15/08/13

G000243870

GRAPHICS
in
DESIGN
and
COMMUNICATION

David Anderson

GILL & MACMILLAN

Gill & Macmillan Ltd

Hume Avenue

Park West

Dublin 12

with associated companies throughout the world

www.gillmacmillan.ie

© David Anderson 2007

978 0 7171 3733 6

Design and print origination in Ireland by O'K Graphic Design, Dublin

Artwork by Peter Bull Art Studio

The paper used in this book is made from the wood pulp of managed forests. For every tree felled, at least one tree is planted, thereby renewing natural resources.

All rights reserved.

No part of this publication may be copied, reproduced or transmitted in any form or by any means without written permission of the publishers or else under the terms of any licence permitting limited copying issued by the Irish Copyright Licensing Agency.

CONTENTS

PART I – PLANE AND DESCRIPTIVE GEOMETRY

PART 1

PLANE AND DESCRIPTIVE GEOMETRY

AREA

PLANE GEOMETRY

1 Basic Constructions

SYLLABUS OUTLINE

Areas to be studied:

• Construction of plane figures. • Construction of loci.

• Circles in contact with points, lines and curves.

Learning outcomes

Students should be able to:

Higher and Ordinary levels

• Construct triangles, quadrilaterals and regular polygons of given side/altitude, inscribed and circumscribed about a circle.

• Apply the principles and properties of plane figures in a problem-solving setting.

Higher level only

• *Use the principle of loci as a problem-solving tool.*

Basic Constructions

To bisect a line AB.

To bisect a line is to divide the line in half.

(1) With A as centre and radius greater than half of AB, draw an arc.

(2) With B as centre, draw another arc having the same radius as Step 1.

(3) The arcs cross, top and bottom, giving the bisector.

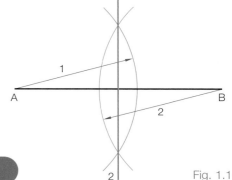

Fig. 1.1

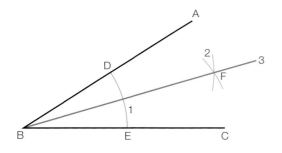

Fig. 1.2

To bisect an angle ABC.

(1) With the vertex B as centre, draw an arc of any radius to hit the arms of the angle AB and BC.

(2) With D and E as centres, swing arcs of equal radius, so they cross as shown, at point F.

(3) F joined back to B bisects the angle.

To construct a perpendicular from A to a given line BC.

(1) With A as centre, scribe an arc having a radius long enough to cut the line AB in two places.

(2) With these two points as centre, draw two arcs of equal radius to cross at D.

(3) Join D back to A to form the perpendicular.

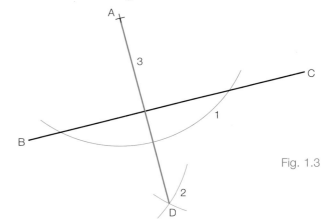

Fig. 1.3

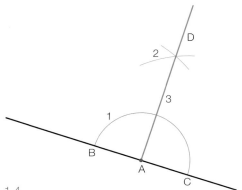

Fig. 1.4

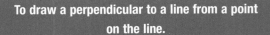

To draw a perpendicular to a line from a point on the line.

(1) Draw a semicircle with A as centre, giving points B and C.
(2) Lengthen the compass and B and C as centres, scribe arcs to cross at point D.
(3) D joined back to A forms the perpendicular.

To divide a line into any number of equal parts.

(1) From one end of the line draw a line at any angle
(2) Using a compass, step down equal spaces on this line. In the diagram we wish to divide the line into four so therefore we step four equal spaces.
(3) Join the last division, point 4, to other end of line AB.
(4) Draw lines parallel to line B4 from points 3, 2 and 1. The line is now divided into four equal divisions.

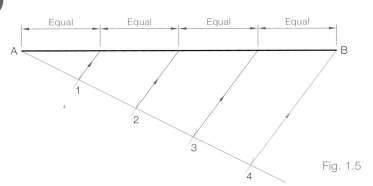

Fig. 1.5

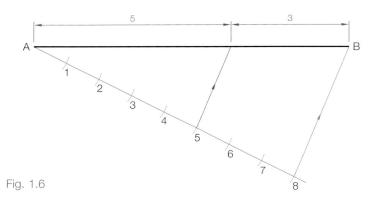

Fig. 1.6

To divide a line into a given ratio (e.g. 5:3).

(1) Add the numbers in the ratio $5 + 3 = 8$.
(2) Set up as above for division of a line stepping eight equal steps.
(3) Join 8 to B.
(4) Draw from 5 parallel to B8 hence dividing AB into the required ratio.

To bisect an angle when we do not have the apex.

Method 1 (Fig. 1.7a)

(1) Draw a line parallel to AB and a set distance away.
(2) Draw a line parallel to CD and the same distance away.
(3) These lines intersect on the bisector at E.
(4) Repeat with a larger or smaller distance to find a second point on the bisector F.

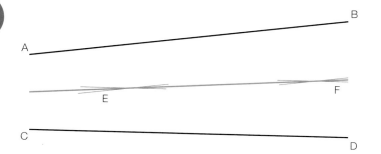

Fig. 1.7a

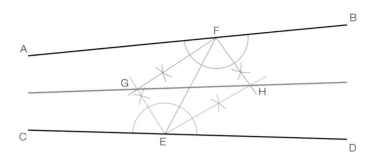

Fig. 1.7b

To divide a line into any number of equal parts.

Method 2 (Fig. 1.7b)

(1) Draw any line EF.
(2) Bisect all the angles to give G and H.
(3) G and H joined give the bisector.

Triangles

Equilateral Triangle (Fig. 1.8)
All sides and angles equal

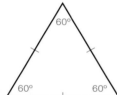

Fig. 1.8

Isosceles Triangle (Fig. 1.9)
Two sides and two angles equal

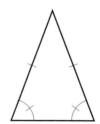

Fig. 1.9

Scalene Triangle (Fig. 1.10)
All sides and angles unequal

Fig. 1.10

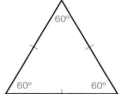

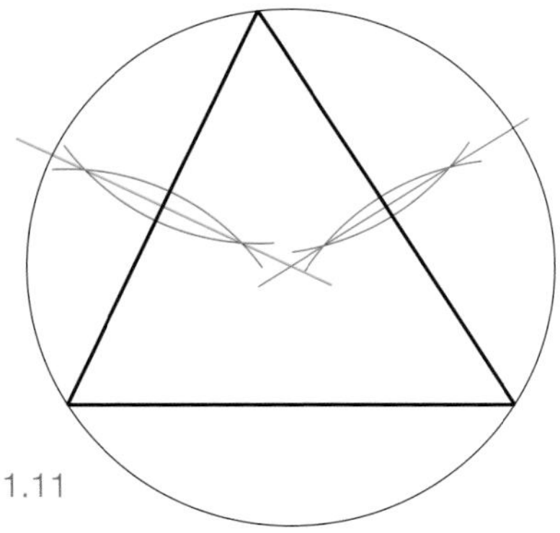

Fig. 1.11

To circumscribe a circle about a triangle (Fig. 1.11)

Bisect any two sides and extend the bisectors until they cross.
The point where they cross is the centre of the circle.

Medians and Centroid (Fig. 1.13)

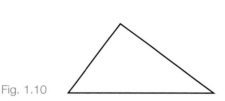

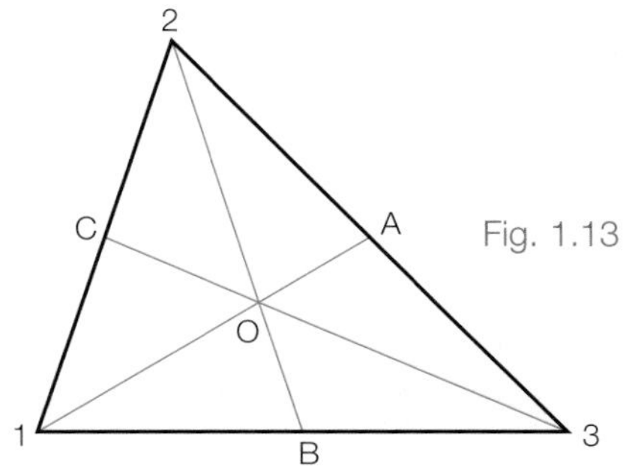

Fig. 1.13

If the midpoints of the sides of a triangle are joined back to the opposite vertex, then the lines produced are called the medians. The medians all cross at the one point called the centroid. The centroid, point O, divides each of the medians, 1A, 2B and 3C in the ratio 1:2.

To inscribe a circle in a triangle (Fig. 1.12)

Bisect any two angles.
Extend the bisectors to cross.
Where they cross is the centre of the circle.

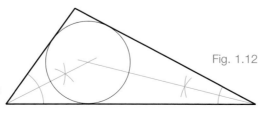

Fig. 1.12

The Circle

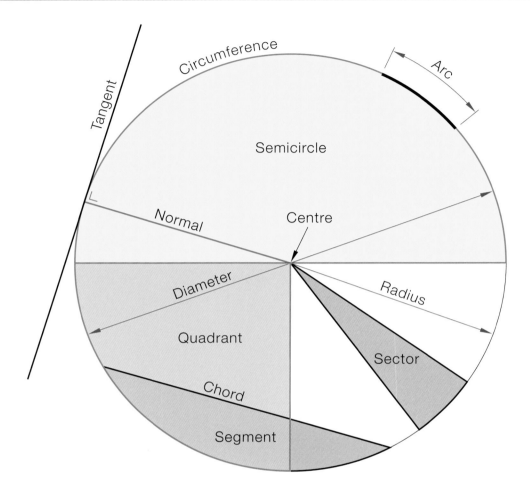

Fig. 1.14

Radius – Distance from the centre to the circumference.

Diameter – A straight line that passes through the centre touching the circumference at both ends. Symbol: ø

Chord – A straight line joining two points on the circumference.

Segment – The area enclosed between a chord and the circle circumference.

Sector – An area enclosed by two radii and the circumference.

Quadrant – A quadrant is a quarter of a circle.

Semicircle – Exactly half of a circle. The area between a diameter and a circumference.

Arc – A piece of the circumference.

Tangent – A straight line that touches the circle at one point, the point of contact.

Normal – A straight line perpendicular to a tangent drawn from the point of contact. The normal passes through the circle centre.

The line that bisects a chord will always pass through the centre point of the circle.

The line that bisects a chord will always pass through the centre point of the circle.

Therefore if you have two chords the centre of the circle can be found as shown in Fig. 1.15.

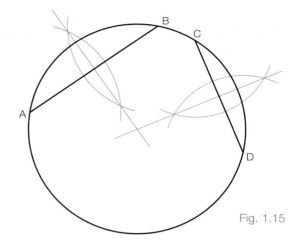

Fig. 1.15

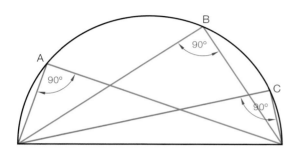

Fig. 1.16

The angle in a semicircle is always a right angle.

(1) Draw a semicircle.
(2) Choose any point A on the circumference.
(3) Join A back to the ends of the diameter.
(4) The enclosed angle is 90°.

Any point chosen on the circumference will give the same answer.

Angles on the same segment of a circle are equal.

The angles at A, B and C will all be identical.

Note: If the segment is smaller than a semicircle, then the angle will be acute. When the segment equals a semicircle, the angle is a right angle as above. When the segment is greater than a semicircle, the angle is obtuse.

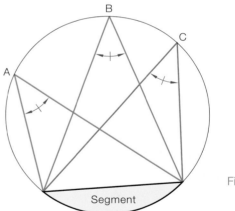

Fig. 1.17

The angle at the centre of a circle is twice that of the angle at the circumference standing on the same chord.

In the diagram we have the chord AB giving us the angle at the centre AOB and the angle at the circumference ACB.

AOB = 2 × ACB

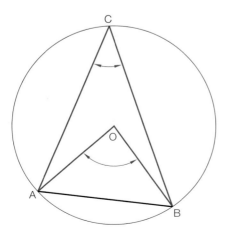

Fig. 1.18

Fig. 1.19

Opposite angles of a cyclic quadrilateral add up to 180°.

A cyclic quadrilateral is one having all four corners on a circle.

Angle A + Angle B = 180°

Angle C + Angle D = 180°

For all quadrilaterals A + B + C + D = 360°

The angle between a tangent and a chord is equal to the angle in the opposite segment.

Angle A = Angle D

Proof: Angle C is a right angle because the angle in a semicircle is always 90°. Therefore Angle B + Angle D must also equal 90° because the sum of the angles in a triangle equal 180°.

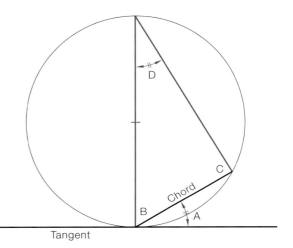

Fig. 1.20a

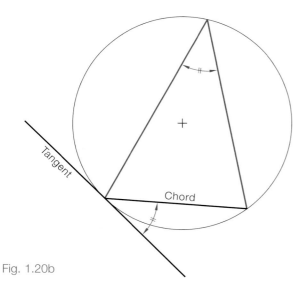

Fig. 1.20b

Angle B + Angle A also equal 90°.

Angle B + Angle D = Angle B + Angle A

Angle D = Angle A

Worked Problems

To construct a triangle given the base, the altitude and the top angle.

All triangles can be circumscribed by a circle. Bisect the base, treating it as a chord. The angle at the circumference is 80°, therefore the angle at the centre will be 160°.

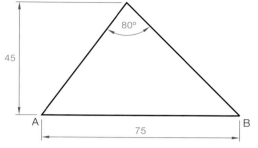

Fig. 1.21

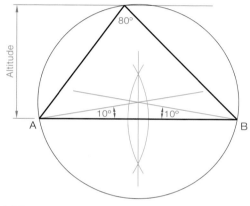

Fig. 1.22

If we create a 10° angle at A and another at B it will create 160° at the centre. Draw the circle. Draw the altitude line parallel to the base, giving two possible solutions for the third vertex of the triangles, Fig. 1.22.

To construct a triangle given the base, one side and the vertical (top) angle.

(1) Treat the base as a chord and bisect it to help find the centre of the circumscribing circle.
(2) Create the vertical angle at A thus forming a tangent.

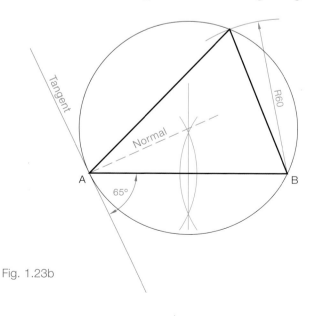

Fig. 1.23b

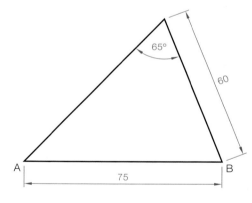

Fig. 1.23a

(3) Produce a normal to this tangent. The normal will pass through the centre of the circumscribing circle.
(4) Using where the normal and the bisector cross as centre, draw a circle to pass through A and B.
(5) The third corner is now located by swinging an arc of radius 60 mm from B to cross the circle, Fig. 1.23b.

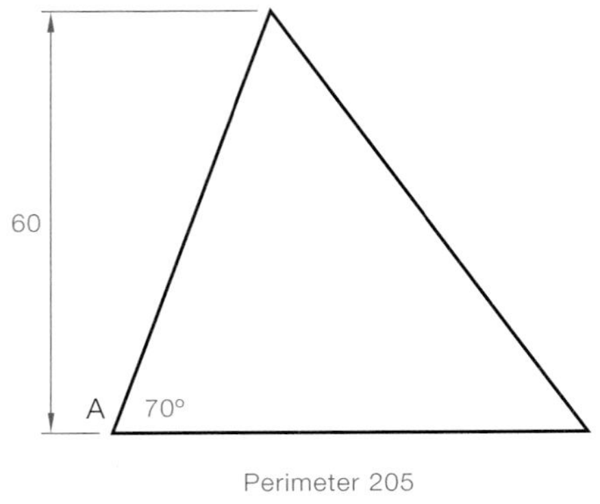

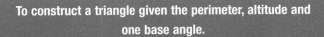

To construct a triangle given the perimeter, altitude and one base angle.

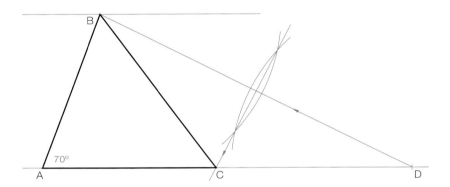

60

A 70°

Perimeter 205

Fig. 1.24a

(1) Draw two parallel lines the altitude apart, i.e. 60 mm.
(2) Draw in the base angle.
 This gives one side of the triangle, AB.
(3) Measure the length of AB and subtract it from the perimeter.
 205 − 65 = 140
 This is the length of the two remaining sides.

(4) Make AD equal to 140 mm.
(5) Join D to B and bisect.
(6) Extend the bisector to give point C.
 ABC is the required triangle.

B

70°

A   C   D

Fig. 1.24b

To construct a triangle given the perimeter and the ratio of the sides.
e.g. perimeter 220 mm, ratio of sides 5:3:4

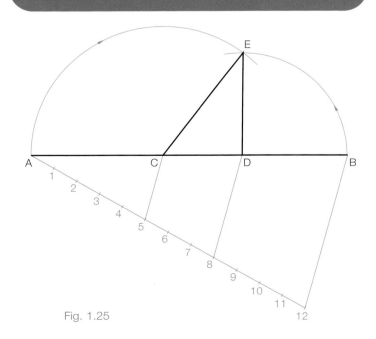

(1) Draw a line AB equal to the length of the perimeter.
(2) Divide the line into the given ratio. AC, CD and DB are the lengths of the sides of the triangle.
(3) With C as centre and AC as radius, scribe an arc.
(4) With D as centre and DB as radius, scribe an arc.
(5) The arcs cross at E. CDE is the required triangle.

Fig. 1.25

Activities

Q1. Draw a line AB, 120 mm long. Divide this line into 9 equal parts.

Q3. Draw a line AB, 120 mm long. Divide this line into the ratio 2:5:4.

Q2. Draw a line AB, 120 mm long. Divide this line into 7 equal parts.

Q4. Draw a line AB, 120 mm long. Divide this line into the ratio 3:5:5.

Q5. Given the line AB with a point P above it. Draw a perpendicular to AB from P using a compass only, Fig. 1.26.

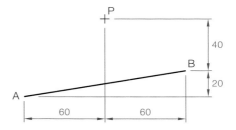

Fig. 1.26

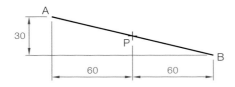

Fig. 1.27

Q6. Given a line AB and a point P on the line. Construct a perpendicular to AB from P using a compass, Fig. 1.27.

Q7. Bisect the angle formed by the lines AB and CD, Fig. 1.28.

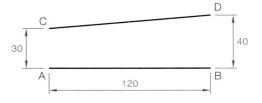

Fig. 1.28

Q8. Construct a triangle of sides 58 mm, 65 mm and 53 mm. Circumscribe a circle about this circle.

Q9. Construct a triangle of sides 95 mm, 45 mm and 75 mm. Inscribe a circle in this triangle.

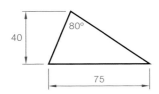

Fig. 1.29

Q10. Construct the triangle shown in Fig. 1.29. Find the centroid of this triangle.

Q11. Construct the triangle shown in Fig. 1.30 and circumscribe a circle around it.

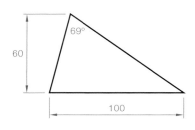

Fig. 1.30

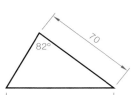
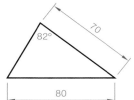

Fig. 1.31

Q12. Construct the triangle shown in Fig. 1.31 and inscribe a circle.

Q13. Construct the triangle shown in Fig. 1.32 given the perimeter, altitude and one base angle.

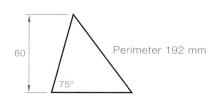

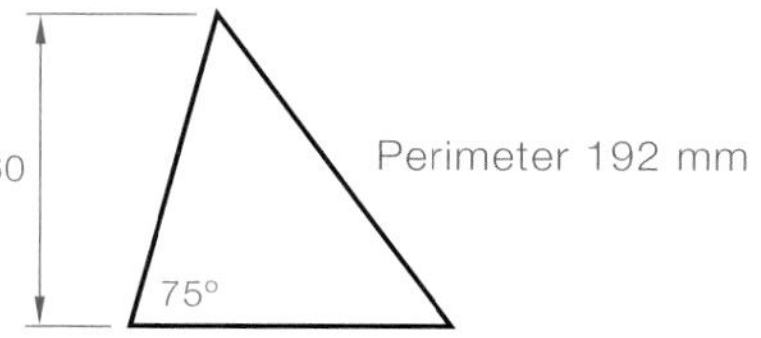

Fig. 1.32

Questions Q15.–Q23.
Construct the following triangles:

Q14. Construct a triangle given the perimeter of 150 mm and the ratio of the sides as 5:4:6. Find the centroid of this triangle.

Q15.

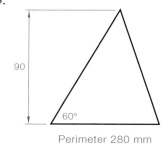

Perimeter 280 mm

Fig. 1.33

Q16.

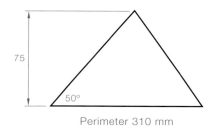

Perimeter 310 mm

Fig. 1.34

Q17.

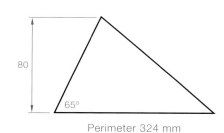

Perimeter 324 mm

Fig. 1.35

Q18.

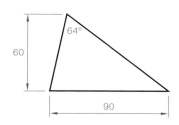

Fig. 1.36

Q19.

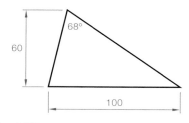

Fig. 1.37

Q20.

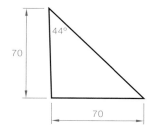

Fig. 1.38

Q21.

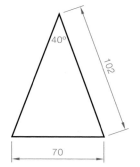

40°

102

70

Fig. 1.39

Q22.

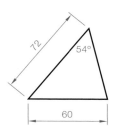

72

54°

60

Fig. 1.40

Q23.

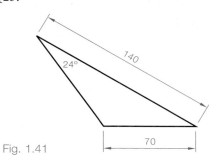

140

24°

70

Fig. 1.41

Q24. Construct a triangle given the perimeter of 180 mm and the ratio of the sides of 4:3:2.

Q25. Construct a triangle given the perimeter of 220 mm and the ratio of the sides of 4:3:5.

Q26. Construct a triangle given the perimeter of 200 mm and the ratio of the sides 7:6:2.

Polygons

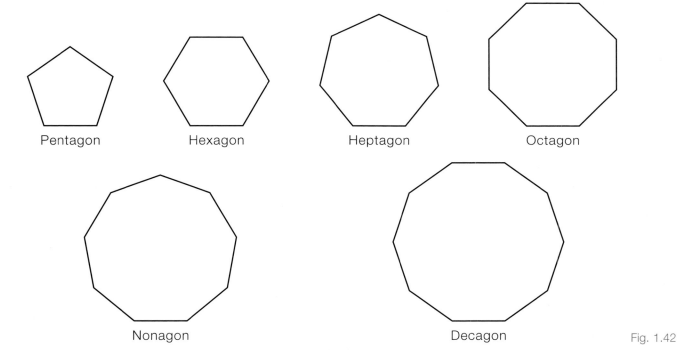

Pentagon   Hexagon   Heptagon   Octagon

Nonagon   Decagon   Fig. 1.42

Definition: A polygon is a plane figure having three or more sides. A regular polygon has all its sides of equal length and all its angles of equal measure.

Construction of a polygon given the base
Method 1: Protractor

The exterior angle for any regular polygon can easily be found by dividing the number of sides required into 360°.

Exterior angle = 360°/Number of sides

For example the exterior angle for a pentagon is 360°/5 = 72º

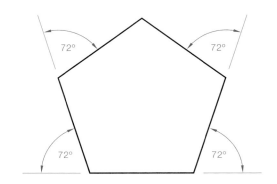

Fig. 1.43

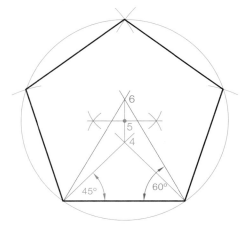

Fig. 1.44

Method 2: Triangle

(1) Draw the base.

(2) On the base, construct a 45° angle from each end as shown in Fig. 1.44. Number the apex as 4.

(3) Produce another triangle on the same base having base angles of 60°. The apex of this triangle is numbered as 6.

(4) Join 4 to 6 and bisect giving point 5.

(5) With 5 as centre, scribe a circle to pass through both ends of the base.

(6) The base stepped round this circle will give the sides of the pentagon.

This method can be used for polygons with more sides but is not very accurate.

The spacing between the centres is the same as that between 4 and 5. As the number of sides increases the accuracy decreases.

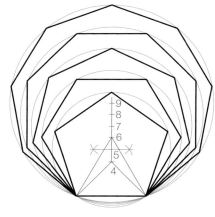

Fig. 1.45

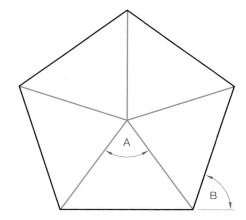

Fig. 1.46

Method 3: Angle at the centre of a polygon

For all regular polygons the angles formed by joining the vertices to the centre will all be equal and will also equal the exterior angle of the polygon.

In Fig. 1.46, Angle A = Angle B

Fig. 1.47

Construct a regular nonagon given the base.

(1) Draw the base.
(2) Since the exterior angle for a nonagon is 40° (360°/9 = 40°) the interior angle will also be 40°. If the top angle of an isosceles triangle is 40°, then the two base angles will be 70°. (Angles in a triangle add up to 180°.) Draw the two base angles finding the nonagon centre at the triangle apex.
(3) Scribe the circle and step the base around it to find the remaining vertices.

To inscribe a regular polygon in a given circle.

(1) Draw the circle and the diameter.
(2) Divide the diameter into the same number of equal parts as there are sides needed on the polygon (7 parts for the heptagon in the diagram).
(3) With the diameter as radius, draw two arcs using the ends of the diameter as centre. The arcs cross at B.
(4) Draw a line from B through 2 on the diameter and extend to hit C on the circle.
(5) AC is one side of the polygon. Step the distance AC around the circumference finding the remaining sides (approximate).

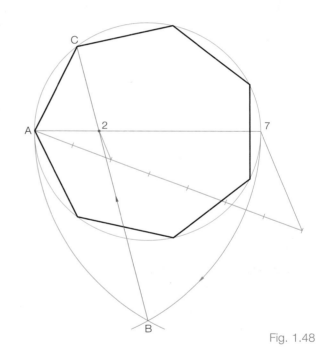

Fig. 1.48

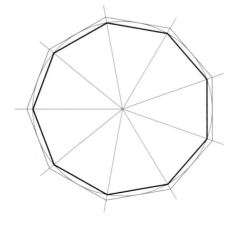

Fig. 1.49

To describe a regular polygon about a given circle.

(1) Draw the given circle.
(2) Inscribe the polygon as described above.
(3) Radiate lines from the centre of the circle through each vertex.
(4) Draw the sides of the required polygon parallel to the sides of the inner polygon.

Circles in Contact with Points, Lines and Curves

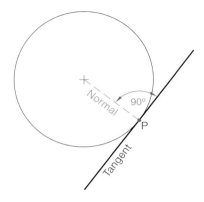

Fig. 1.50

To draw a tangent to a circle from a point P on the curve.

Join P back to the centre of the circle giving the normal. The tangent can be constructed perpendicular to the normal at P.

To draw a tangent to a circle from a point P outside the circle.

The solution is based on the fact that the normal is always perpendicular to the tangent and that the angle in a semicircle is always a right angle.

(1) Join P to C and bisect.

(2) Draw a semicircle on line CP to cut the circle at A.

(3) Point A is the point of contact and PA is the tangent.

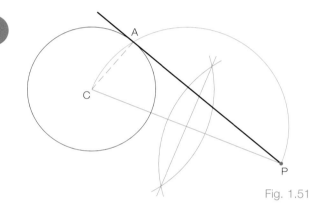

Fig. 1.51

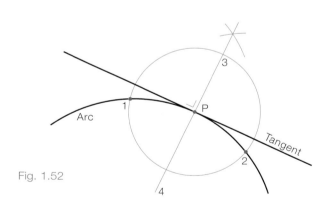

Fig. 1.52

Tangent to an arc when we do not have the centre.

(1) With P as centre, draw a circle finding points 1 and 2.

(2) Use points 1 and 2 to bisect, giving line 3,4.

(3) The tangent is drawn perpendicular to line 3,4.

To draw a tangent to a circle, parallel to a given line.

(1) With centre C, draw an arc across the given line at A and B.

(2) Bisect AB giving D.

(3) Join D back to C giving the normal.

(4) The point of contact is found and the tangent is drawn parallel to the original line.

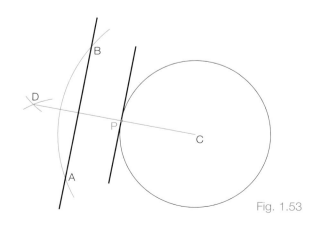

Fig. 1.53

External tangent to two unequal circles.

(1) Join the centres and bisect.
(2) Draw a semicircle.
(3) Step the radius of the small circle r inside the circumference of the large circle, giving point A.
(4) Draw the circle through A as shown.
(5) This circle crosses the semicircle at B which is a point on the normal.
(6) Draw the normal. The normal for the smaller circle will be parallel to this.
(7) Draw the tangent, Fig. 1.55.

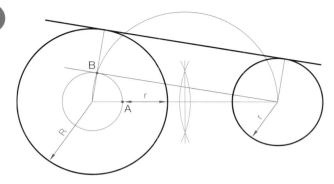

Fig. 1.54

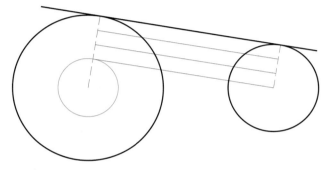

Fig. 1.55

T out r in
External tangent step the radius of the small circle in.

This construction is based on the fact that if the two circles increase or decrease in radius by the same amount, the external tangents to them will remain parallel. The small circle is reduced to a point by subtracting its radius. The larger circle must be reduced in size by a similar amount. The problem is now reduced to that of drawing a tangent to a circle from a point outside it.

Internal tangent to two unequal circles.

(1) Join the centres and bisect.
(2) Draw a semicircle.
(3) Step the radius of the small circle r outside the circumference of the large circle giving point A.
(4) Draw the arc from A as shown.
(5) This arc crosses the semicircle at B which is a point on the normal.
(6) Draw the normals and the tangent.

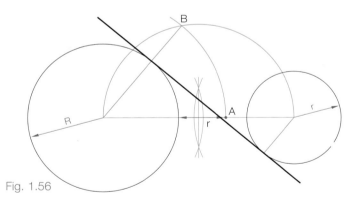

Fig. 1.56

This construction is based on the fact that when the tangent is internal, by increasing the radius of the larger circle the smaller circle must decrease by a similar amount if the tangents are to remain parallel. Increase the large circle by the radius r of the small circle will result in the small circle being reduced to a point.

T in r out
Internal tangent step the radius of the small circle out.

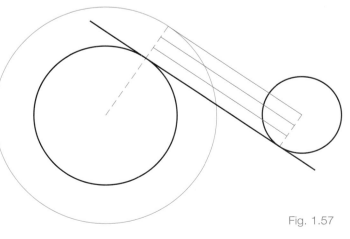

Fig. 1.57

Activities

Q1. Given the base of a pentagon as 40 mm. Construct the pentagon using two methods.

Q2. Construct a heptagon having a base of 35 mm using the triangle method.

Q3. Draw a circle of 90 mm diameter. Inscribe a pentagon in this circle.

Q4. Describe a nonagon about a circle of radius 40 mm.

Q5. Inscribe a pentagon in a circle of 90 mm diameter.

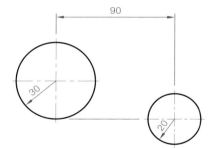

Fig. 1.60

Q8. Draw an external tangent to the two given circles, Fig. 1.60.

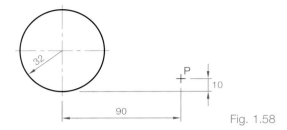

Fig. 1.58

Q6. Draw both tangents to the circle from point P showing clearly the points of contact, Fig. 1.58.

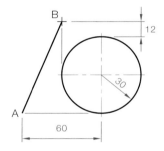

Fig. 1.59

Q7. Construct a tangent to a given circle, parallel to a given line AB, Fig. 1.59.

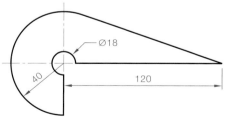

Fig. 1.61

Q9. Draw the centre square shown in the diagram Fig. 1.61.

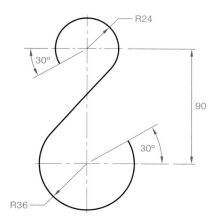

Fig. 1.62

Q10. Draw the metal hook shown in Fig. 1.62.

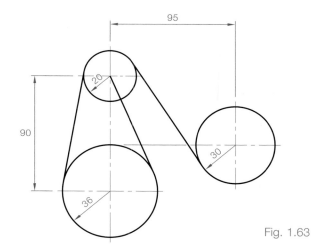

Fig. 1.63

Q11. Draw the pulley system shown in Fig. 1.63.

Tangent Curves

To construct the tangent arc shown, to two given circles.

(1) From the centre of the large circle draw an arc equal to R + 50 = 30 + 50 = 80.

(2) From the centre of the small circle draw an arc equal to r + 50 = 16 + 50 = 66.

(3) The centre is found where these two arcs cross. An arc of radius 50 mm will form a tangent to the two circles.

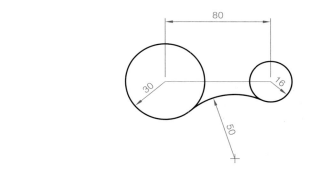

Fig. 1.64

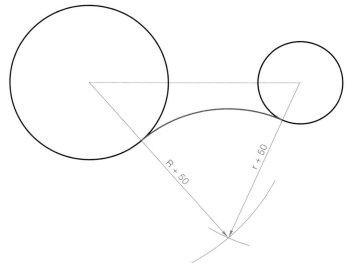

Fig. 1.65

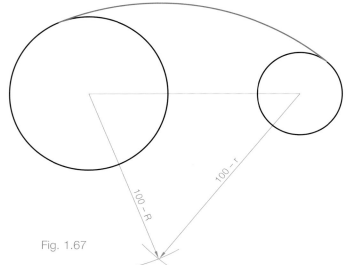

Fig. 1.66

Fig. 1.67

To construct a tangent arc to enclose two given circles.

(1) From the centre of the large circle draw an arc equal to 100 − R = 100 − 30 = 70.
(2) From the centre of the small circle draw an arc equal to 100 − r = 100 − 16 = 84.
(3) The centre is found where these two arcs cross. An arc of radius 100 mm will form a tangent curve to the two circles.

To construct an internal tangential arc to two given circles.

(1) From the centre of the large circle draw an arc equal to 80 + R = 80 + 30 = 110.
(2) From the centre of the small circle draw an arc equal to 80 − r = 80 − 16 = 64.
(3) The centre is found where the two arcs cross. An arc drawn with radius 80 mm will form an internal tangent to the two circles.

There are four possible combinations of arcs to give four possible internal tangents.

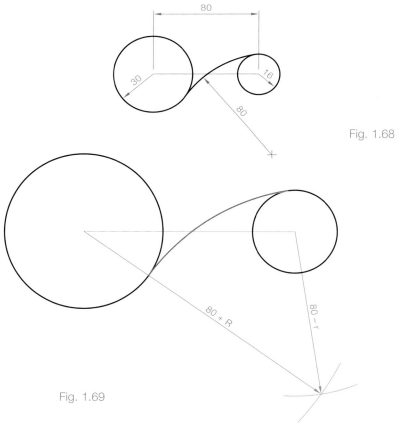

Fig. 1.68

Fig. 1.69

Circles Touching Points and Lines

> ### To draw a circle of given radius to touch two arms of an angle.

(1) Draw a line parallel to AC the radius of the required circle away.

(2) Draw a similar line parallel to AB.

(3) The lines cross, giving the circle centre.

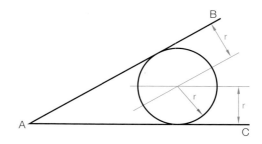

Fig. 1.70

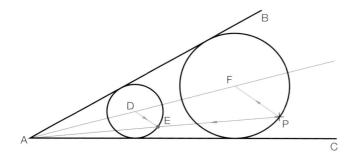

Fig. 1.71

> ### To draw a circle to touch the two arms of an angle and a given point P.

(1) Bisect the angle BAC. The centre of the required circle must rest on this bisector.

(2) Draw the circle having its centre D on the bisector.

(3) Join point P back to the corner A.

(4) The line PA strikes circle D at E. Join D to E.

(5) From P draw a line parallel to line DE finding point F, the centre of the required circle.

> ### To draw a circle to touch a given line AB at a given point D and to pass through a point P.

(1) AB will be a tangent to the circle and D will be the point of contact.

A perpendicular from D will therefore form the normal and will pass through the centre.

(2) Join DP.

(3) Bisect DP. The line DP will form a chord to the circle and therefore the bisector of this chord will also pass through the circle centre.

(4) Point C is found where the bisector and the perpendicular meet.

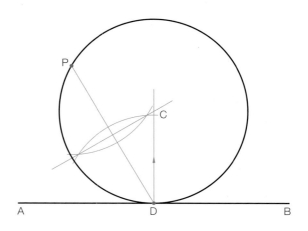

Fig. 1.72

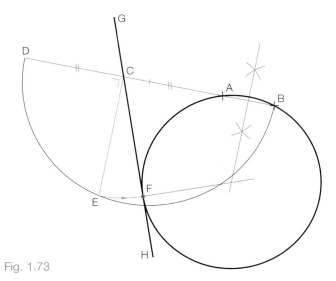

Fig. 1.73

To draw a circle to pass through two given points A and B and to touch a given line GH.

(1) Join A to B and bisect (chord).
(2) Extend AB to the line GH, finding point C.
(3) Extend BC further to D so that the length of CA equals CD.
(4) Bisect the line DB and draw a semicircle.
(5) Draw CE perpendicular to DB.
(6) Make CF equal in length to CE. Point F is the point of contact.
(7) A perpendicular from F to the line GH will find the centre.
(8) Draw the circle.

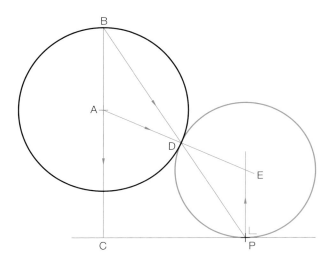

Fig. 1.74

To draw a circle to touch a given point p and a given circle.

(1) Draw a vertical line through the centre of the given circle. Line BAC.
(2) Draw a horizontal line through point P to C.
(3) Erect a perpendicular to line CP at point P. The centre of the required circle will be on this line.
(4) Join B to P, cutting the given circle at D. D will be the point of contact.
(5) A line from A through D to E will find the circle centre.

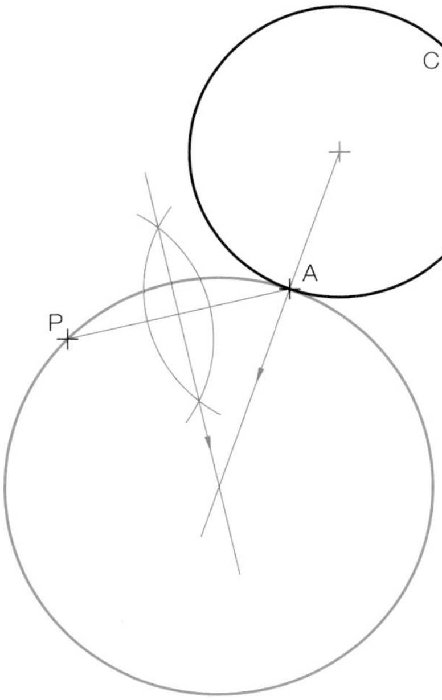

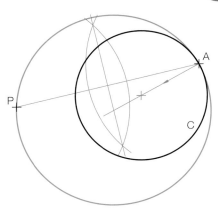

Fig. 1.75a

To draw a circle to touch a given circle C at a point A on the circumference and to pass through a given point

(1) Join A to P and bisect. AP will be a chord and therefore the bisector of this chord will pass through the centre.
(2) Join A and the centre of the original circle and extent to hit the bisector. If two circles are in contact then their centres and the point of contact will be in line.
(3) Draw the circle.

Fig. 1.75b

To draw a circle to touch a given circle C and to pass through two given points A and B.

(1) Join A to B and extend.

(2) Bisect AB (chord).

(3) Draw any circle on this bisector such that it passes through AB and cuts through circle C in two places, D and E.

(4) Join D to E and produce to intersect AB produced. This locates point F.

(5) From F draw a tangent to the given circle. The normal is also drawn.

(6) The normal extended will intersect the bisector at G which will be the centre of the required circle.

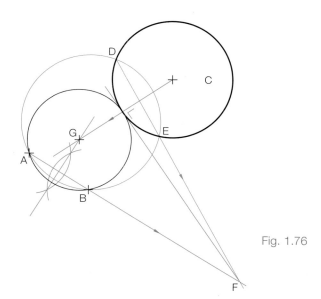

Fig. 1.76

Use of Loci

Many of the previous problems can be solved by the use of loci.

Definition: A locus is the path followed by a point while obeying certain conditions.

A circle, for example, is the locus/path of a point that remains a set distance (the radius) from another point (the centre).

To draw a circle to pass through two given points A and B and to touch a given line GH.

This problem was solved by an alternative method in Fig. 1.73.

(1) Join A and B and bisect.

> The bisector of a line is the locus of all points which are equidistant from the end points of that line.

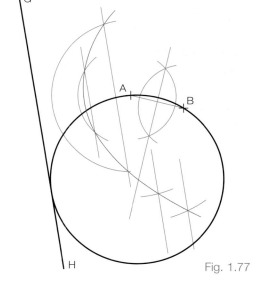

Fig. 1.77

(2) Draw the locus of points which are equidistant from A and the line GH.

Draw a line 20 mm from GH and parallel to it. Draw an arc of radius 20 mm having point A as centre. Arc and line cross giving a point on the locus. Repeat as above but drawing the line 30 mm from GH and the arc of radius 30 mm.

Repeat until the locus is long enough to cross the bisector of chord AB.

Join all the points to give a smooth curve.

(3) Where the bisector and locus cross gives the centre of the required circle.

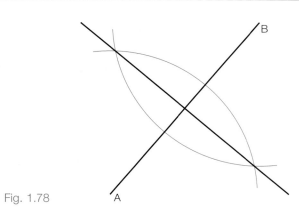

Fig. 1.78

HIGHER LEVEL

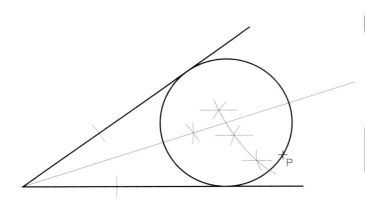

Fig. 1.79

To draw a circle to touch the two arms of an angle and a given point P.

This problem was solved by an alternative method in Fig. 1.71.

(1) Bisect the angle.

> **The bisector of an angle is the locus of all points which are equidistant from both arms of the angle.**

(2) Draw the locus of points which are equidistant from point P and one of the arms of the angle.

(3) The locus and bisector cross at the circle centre.

To draw a circle to touch a given circle C and to pass through two given points A and B.

Already answered using alternative method, Fig. 1.76.

(1) Join A to B and bisect.

(2) Draw a locus of points which are equidistant from one of the points (e.g. B) and the circumference of the circle.
With B as centre draw an arc of radius 20 mm.
With centre of circle C as centre add 20 mm to the radius of circle C and draw an arc.
The two arcs intersect giving points on the locus.
Repeat with larger measurements to plot the locus.

(3) The locus and the bisector of AB intersect at the centre of the required circle.

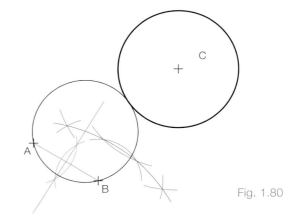

Fig. 1.80

To draw a circle to touch three given circles A, B and C.

(1) Plot the locus of points that are equidistant from the circumference of circle A and circle B.

(2) Plot a second locus of all points that are equidistant from the circumference of circle A and circle C.

(3) Where these two loci cross gives a point which is equidistant from the circumference of all three circles. The centre of the required circle.

(4) Draw the circle.

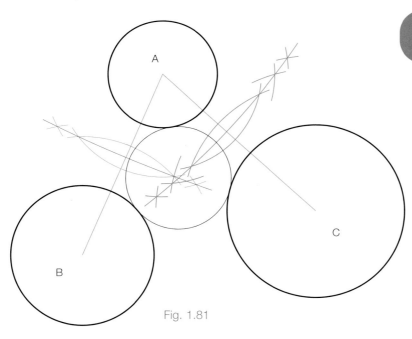

Fig. 1.81

To draw a circle to touch two given circles A and B and to touch a given line CD.

(1) Plot the locus of points that are equidistant from the circumference of A and the line CD.
(2) Plot the second locus of points that are equidistant from the circumference of B and the line CD.
(3) Where the loci cross is the centre of the required circle, Fig. 1.82.

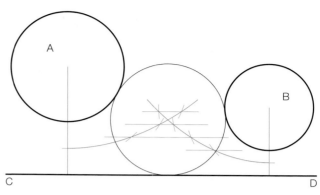

Fig. 1.82

Activities

Q1. Draw a circle of radius 18 mm to touch the two given circles, Fig. 1.83.

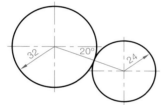

Fig. 1.83

Q2. Draw a circle to touch the two given circles and having a radius of 60 mm, Fig. 1.84.

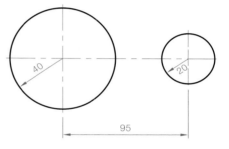

Fig. 1.84

Q3. Draw the machine part shown in Fig. 1.85.

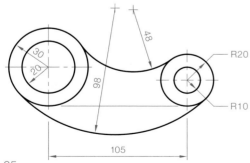

Fig. 1.85

Q4. Shown is the head of a spanner, Fig. 1.86. Construct this showing all centre points and points of contact.

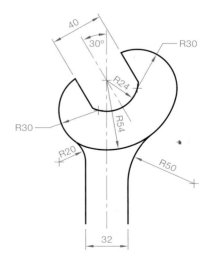

Fig. 1.86

Q5. Draw the door handle shown in Fig. 1.87.

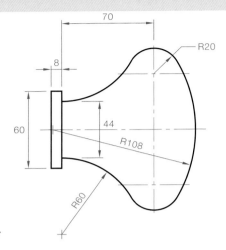

Fig. 1.87

Q6. Construct the vase shown in Fig. 1.88. The shape is symmetrical.

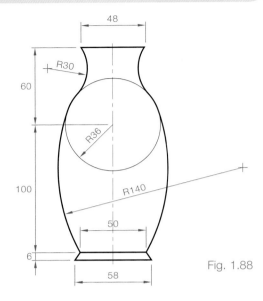

Fig. 1.88

Q7. Draw a circle to touch the two arms of the given angle and to touch point P, Fig. 1.89.

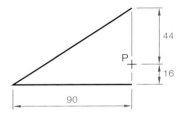

Fig. 1.89

Q8. Given a line, a point A on the line and a point P off the line. Draw a circle tangential to the given line at A and to pass through point P, Fig. 1.90.

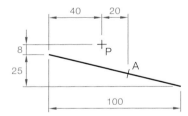

Fig. 1.90

Q9. To draw a line to pass through the two given points A and B and be tangential to the given line CD, Fig. 1.91.

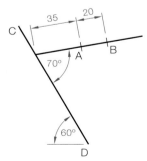

Fig. 1.91

Q10. Draw a circle to touch the given circle and a point P outside the circle, Fig. 1.92.

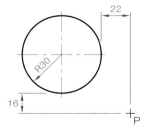

Fig. 1.92

Q11. Draw a circle to touch the given circle and pass through a point P outside the circle, Fig. 1.93.

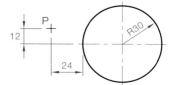

Fig. 1.93

Q12. For both Figures 1.94a and 1.94b draw a circle to touch the given circle at point A and to pass through point P.

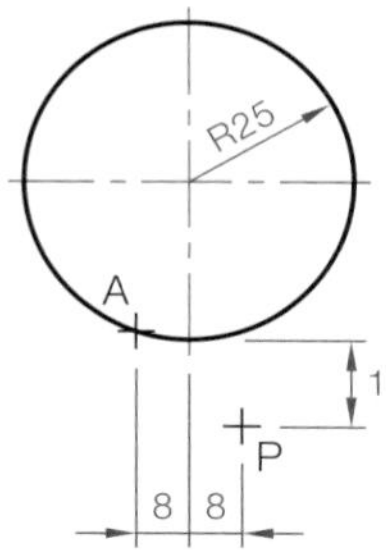

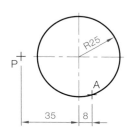

Fig. 1.94a

Fig. 1.94b

Q13. Draw a circle to pass through points P_1 and P_2 and to touch a given circle, Fig. 1.95.

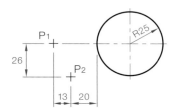

Fig. 1.95

Q14. Construct the figure shown in Fig. 1.96. Hint: See Fig. 1.20 in this chapter.

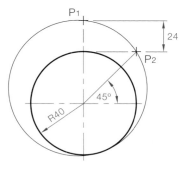

Fig. 1.96

Q15. Draw the figure shown in Fig. 1.97.

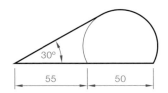

Fig. 1.97

Solve all the following problems by the use of loci.

Q16. Draw a circle to touch line AB and to pass through P₁ and P₂, Fig. 1.98.

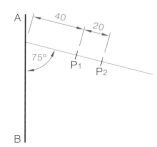

Fig. 1.98

Q17. Draw a circle to pass through a given point P and to touch the two arms of the angle, Fig. 1.99.

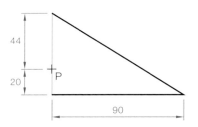

Fig. 1.99

Q18. Draw a circle to touch two given points and a given circle, Fig. 1.100.

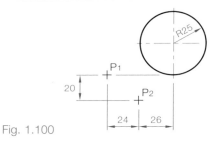

Fig. 1.100

Q19. Draw a circle to touch three given circles, Fig. 1.101.

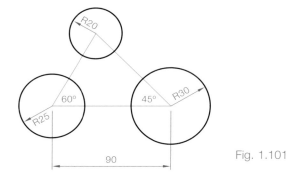

Fig. 1.101

Q20. Draw a circle to touch the two given circles and to touch the given line AB, Fig. 1.102.

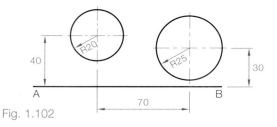

Fig. 1.102

Q21. Draw the figure shown in Fig. 1.103.

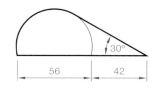

Fig. 1.103

Q22. Draw a circle to touch a given point P and two given circles, Fig. 1.104.

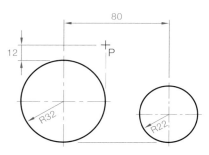

Fig. 1.104

2
AREA

PROJECTION SYSTEMS

2 Orthographic and Auxiliary Projection

SYLLABUS OUTLINE

Areas to be studied:
• Definition of a plane. • Principal planes of reference.
• Auxiliary views, *including second and subsequent auxiliary views.* • True shapes of surfaces and true lengths of lines.

Learning outcomes
Students should be able to:

Higher and Ordinary levels

- Represent three-dimensional objects in logically arranged two-dimensional views.
- Apply their knowledge of reference planes and auxiliary projection planes to solving problems using a first auxiliary view.
- Present drawings in first-angle orthographic conventional views.
- Determine the projections, inclinations, true length and true shape, of lines and planes.

Higher Level only

- *Apply their knowledge of reference planes and auxiliary projection planes to solving problems using a first auxiliary view and subsequent auxiliary views.*
- *Present drawings in third-angle orthographic conventional views.*
- *Determine the projections of lines given the angles of inclination to the principal planes of reference.*

Plane

A plane is a flat surface with no thickness. If two points are selected on a plane and joined with a straight line, then the straight line will lie on the plane along its full length. Planes are considered to have no boundaries, to be limitless. We usually draw edges to the planes to help our visualisation of them.

Fig. 2.1 shows the principal planes of reference. Two planes, one vertical and one horizontal, intersect along the straight line xy. These planes divide space into four sections: first, second, third and fourth angles. When representing objects we generally place them in the first angle or the third angle and project their image onto the horizontal plane and the vertical plane. This gives first-angle projection and third-angle projection.

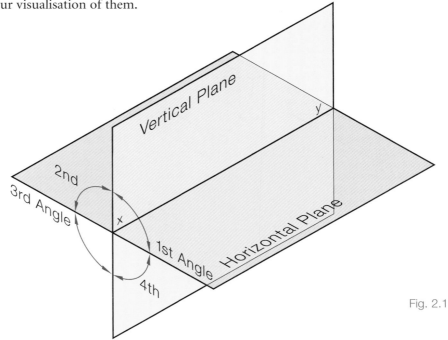

Fig. 2.1

First-angle Projection

The object to be drawn is positioned in the First Angle of the intersecting vertical and horizontal planes. When we view from directly in front of the object we see the **Front Elevation**. The view that we see is projected onto the vertical plane behind. When we view from directly above the object we see the **Plan**. The view that we see is projected onto the horizontal plane below, see Fig. 2.2.

Note: The plane that we project onto must always be perpendicular to our line of sight.

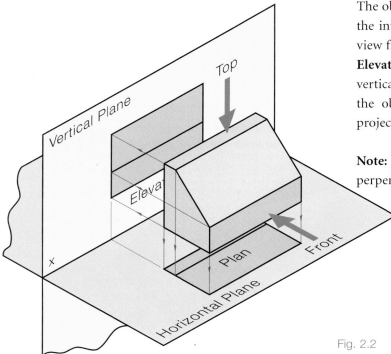

Fig. 2.2

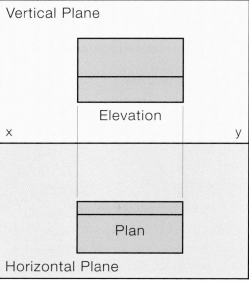

Fig. 2.3

We now fold the horizontal plane down in line with the vertical plane. The plane is hinged about the xy line. This gives two views of the one object. The elevation is always directly above the plan.

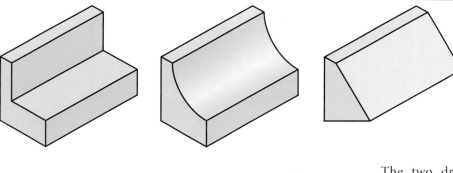

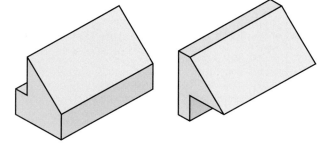

Fig. 2.4

The two drawings together give us a lot of information about the object but not the complete picture. This plan and elevation could represent any of the objects in Fig. 2.4. To represent the object completely we need a third view, a view from the side. When viewing from the side we need to introduce a new vertical plane onto which we project our image.

The plane must be perpendicular to the line of sight (Fig. 2.5). When we consider all three views together we have a complete representation of the object.

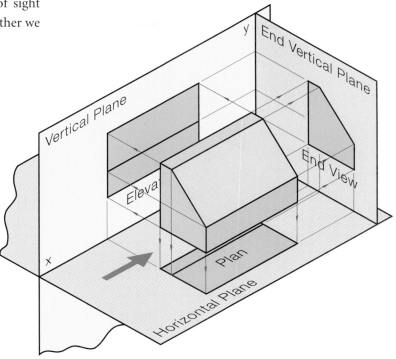

Fig. 2.5

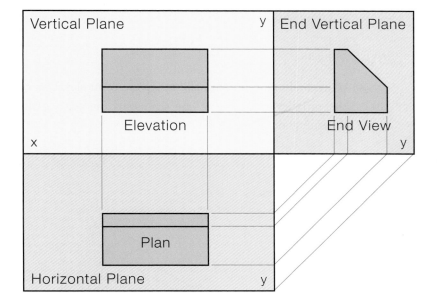

Fig. 2.6

The line of intersection between the two vertical planes is called the yy line. All three planes are folded out flat as seen in Fig. 2.6. The horizontal plane is folded down, hinging along the xy line and the end vertical plane swings back hinging along the yy line. All three planes now lie on one plane.

As was mentioned earlier, the vertical planes and horizontal plane are limitless in size. When drawing objects in this format, **orthographic projection**, we dispense with the plane edges and just use the hinge lines, i.e. xy line and yy line. In this example, for clarity, the object was raised up above the horizontal plane. Usually the object is placed on the horizontal plane. This means that the elevations will be on the xy line.

The XY Line

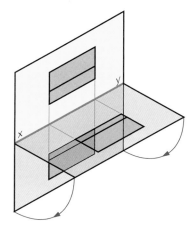

Fig. 2.7

It is worth noting at this stage that the xy line represents several things:

(1) The line of intersection between the vertical and horizontal planes, Fig. 2.7.

(2) The xy line is the hinge line about which the horizontal plane drops down in line with the vertical plane, Fig. 2.7.

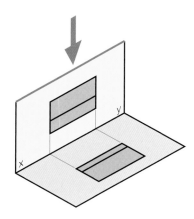

Fig. 2.8

(3) When looking straight down to see the plan, the xy line represents the edge of the vertical plane, Fig. 2.8.

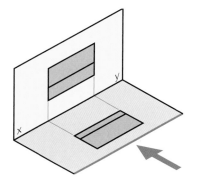

Fig. 2.9

(4) When looking in horizontally to see the front elevation or the end elevation, the xy line represents the edge of the horizontal plane. Fig. 2.9.

Fig. 2.10 shows a pictorial view of an object.

(i) Draw a front elevation of the object looking in the direction of arrow A.

(ii) Project a plan from the front elevation.

(iii) Project an end elevation looking in the direction of arrow B.

(1) Draw the xy line first.

(2) Set up a box that will contain the front elevation on this xy line. The height will be 70 mm and the length will be 104 mm.

(3) The box for the plan is usually drawn next. The plan will be the same length and directly below the front elevation. The size of the gap between the plan and the xy line is chosen to give a nice drawing layout.

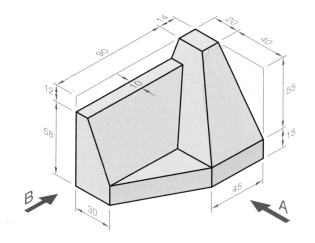

Fig. 2.10

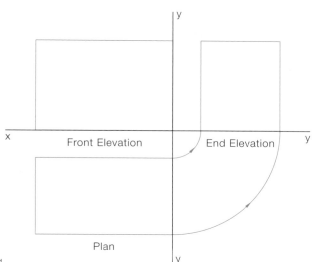

Fig. 2.11

(5) The details of the three views are built up as shown in Fig. 2.12.

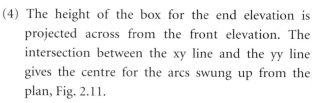

Fig. 2.13 shows a pictorial view of a solid.
(i)   Draw a front elevation looking in the direction of arrow A.
(ii) Draw an end elevation viewing in the direction of arrow B.
(iii) Project a plan from the front elevation.

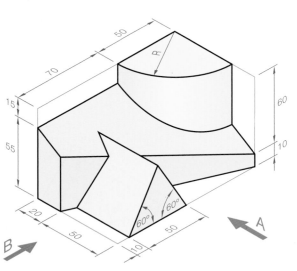

Fig. 2.13

(2) The views are built up in stages. None of the three drawings can be completed on their own without using information from the other two views. In order to simplify the appearance of the drawing in Fig. 2.14 many of the construction lines have been left out.

(4) The height of the box for the end elevation is projected across from the front elevation. The intersection between the xy line and the yy line gives the centre for the arcs swung up from the plan, Fig. 2.11.

These arcs represent the end vertical plane as it swings around into place.

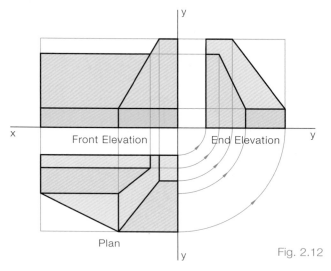

Fig. 2.12

(1) Since arrow A points to the left the front elevation is drawn on the left. Start with the xy line and the three boxes to contain the views in their correct positions. Arrow B points to the right so the end view is on the right.

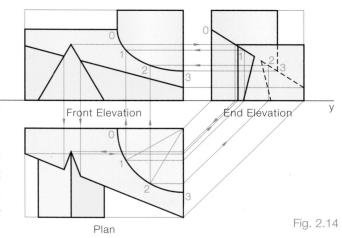

Fig. 2.14

Auxiliary Elevation

The front elevation, end elevations and plan, together give a huge amount of information about the object being drawn. We looked from in front of the object, from the sides and from above the object to obtain these views. The views themselves were projected onto the principal planes of reference. An object can of course be viewed from any direction and the image projected onto a new plane. Remember, the plane onto which an image is projected must be perpendicular to the line of sight. An image projected onto a vertical plane is an elevation. To see an image on a vertical plane we must view horizontally. An auxiliary elevation, therefore, is a view parallel to the horizontal plane and at an angle between 0° and 90° to the vertical plane.

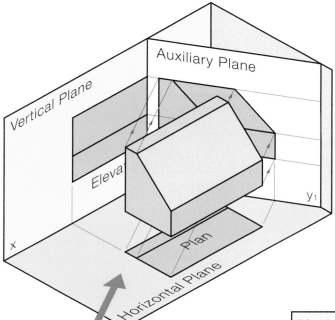

Fig. 2.15

The diagram Fig. 2.15 shows the principal planes of reference. The front elevation and plan are projected in the normal way. To view in the direction of the arrow we must introduce a new vertical plane, as shown, perpendicular to the line of sight. This auxiliary plane intersects the horizontal plane along a line which we call the x_1y_1 line. The view of the object may now be projected onto this plane.

Since the line of sight is horizontal the image is an elevation. The heights used in the auxiliary elevation will be the same heights as in all the other elevations. Fig. 2.16 shows the planes folded down flat. The projection lines are always perpendicular to the xy line. It should be noted that the auxiliary plane can be close to the object or far away from the object, it will not affect the image in any way because the projection lines are parallel.

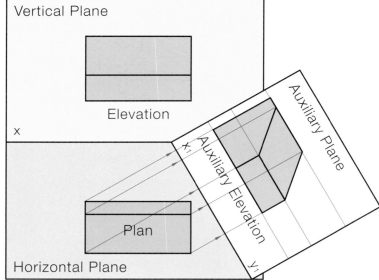

Fig. 2.16

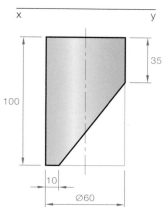

Fig. 2.17

The drawing Fig. 2.17 shows the plan of a cylinder resting on the horizontal plane. The cylinder has been cut by a simply inclined plane.

(i)   Draw the given plan and project an elevation.
(ii) Draw a new elevation that will show the true shape of the cut surface.

(1) Draw the plan.

(2) The elevation will be a circle.

(3) Divide the elevation into twelve parts and index.

(4) Project these divisions down to the cut surface of the plan.

(5) The cut surface is an edge view in plan. View perpendicular to an edge view and we see the true shape. Draw the x_1y_1 parallel to the cut surface.

(6) Project points up from the plan and take the heights of each point from the elevation.

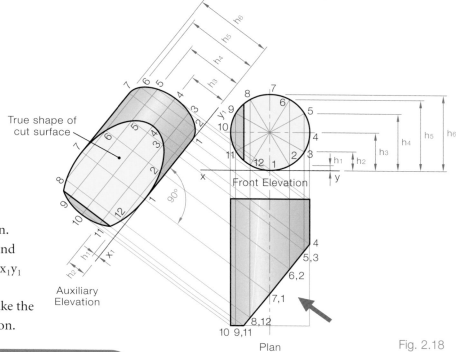

Fig. 2.18

Fig. 2.19 shows the plan and elevation of an object which has been cut by a vertical plane as shown.

(i)   Draw the given views.
(ii) Draw an auxiliary elevation of the object that will show the cut surface as a true shape.

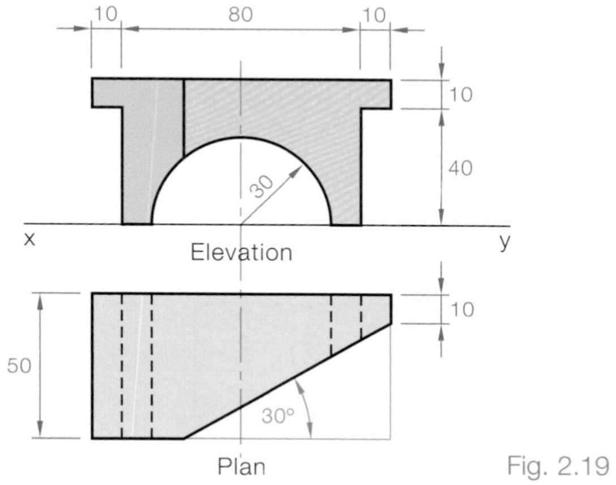

Fig. 2.19

(1) Divide the semicircle into six and index the points.

(2) The cut surface is at 30° in the plan so the x_1y_1 will be at 30° and the viewing angle at 60°.

(3) Project the points from the plan and take heights from the elevation.

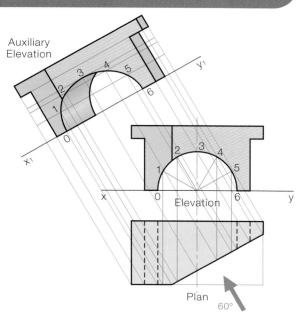

Fig. 2.20

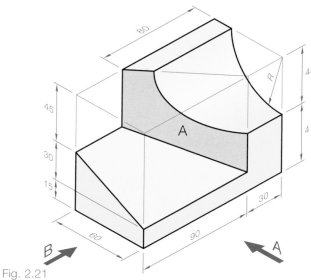

Fig. 2.21

A pictorial drawing of a solid is shown in Fig. 2.21.

(i)   Draw an elevation of the solid viewing in the direction of arrow A.

(ii)   Project a plan.

(iii) Draw an end elevation viewing in the direction of arrow B.

(iv)   Project a new elevation that will show the true shape of surface A.

(1) Draw the xy line and set up the boxes for the views. The front elevation will be on the left and the end elevation to the right.

(2) The end elevation and the plan can be completed without difficulty.

(3) The curve in the front elevation is found by dividing the quadrant in the end elevation giving 0, 1, 2 and 3. These points are projected down to the plan and up to the front elevation. They are then projected across from the end view. Where the lines intersect gives points on the curve, Fig. 2.22.

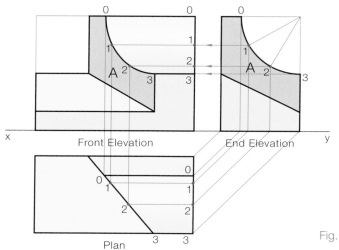

Fig. 2.22

(4) In order to see the surface A as a true shape we must view it straight on. Surface A is seen as an edge view in the plan. We view perpendicular to this edge view.

(5) Draw x_1y_1 (the new vertical plane) parallel to surface A in plan and perpendicular to the line of sight.

(6) Project the points as for an ordinary elevation. Every point must be brought up including the two sets of points on the curves.

(7) The heights of all points on the auxiliary elevation will be the same as the corresponding points on the other elevations. The true shape is found in the auxiliary.

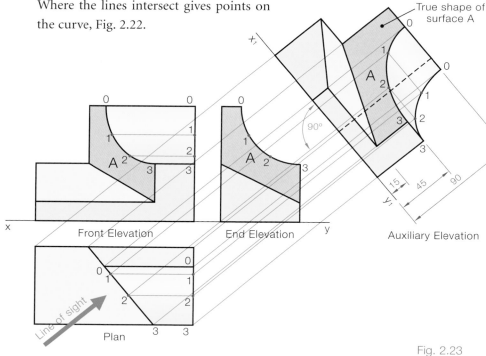

Fig. 2.23

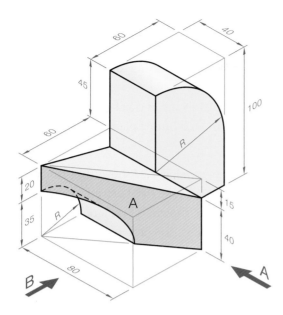

Fig. 2.24

(1) The front elevation will be on the left because we are viewing from the right. The end elevation will be to the right of the front elevation. Draw the xy line and draw the boxes for the various views.

(2) The curve in the end view is found by dividing the quadrant in the front elevation and projecting points 0, 1, 2 and 3 round through the views.

(3) Surface A is seen as an edge view in the plan, so to see a true shape of A perpendicular to the edge view, x_1y_1 is drawn perpendicular to the line of sight.

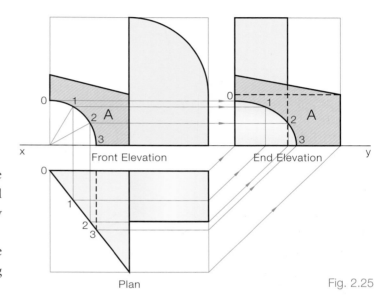

Fig. 2.24 shows a pictorial drawing of an object.
(i) Draw an elevation of the solid viewing in the direction of arrow A.
(ii) Project a plan from the elevation.
(iii) Project an end elevation viewing in the direction of arrow B.
(iv) Project a new elevation of the solid that will show the true shape of surface A.

Fig. 2.25

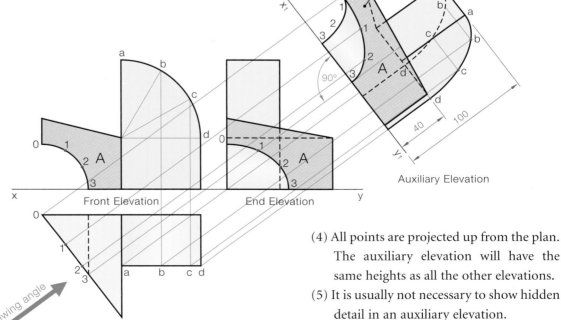

Fig. 2.26

(4) All points are projected up from the plan. The auxiliary elevation will have the same heights as all the other elevations.

(5) It is usually not necessary to show hidden detail in an auxiliary elevation.

Auxiliary Plans

When viewing an object to see its plan we are viewing from directly above that object. The line of sight is vertical and is therefore parallel to the vertical plane. The view is projected onto the horizontal plane.

When viewing an object to get an auxiliary plan we continue to view parallel to the vertical plane, but at an angle between 0° and 90° to the horizontal plane. As is always the case, the view is projected onto a plane that is perpendicular to the line of sight.

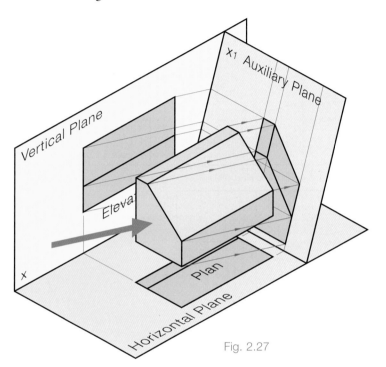

Fig. 2.27

The diagram Fig. 2.27 shows the principal planes of reference. The front elevation and plan of an object are shown. These are projected in the normal way. To view in the direction of the arrow we introduce a new plane perpendicular to the line of sight. The line of sight is inclined to the horizontal plane and parallel to the vertical plane. The auxiliary plane is inclined to the horizontal plane and perpendicular to the vertical plane. The x_1y_1 is the line of intersection between the auxiliary plane and the vertical plane. Since the line of sight is parallel to the vertical plane, the auxiliary plan which is produced will be the same distance from the x_1y_1 as the ordinary plan is from the xy line.

As before, the plane itself can be positioned close to, or far away from, the object as long as it is at the correct angle.

Fig. 2.28 shows the planes folded back.

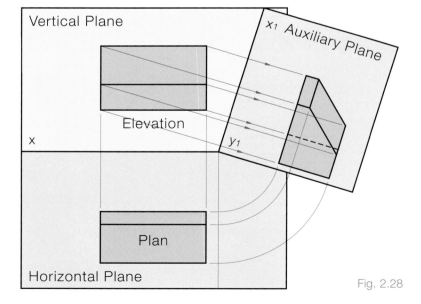

Fig. 2.28

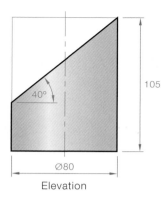

Fig. 2.29

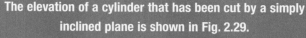

The elevation of a cylinder that has been cut by a simply inclined plane is shown in Fig. 2.29.

(i)   Draw the given elevation and project a plan and an end elevation.

(ii)   Project a new plan of the cylinder that will show the true shape of the cut surface.

(1) Draw the elevation. The plan, even though the cylinder is truncated, will be a circle.

(2) Divide the plan into twelve equal divisions.

(3) Project 0 to 11 up to the sloped surface in elevation and across to the end view.

(4) Project the same points 0 to 11 from the plan to the end view. The points in the end view are found where the corresponding lines cross, Fig. 2.30.

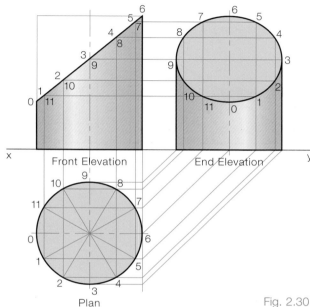

Fig. 2.30

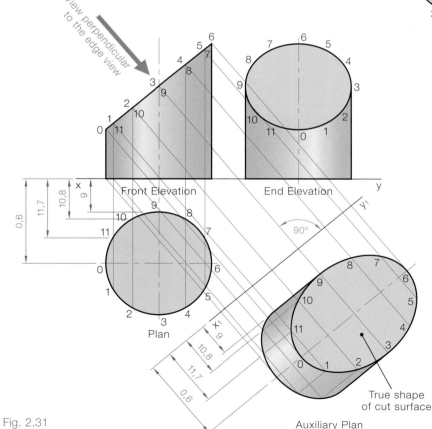

Fig. 2.31

(5) The front elevation shows the edge view of the cut surface. To see the true shape we view perpendicular to the edge view.

(6) The x_1y_1 will be drawn parallel to the edge view, which will be perpendicular to the line of sight.

(7) Project down the points from the elevation.

(8) The distance from the xy line to point 9 is taken on the compass and measured on the appropriate line from the x_1y_1 line. This locates point 9 in the auxiliary plan.

(9) All other points are found in the same way, Fig. 2.31.

The pictorial drawing of a solid is shown in Fig. 2.32.

(i) **Project a front elevation of the solid, viewing in the direction of arrow A.**

(ii) **Draw an end elevation, viewing in the direction of arrow B.**

(iii) **Project a plan.**

(iv) **Project a new plan of the solid showing the true shape of surface S.**

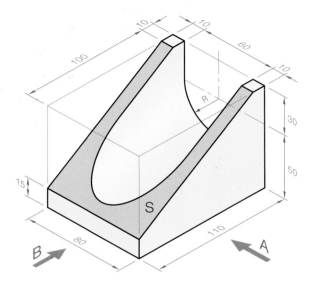

Fig. 2.32

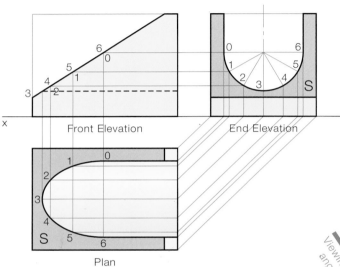

Fig. 2.33

Always think through the problem before starting to plan how the various components of the solution will be positioned on the sheet.

(1) Front elevation will be on the left and the end elevation to its right, Fig 2.33.

(2) Both elevations need to be completed before the plan. The curve in the plan is found in the usual way.

(3) To see the true shape of a surface we view perpendicular to the edge view.

(4) The construction is clearly shown from the illustration Fig. 2.34.

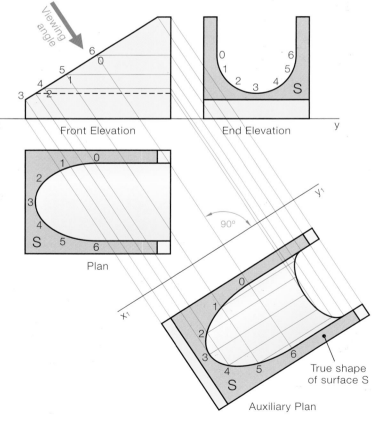

Fig. 2.34

Fig. 2.35 shows a pictorial view of a solid.

(i) Draw the front elevation of the solid looking in the direction of arrow A.

(ii) Project a plan from the front elevation.

(iii) Project an end elevation viewing in the direction of arrow B.

(iv) Construct an auxiliary plan that will show the true shape of surface S.

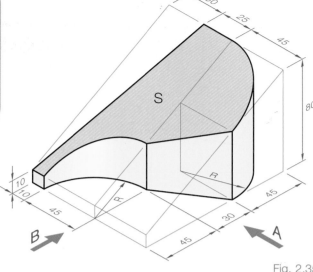

Fig. 2.35

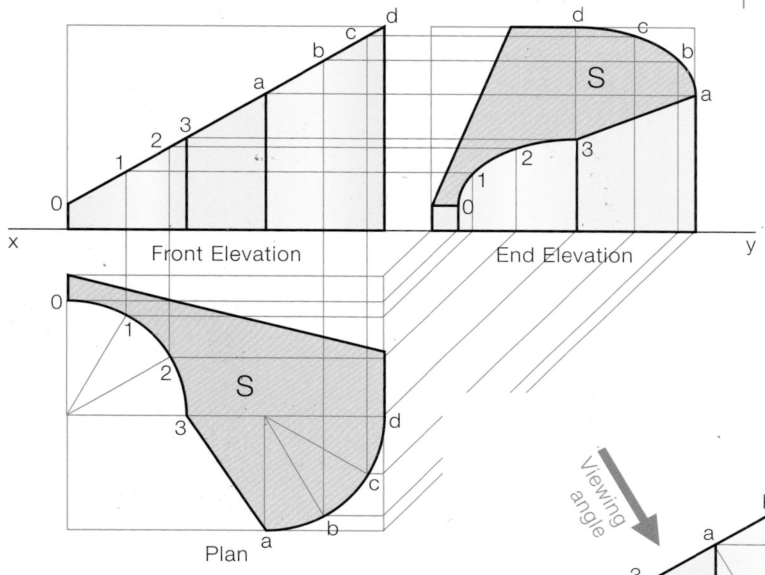

(1) Draw the front elevation, end elevation and plan. Ensure that you leave enough space for the auxiliary plan which will be down on the right.

(2) Surface S appears as an edge view in the front elevation. View perpendicular to this edge view to see surface S as a true shape.

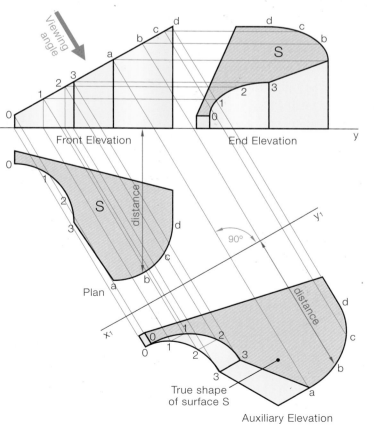

Fig. 2.36

(3) From each point in the elevation, project lines in the direction of the viewing angle.

(4) Draw the x_1y_1 line perpendicular to the lines of projection.

(5) For any point on the plan we take the distance the point is from the xy line and transfer this distance from x_1y_1 to locate the point in the auxiliary plan, see Fig. 2.37.

True shape of surface S

Auxiliary Elevation

Fig. 2.37

Further Uses of Auxiliary Views

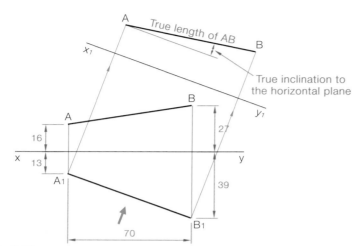

Fig. 2.38

To find the true length of a line AB and to find its inclination to the horizontal plane.

(1) To see the true inclination of the line to the horizontal plane we use an auxiliary elevation. We view perpendicular to the plan of the line.

(2) Draw the x_1y_1 line parallel to the line in plan.

(3) Project the new elevation which shows both the true length and the true inclination to the horizontal plane (HP).

To find the true length of a line AB and to find its inclination to the vertical plane.

(1) Set up the plan and elevation to the same measurements as Fig. 2.38.

(2) To see the true inclination to the vertical plane an auxiliary plan must be projected.

(3) View perpendicular to line AB in elevation.

(4) Draw x_1y_1 parallel to line AB in elevation.

(5) Project the auxiliary plan showing the true length and the required inclination.

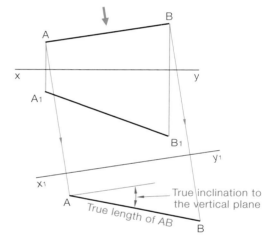

Fig. 2.39

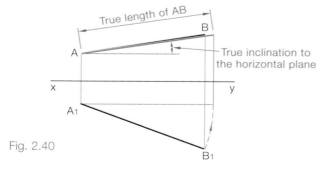

Fig. 2.40

To find the true length of a line AB and to find its inclination to the horizontal plane.

Alternative Method

In Fig. 2.38 we moved our line of sight to view the line straight on and thus see its true length and angle. In this method we rotate the line so that it is parallel to the vertical plane and hence will show its true length and true angle in elevation.

(1) Rotate line AB in plan about point A until it is parallel to the xy line.

(2) Project the end of the new line to elevation and project point B in elevation across to meet it.

To find the true length of a line AB and to find its inclination to the vertical plane.

Alternative Method

Similar construction as Fig. 2.40 except the line is rotated in elevation giving the true length and angle in plan.

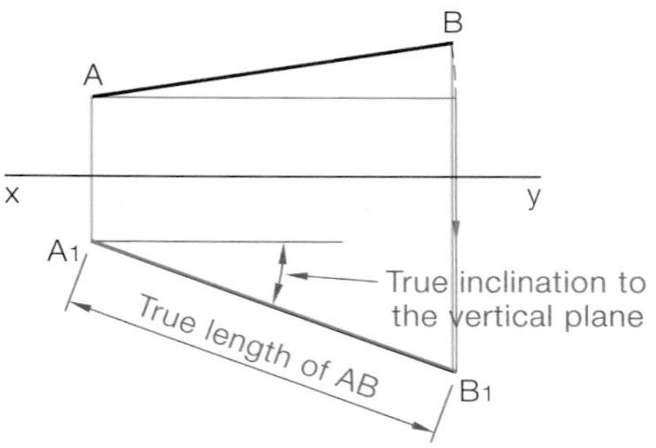

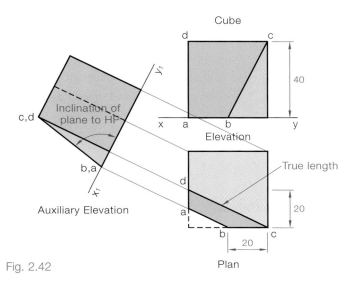

Fig. 2.41

Fig. 2.42

To find the inclination of a plane abcd to the horizontal plane.

Lines dc and ab are horizontal, and are therefore seen as true lengths in the plan. Project an auxiliary elevation, viewing in the direction of the true lengths. The plane abcd will appear as an edge view in the auxiliary and the angle can be seen.

Note:

(1) **A line on a plane parallel to the xy line in elevation will appear as a true length in plan.**
The converse is also true.

(2) **A line on a plane parallel to the xy line in plan will appear as a true length in elevation.**

(3) **When a line on a plane appears as a true length, viewing along the true length will show an edge view of that plane.**

Activities

Q1. Fig. 2.43 (2.44) shows the plan and elevation of an object. Make a pictorial drawing showing the planes of reference and demonstrating how the views are projected.

Q2. Make a pictorial drawing showing the planes in question one rebatted in line with the vertical plane. Show the elevation and plan in their respective positions on the planes.

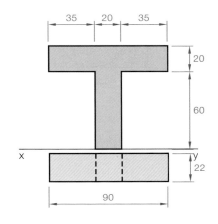

Fig. 2.43 (2.44)

Q3. Fig. 2.45 shows the elevation and plan of a solid. Draw the given views and project an end view looking from the left.

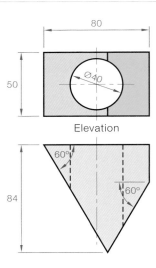

Elevation

84

Fig. 2.45

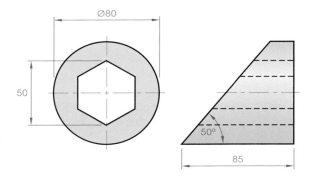

Fig. 2.46

Q4. Two views of a shaped cylinder are shown in Fig. 2.46. Draw the given views and project a plan.

AUXILIARY ELEVATIONS

Q5. Given the plan and elevation in Fig. 2.47. Draw the given views and project an auxiliary elevation in the direction of arrow A.

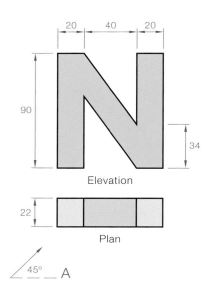

Elevation

Plan

45° _ A

Fig. 2.47

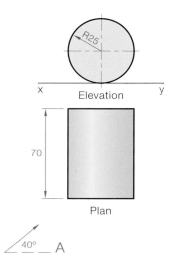

Plan

40° _ A

Fig. 2.48

Q6. The diagram Fig. 2.48 shows the plan and elevation of a cylinder lying on the horizontal plane. Draw the given views and project an auxiliary elevation of the solid viewing in the direction of arrow A.

Q7. The diagram Fig. 2.49 shows the plan, elevation and end view of a solid. Draw the given views and project an auxiliary elevation in the direction of the arrow A.

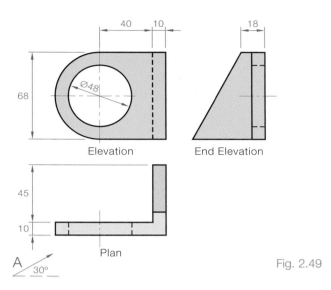

Fig. 2.49

Q8. The drawings in Fig. 2.50 show the projections of a shaped block with a hole drilled through the centre. Project the given views and project a new elevation of the solid which includes the true shape of surface A.

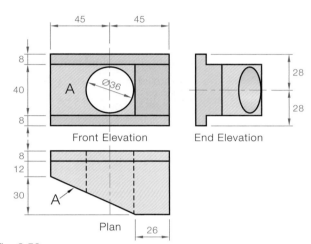

Fig. 2.50

Q9. The diagram Fig. 2.51 shows the front elevation, end elevation and plan of a shaped solid. Draw the given views and project an auxiliary elevation in the direction of the arrow.

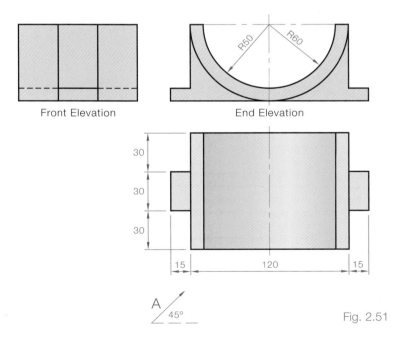

Fig. 2.51

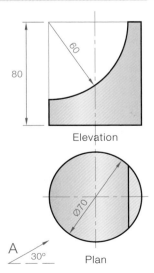

Fig. 2.52

Q10. Draw the given views Fig. 2.52 and project an end elevation. Project a new elevation viewing in the direction of arrow A.

Q11. Draw the given views, Fig. 2.53, of a rectangular-based pyramid. Project a new plan that will show the true shape of surface A.

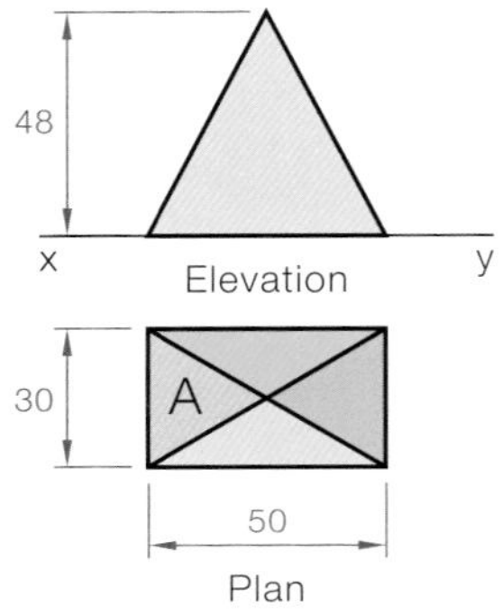

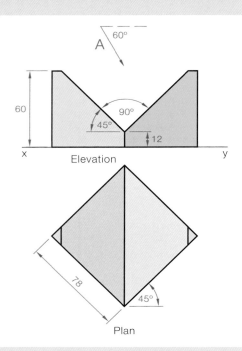

Fig. 2.54

Plan

Elevation   Fig. 2.53

Q12. The plan and elevation of a vee-block are shown, Fig. 2.54. Draw the two given views and project an auxiliary plan looking in the direction of arrow A.

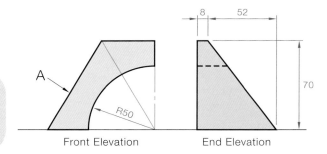

Front Elevation   End Elevation

Fig. 2.55

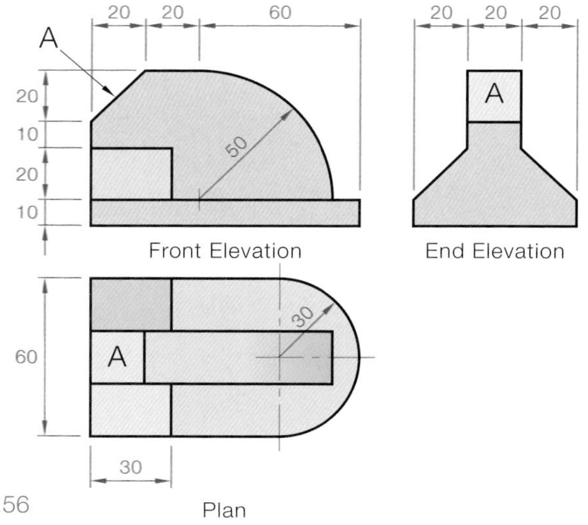

Q13. Fig. 2.55 shows the front and end elevations of a solid. Project a plan of the solid. Project an auxiliary plan showing the true shape of surface A.

Front Elevation   End Elevation

Plan

Fig. 2.56

Q14. Draw the given front elevation, end elevation and plan, Fig. 2.56. Project a plan that will show the true shape of surface A.

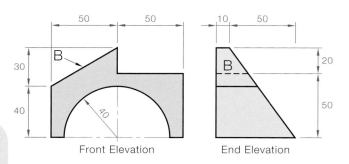

Front Elevation   End Elevation

Fig. 2.57

Q15. Given the front elevation and plan, Fig. 2.57. Draw the given views and project a plan. Project a new plan of the solid showing the true shape of surface B.

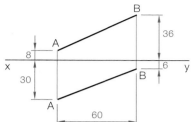

Fig. 2.58

Q16. Given the plan and elevation of a line AB, Fig. 2.58. Find the true length of the line and its true inclination to the horizontal plane using an auxiliary view.

Q17. Given the plan and elevation of a line CD, Fig. 2.59. Find the true length of the line and its inclination to the horizontal plane using the rotation method.

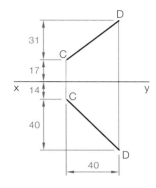

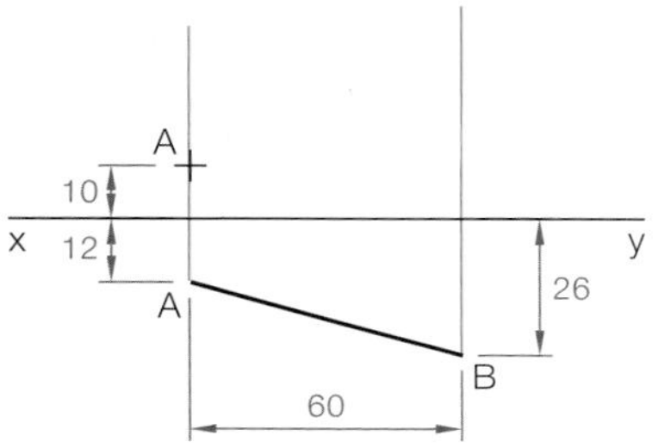

Fig. 2.59

Fig. 2.60

Q18. Given the plan of a line AB and the elevation of one end of the line, A, Fig. 2.60. The true inclination of this line is to be 30° to the horizontal plan. Draw the elevation.

Q19. Given the elevation of a line CD and the plan of one end of the line, C, Fig. 2.61. If the true length of this line is to be 80 mm, complete the plan.

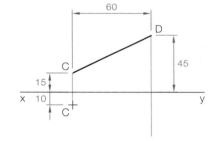

Fig. 2.61

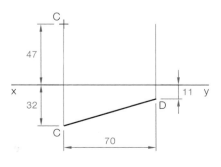

Fig. 2.62

Q20. Given that a line AB has a true length of 70 mm. End A rests somewhere on line A in plan and A₁ in elevation. End B rests somewhere on line B in plan and B₁ in elevation. Find the elevation and plan of the line.

Q21. Given the elevation of a line CD and the elevation of one end of the line, C, Fig. 2.63. If the true length of the line is 76 mm, complete the elevation.

Fig. 2.63

Third-angle Projection

Third-angle projection is the system of orthographic projection which is more favoured in America whereas first-angle projection is more favoured in Europe. The object to be drawn is placed in the third angle of the intersecting reference planes. The views are found by looking **through** the planes.

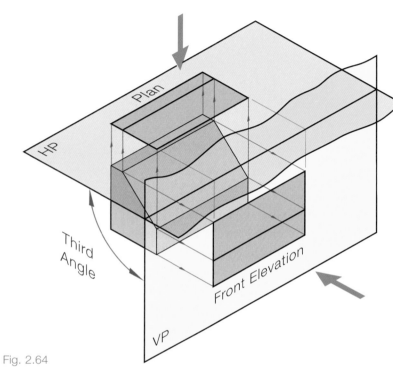

Fig. 2.64

Fig. 2.64 shows the arrangement of planes and object. The front elevation is found by looking through the vertical plane. The view that is seen is what is projected onto the plane. Similarly for the plan, we look down through the vertical plane. The view that is seen is projected up to the horizontal plane.

The horizontal plane is hinged about the xy line until it is vertical. The plan, therefore, is above the xy line and the front elevation is below the plan and the xy line.

The two end views are drawn in line with the front elevation, Fig. 2.65. They can be projected in a similar way as was done in first-angle projection. It should be noted that we are viewing through the plane and then projecting the image back onto the same plane. The end elevation on the left, therefore, will be the view from the left and the end elevation to the right of the front elevation will be the view from the right of the object.

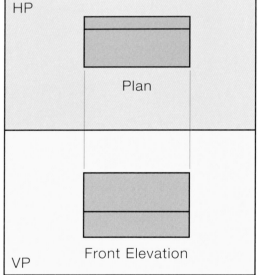

Fig. 2.65

Symbol
The angle of projection must be stated on a drawing either by using text or by using the appropriate symbol, Figures 2.66a and 2.66b.

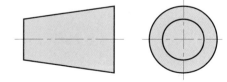

Fig. 2.66a

First-angle Projection

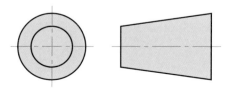

Fig. 2.66b

Third-angle Projection

HIGHER LEVEL

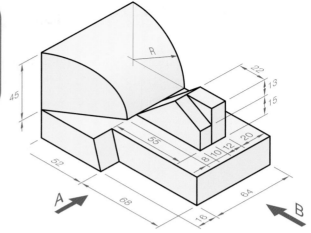

A pictorial drawing of an object is shown in Fig. 2.67.
Using third-angle projection draw:
(i)   A front elevation looking in the direction of arrow A.
(ii) A plan.
(iii) An end elevation projected from the other two views.

Fig. 2.67

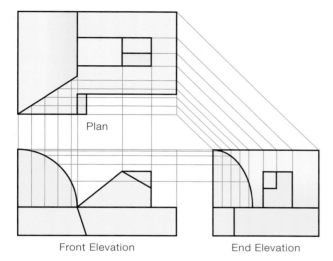

Plan

Front Elevation   End Elevation

(1) Set up the relative positions of the three views. The
    arrow A is pointing from the left so the front
    elevation will be drawn on the left.
(2) The plan is directly above the front elevation.
(3) The arrow B is viewing from the right so the end
    elevation will be to the right of the front elevation.
(4) The symbol must be used to indicate third-angle
    projection, Fig. 2.68.

Fig. 2.68

Fig. 2.69 shows a pictorial view of a shaped block. Using
third-angle projection draw:
(i)   A front elevation viewing in the direction of arrow A.
(ii) A plan.
(iii) An end elevation viewed in the direction of arrow B.

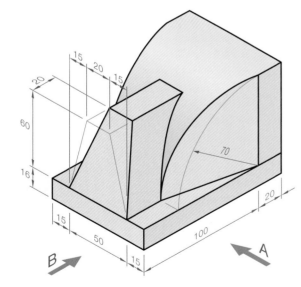

Fig. 2.69

Fig. 2.70 shows a possible arrangement for the xy
line and the yy line. The construction of the views
themselves should be straightforward.

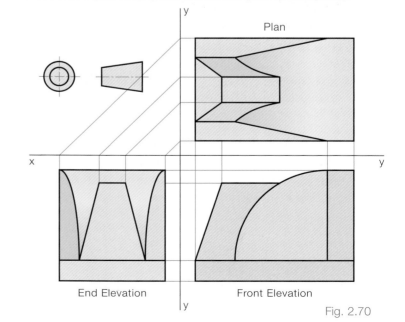

End Elevation   Front Elevation

Fig. 2.70

HIGHER LEVEL

Third-angle Auxiliary Views

The projection of auxiliary views, in third-angle projection, follow the same rules as in first angle. Fig. 2.71 shows an auxiliary elevation projected and Fig. 2.72 shows an auxiliary plan projected.

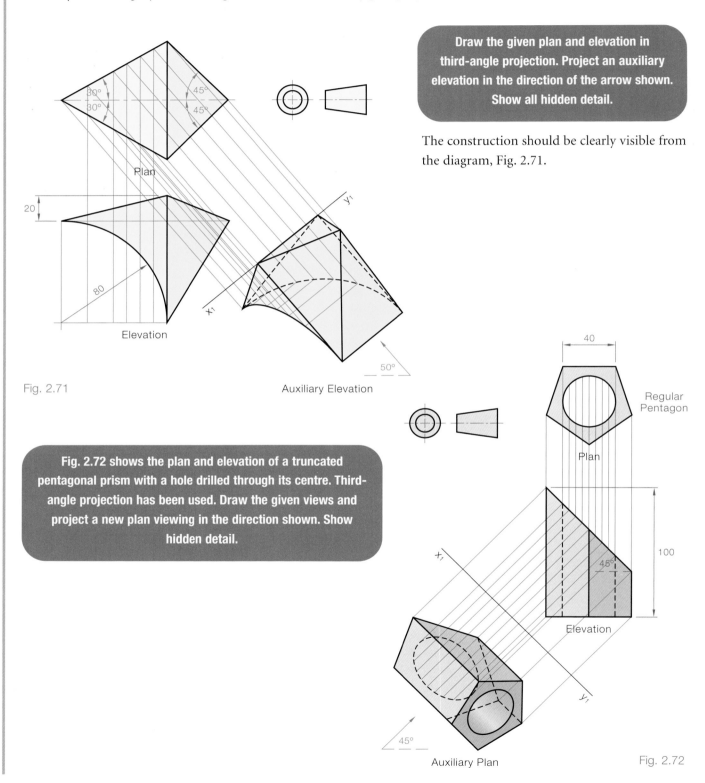

Draw the given plan and elevation in third-angle projection. Project an auxiliary elevation in the direction of the arrow shown. Show all hidden detail.

The construction should be clearly visible from the diagram, Fig. 2.71.

Fig. 2.71

Fig. 2.72 shows the plan and elevation of a truncated pentagonal prism with a hole drilled through its centre. Third-angle projection has been used. Draw the given views and project a new plan viewing in the direction shown. Show hidden detail.

Fig. 2.72

HIGHER LEVEL

Second Auxiliary Views

Once an auxiliary view is constructed it can be used as a basis for another auxiliary. The second auxiliary can be used to get a third auxiliary view and so on. An auxiliary plan can only be projected from an elevation or an auxiliary elevation. Similarly an auxiliary elevation can only be projected from a plan or an auxiliary plan.

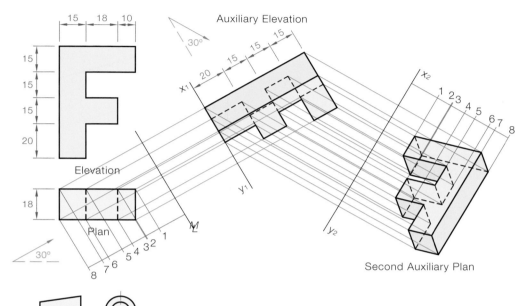

Fig. 2.73

HIGHER LEVEL

(1) Draw the elevation, plan and auxiliary elevation in the normal way, Fig. 2.73.

(2) The new line of sight is shown at 30° to the x_1y_1. Set up the x_2y_2 perpendicular to this line of sight.

(3) Points are projected from the auxiliary elevation in the direction of the line of sight.

(4) The distances for the second auxiliary plan are measured from the x_1y_1 back to the plan for each point. It is often useful to put a line, parallel to the x_1y_1 line, closer to the plan. This line is called a **measuring line** or a **datum line**. Measuring from the measuring line to the plan instead of from the x_1y_1 line to the plan has the effect of bringing the second auxiliary plan closer to the x_2y_2 line.

Note:

- Lines that are parallel remain parallel in all views.
- When finding distances for an auxiliary you measure from the xy line before the one for the view being found, e.g. if projecting a fourth auxiliary we would be drawing it from x_4y_4. Measurements would be taken from the previous xy line, i.e. x_3y_3.
- When finding distances for an auxiliary you measure to the view before the view being projected from, e.g. if projecting a fourth auxiliary, the view would be projected from the third auxiliary, therefore the measurements are taken from the second auxiliary.

Applications of Second Auxiliary View

H I G H E R   L E V E L

> **To project the point view of a line.**

A point view of a line is when a view is taken down the length of the line and the whole line is only seen as a point. Only the end of the line is seen and it is a dot.

> **To obtain a point view of a line, a view is projected to show the true length of the line. A subsequent view is then taken viewing along the true length.**

(1) Project the plan and elevation of the line.

(2) Draw x_1y_1 parallel to the line in plan and project an auxiliary elevation. This auxiliary elevation shows line AB as a true length.

(3) The second auxiliary is projected from the first, viewing along the true length. The x_2y_2 is perpendicular to the true length.

(4) Both A and B end on the same point, as they are both distance d from the x_1y_1 in the plan.

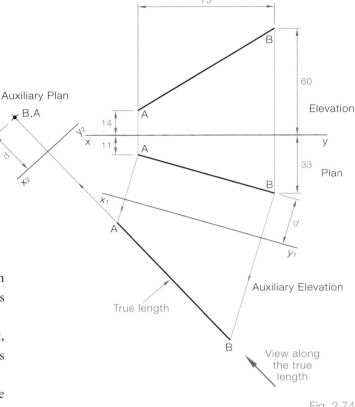

Fig. 2.74

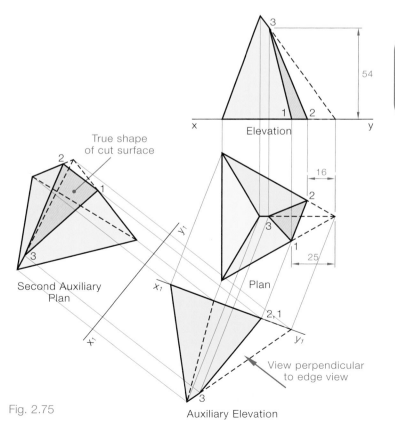

Fig. 2.75

> **Given a tetrahedron of 75 mm side which is cut as shown in Fig. 2.75. Project a view of the given solid showing the true shape of the cut surface.**

(1) The edge 1,2 is horizontal and is therefore seen as a true length in plan.

> **If we view along the true length of a line, the plane on which the line rests will be seen as an edge view.**

Project the auxiliary elevation with x_1y_1 perpendicular to 1,2 in plan.

(2) Project perpendicular to the edge view to show the true shape. Draw x_2y_2 parallel to the edge view. Distances for the second auxiliary plan are taken from the x_1y_1 back to the plan.

HIGHER LEVEL

> **Given the solid, Fig. 2.76.**
> **Side 1,2 = 60 mm, side 1,3 = 75 mm, side 2,3 = 80 mm.**
> **Find the true angle between surface A and B.**

(1) Line 0,3 is the line of intersection between the two planes. Project either an auxiliary elevation or auxiliary plan to show this line as a true length. In Fig. 2.76 x_1y_1 is drawn parallel to 0,3 in the elevation. The auxiliary plan will show 0,3 as a true length.

(2) Project a point view of 0,3. View in the direction of the true length. The x_2y_2 line is perpendicular to the true length. When this view is projected, both plane A and plane B are seen as edge views. The angle between the planes is clearly seen. This angle is called the **dihedral angle**.

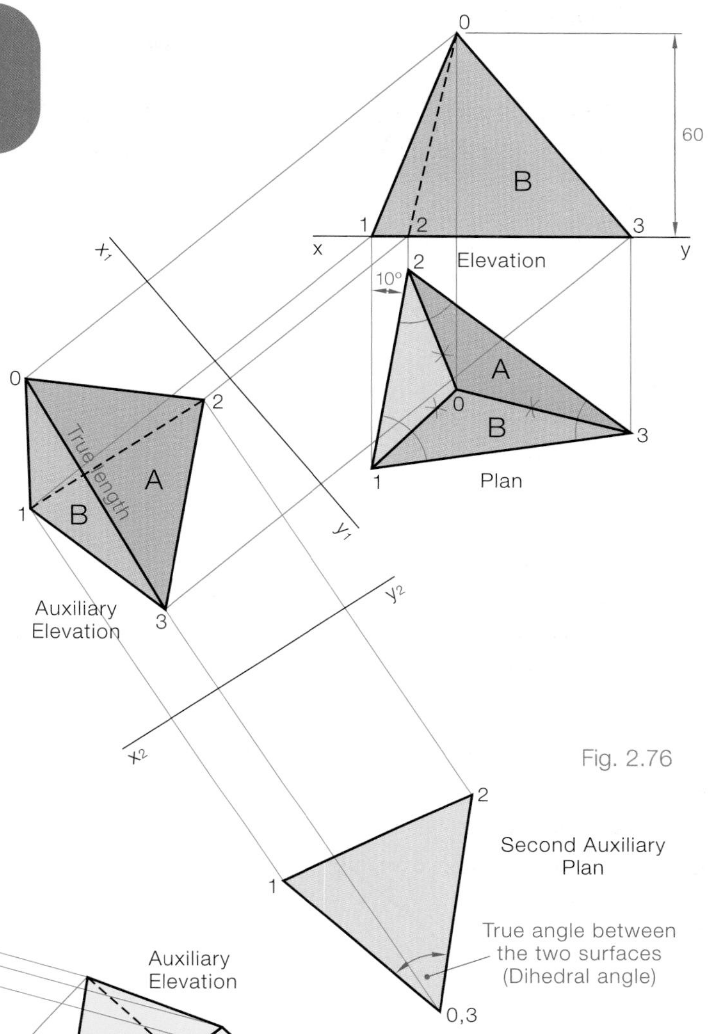

Fig. 2.76

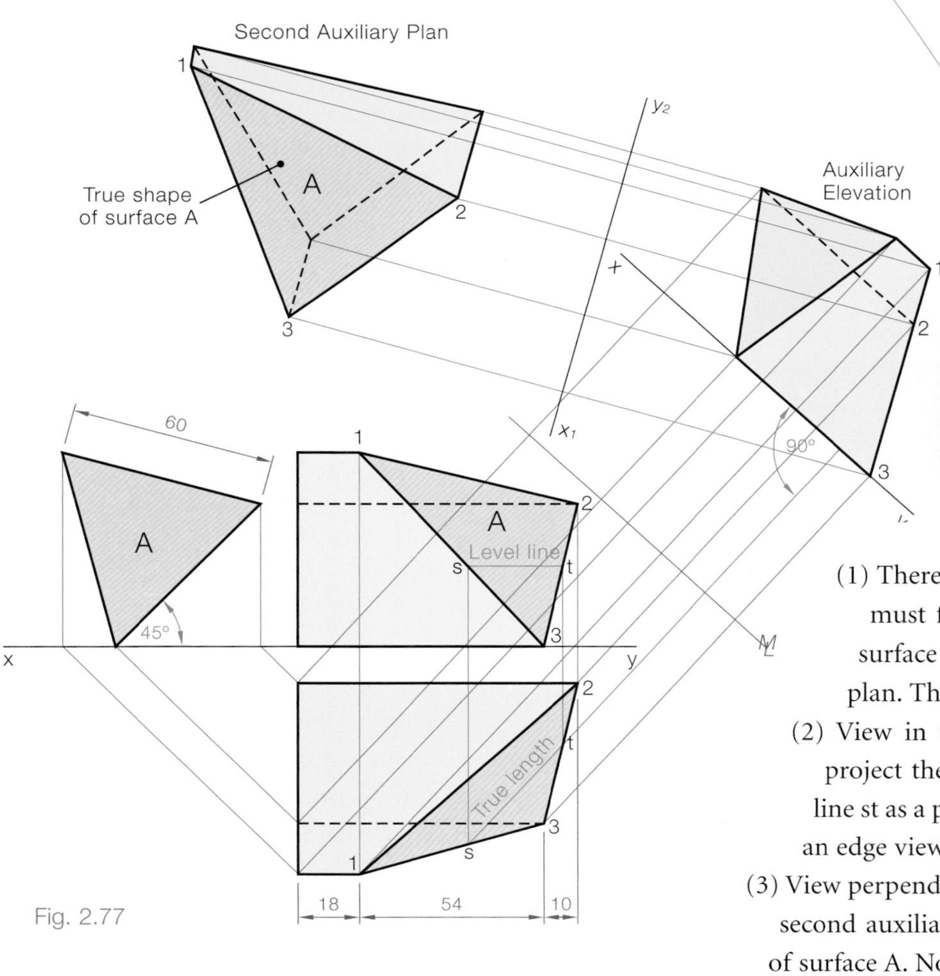

> **Fig. 2.77 shows an equilateral triangular prism which has been cut as shown. Project a view of the solid to show a true shape of the cut surface A.**

(1) There is no true length on surface A so we must find one. Draw a horizontal line on surface A in elevation, line st. Find st in plan. This line is a true length.

(2) View in the direction of the true length to project the auxiliary elevation. This shows the line st as a point view and the plane it rests on as an edge view.

(3) View perpendicular to the edge view to project the second auxiliary plan which shows the true shape of surface A. Note the measuring line.

Fig. 2.77

Projection of Lines Given Angles of Inclination

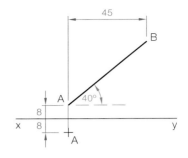

Fig. 2.78

> **Given the elevation of a line AB and its true inclination to the horizontal plane as 30°. Draw the plan of the line given one point.**

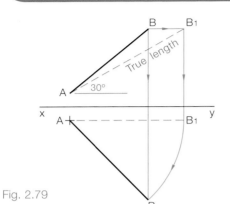

Fig. 2.79

(1) The heights of A and B will remain the same. Draw a line starting at A in elevation and at the correct angle.

(2) Project B across to intersect this line at B.

(3) Project to plan. Since it is a true length in elevation it must be parallel to the xy line in plan.

(4) Rotate the line about point A in plan.

(5) Drop point B from elevation to intersect the rotation.

> **Given the elevation of a line AB and its true inclination to the vertical plane as 20°. Given one point on the plan, complete the plan.**

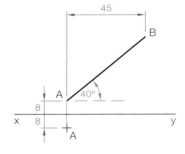

Fig. 2.80

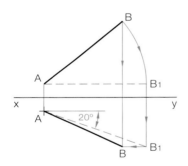

Fig. 2.81

(1) Rotate line AB about A in elevation until it is horizontal.

(2) Project to plan. The line when horizontal will make an angle of 20° to the xy line. Draw the line from A at 20° to the xy line, locating point B.

(3) B_1 can be projected across locating B in plan as shown in Fig. 2.81.

> **Given the plan of a line AB and the elevation of point B. The true length of the line is 60 mm. Find the elevation of the line.**

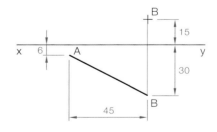

Fig. 2.82

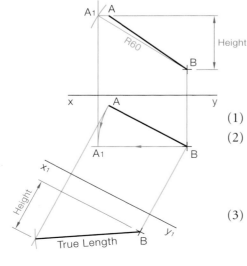

Fig. 2.83

(1) Two approaches to solving this problem are shown in Fig. 2.83.

(2) The line is rotated about point B in plan until it is parallel to xy, giving A. A projection line is brought vertically from A_1 to elevation. The true length of AB is swung from B in elevation finding A_1. Point A is found in elevation by projection.

(3) The alternative method uses an auxiliary view. The construction is self-explanatory.

HIGHER LEVEL

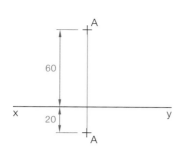

Fig. 2.84

Given the true length of a line AB, its true angle to the vertical plane and its true angle to the horizontal plane. Draw a plan and elevation of the line.
Length = 60 mm, Angle to vertical plane (VP) = 20°, Angle to HP = 40°.

(1) Locate point A in plan and elevation.
(2) From A in the elevation, draw a line that is 60 mm long and is inclined at 40° to the horizontal plane.
(3) Rotate this line about a vertical axis through A. This forms a cone with A as apex having every generator 60 mm long and inclined at 40° to the horizontal plane, Figures 2.85 and 2.86.

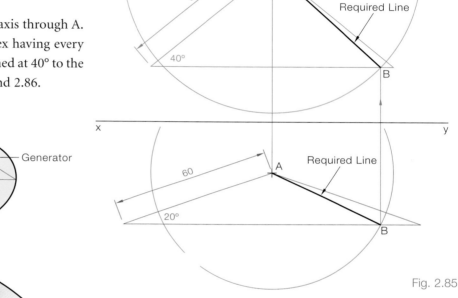

Fig. 2.85

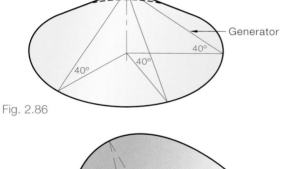

Fig. 2.86

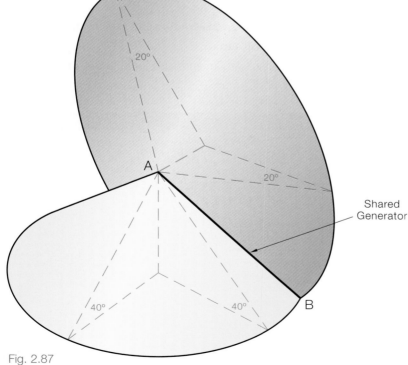

Fig. 2.87

(4) Draw the cone in plan.
(5) From A in plan draw a line that is 60 mm long and is inclined at 20° to the vertical plane.
(6) Rotate this line about a horizontal axis through A. This forms a cone with A as apex having every generator 60 mm long and inclined at 20° to the vertical plane.
(7) The two cones produced will intersect along a shared generator in two locations. Either of these is the required line, Fig. 2.87.

HIGHER LEVEL

Activities

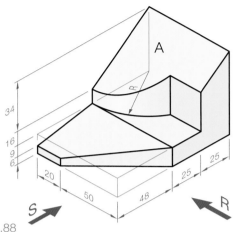

Fig. 2.88

Q1. The diagram, Fig. 2.88, shows a shaped solid.
(i)   In third-angle projection draw a front elevation viewing in the direction of arrow R.
(ii) Draw an end view looking in the direction of arrow S.
(iii) Project a plan from these views.
(iv) Project a new plan of the solid that will show the true shape of surface A.

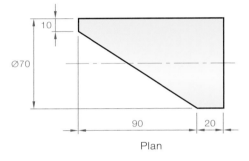

Plan

Fig. 2.89

Q2. The diagram, Fig. 2.89, shows the plan of a cylinder which has been cut by a vertical plane. In third-angle projection draw:
(i)   The front elevation.
(ii) An end elevation viewing from the left.
(iii) An auxiliary elevation viewing perpendicularly to the cut surface. Include hidden detail and the third-angle symbol.

Q3. The object shown in Fig. 2.90b is to be tilted at 30° to the horizontal plane as shown in Fig. 2.90a.
(i)   In third-angle projection draw the given elevation and project an auxiliary plan to show the true shape of the top surface.
(ii) Using these views, project a plan and an end view looking in from the left.
(iii) Draw in the third-angle symbol.

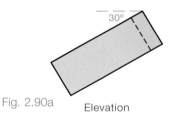

Fig. 2.90a   Elevation

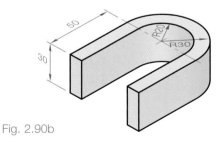

Fig. 2.90b

Q4. The diagram in Fig. 2.91 shows the elevation and plan of a letter.
(i)   Draw the given views.
(ii) Project an auxiliary elevation onto the x_1y_1.
(iii) Project a second auxiliary plan onto x_2y_2.

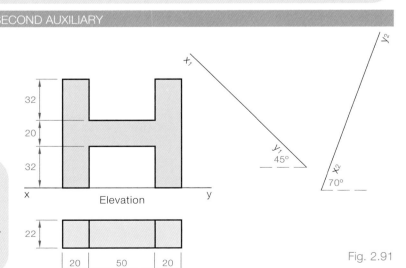

Fig. 2.91

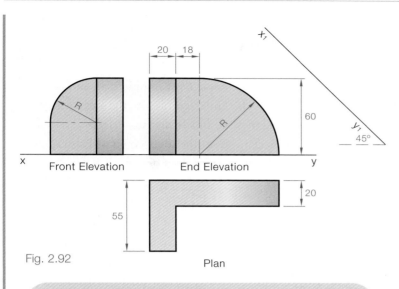

Fig. 2.92

HIGHER LEVEL

Q5. Draw the views indicated in Fig. 2.92 and project an auxiliary elevation and a second auxiliary plan on the xy lines shown.

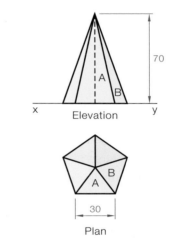

Fig. 2.93

Q6. The diagram, Fig. 2.93, shows the plan and elevation of a regular pentagonal prism.
(i) Draw the given views.
(ii) Project a new elevation showing the true length of the line of intersection between surfaces A and B.
(iii) Project a second auxiliary plan showing the dihedral angle between surfaces A and B.

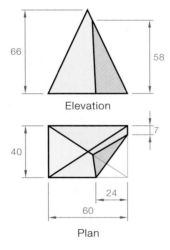

Fig. 2.94

Q7. A rectangular-based pyramid has been cut by a plane as shown in Fig. 2.94.
(i) Draw the given views.
(ii) Project an auxiliary elevation which will show the true angle the cutting plane makes with the horizontal plane.
(iii) Project a second auxiliary plan showing the true shape of the cut surface.

Q8. In end view AB = 60 mm, BC = 70 mm and AC = 50 mm, Fig. 2.95.
(i) Draw the given views.
(ii) Project an auxiliary plan showing the true angle between plane ABC and the vertical plane.
(iii) Project a second auxiliary elevation to show the true shape of ABC.

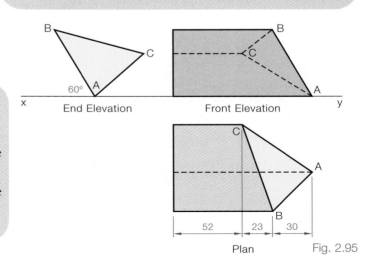

Fig. 2.95

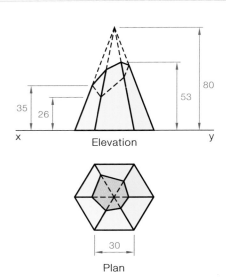

Fig. 2.96

Q9. A hexagonal-based pyramid has been cut by a plane. Three points on the cut surface are given, Fig. 2.96.

(i) Draw the complete pyramid in plan and elevation.

(ii) Locate the three points on the cut surface and using these complete the cut surface.

(iii) Project a view of the solid which will also show the true shape of the cut surface.

Q10. Given the true length of a line as 70 mm, its true angle to the horizontal plane as 45° and its true angle to the vertical plane as 30°, Fig. 2.97. Given the projections of one end of the line complete the plan and elevation.

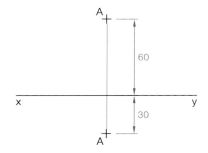

Fig. 2.97

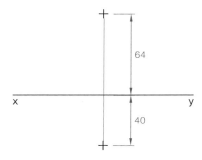

Fig. 2.98

Q11. Given the projections of a point B. This point is one end of a line which has a true length of 70 mm, a true angle to the horizontal plane of 40° and a true angle to the vertical plane of 32°, Fig. 2.98. Find the plan and elevation of this line.

Q12.

(i) Draw the given views of the object in Fig. 2.99.

(ii) Project an auxiliary to show the true length of line 1,2.

(iii) Find the dihedral angle between surfaces A and B.

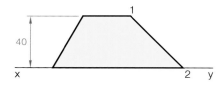

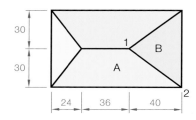

Fig. 2.99

3 Sections of Solids

SYLLABUS OUTLINE

Areas to be studied:

• Sectional views. • Projection of cube and tetrahedron, *their inscribed and circumscribed spheres.*

Learning outcomes

Students should be able to:

Higher and Ordinary levels

• Solve problems that involve the intersection of solids by simply inclined planes and obliquely inclined planes, using horizontal and vertical section planes.

• Represent in two dimensions the cube and tetrahedron from given information.

Higher level only

• Solve problems that involve the intersection of solids by simply inclined planes and obliquely inclined planes using simply inclined section planes.

• Determine the incentre and circumcentre of cube and tetrahedron.

Section Planes

A sectional plane is a plane which slices through an object. These planes can be horizontal, vertical, simply inclined or oblique. Sectional planes are used to reveal the inside of an object or can be used to help solve the interpenetration of solids. See Figures 3.1, 3.2, 3.3 and 3.4.

HORIZONTAL SECTION PLANE

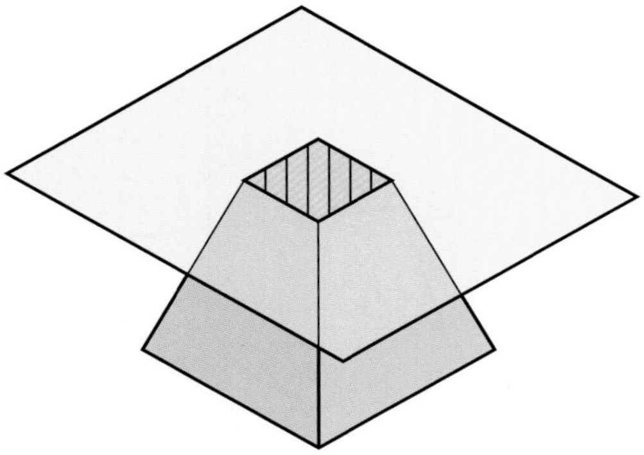

Fig. 3.1a

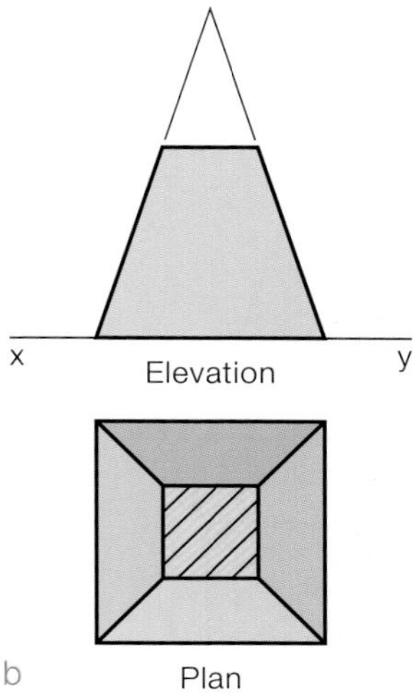

Elevation

Plan

Fig. 3.1b

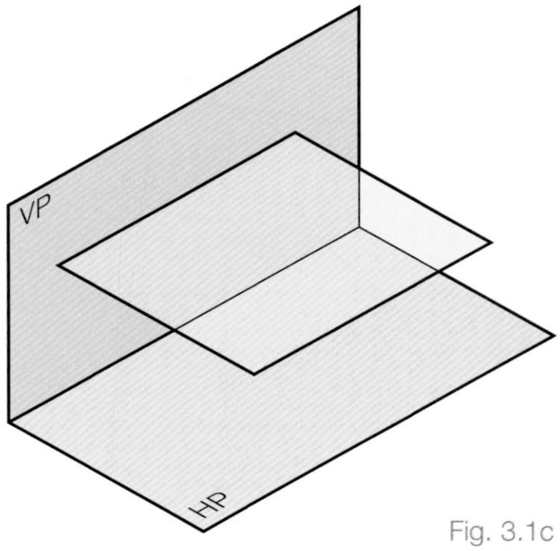

Fig. 3.1c

VERTICAL SECTION PLANE

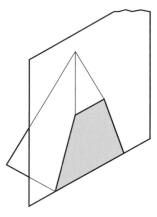

Fig. 3.2a

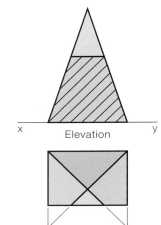

x   y
        Elevation

Plan

Fig. 3.2b

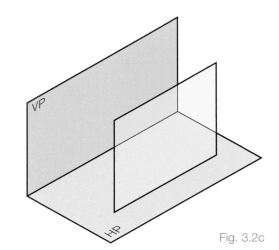

VP

HP

Fig. 3.2c

SIMPLY INCLINED SECTION PLANE

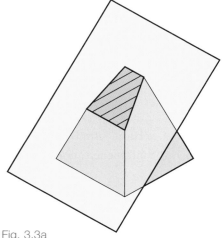

Fig. 3.3a

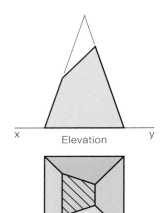

x   y
        Elevation

Plan

Fig. 3.3b

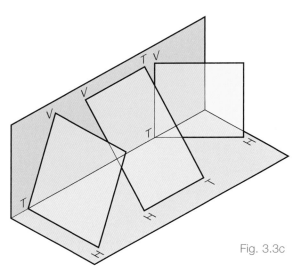

Fig. 3.3c

OBLIQUE SECTION PLANE

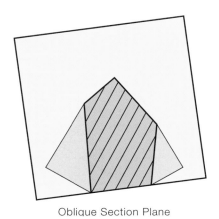

Oblique Section Plane

Fig. 3.4a

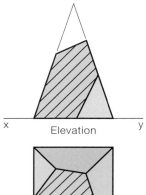

x   y
        Elevation

Plan

Fig. 3.4b

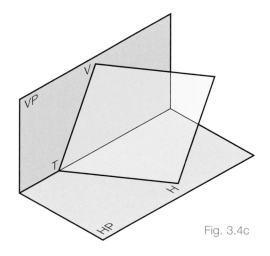

VP

V

T

H

HP

Fig. 3.4c

Traces of a Plane

When a plane meets another plane the line of intersection will always be a straight line. If a plane is extended to meet the horizontal plane the straight line produced is called the **horizontal trace**. Similarly, if a plane is extended to meet the vertical plane the straight line produced is called the **vertical trace**. When the plane intersects both planes simultaneously it will have both a horizontal trace and a vertical trace. These traces will always meet on the xy line except for one type of plane shown in Fig. 3.5, a doubly inclined plane. In this case the traces run parallel to the xy line.

Fig. 3.5 shows the plane pictorially while Fig. 3.6 shows the representation of the same plane in orthographic projection.

All planes can be represented, in orthographic, by their traces. Fig. 3.7 shows a number of plane types in a pictorial view while Fig. 3.8 shows the corresponding orthographic representation of the same planes.

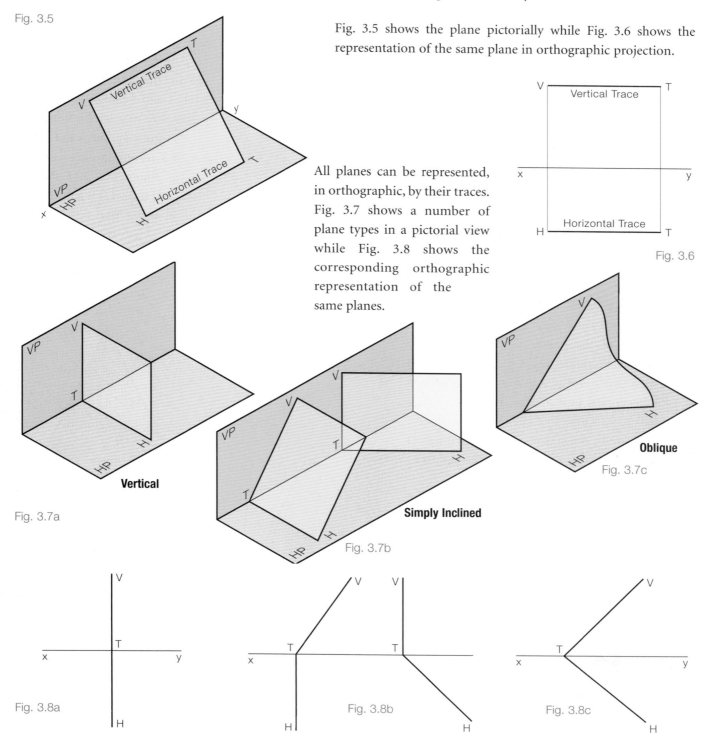

Fig. 3.5

Fig. 3.6

Vertical
Fig. 3.7a

Simply Inclined
Fig. 3.7b

Oblique
Fig. 3.7c

Fig. 3.8a

Fig. 3.8b

Fig. 3.8c

Projection of Solids Cut by Simply Inclined Planes

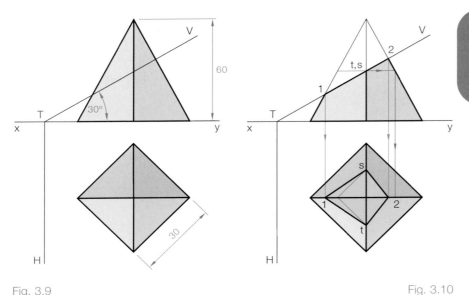

Fig. 3.9

Fig. 3.10

Fig. 3.9 shows the plan and elevation of a pyramid that is to be cut by the simply inclined plane VTH. Draw the plan and elevation of the cut solid.

(1) The simply inclined plane appears as an edge view in elevation so the cut points 1 and 2 can be clearly seen and projected to plan.

(2) Points s and t cannot be projected in this way. We take a horizontal section through points s and t. If we draw this section in plan we locate the two points. Fig. 3.11 shows a pictorial of the pyramid, the cutting plane and the horizontal section used to find points s and t.

Fig. 3.12 shows the plan and elevation of a cone that is to be cut by the simply inclined plane VTH. Draw the plan and elevation of the cut solid.

(1) Points 3 and 4 are easily found.

(2) The rest of the points are found by using horizontal sections. Take a section at any level in elevation giving points 2 and 1. The section will be circular in plan. The circle has a radius equal to R_1. Draw this circle in plan. Project points 1 and 2 down from elevation to intersect this circle, locating points 1 and 2 in plan.

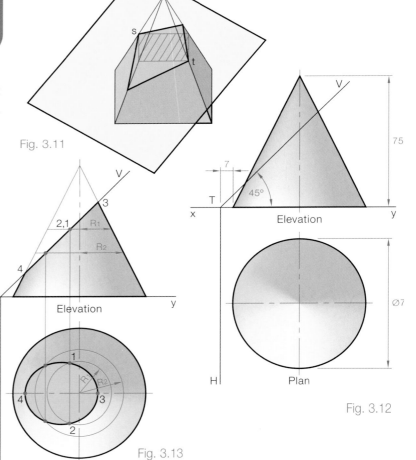

Fig. 3.11

Fig. 3.13

Fig. 3.12

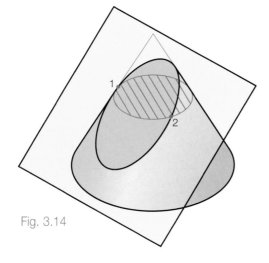

Fig. 3.14

The plan of a sphere resting on the horizontal plane is shown in Fig. 3.15. The sphere is to be cut by the simply inclined plane S–S. Find the plan and elevation of the cut solid using vertical section planes.

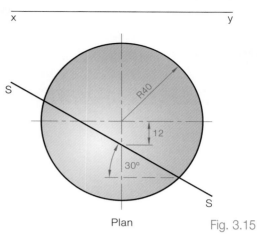

Plan

Fig. 3.15

(1) Each point on the cut surface is found by taking vertical sections. A vertical section parallel to the vertical plane is taken in plan. This section will be circular in elevation, Fig. 3.16.

(2) The intersection between the vertical section plane and section plane S–S in plan is projected to elevation, giving p and q, Fig 3.17.

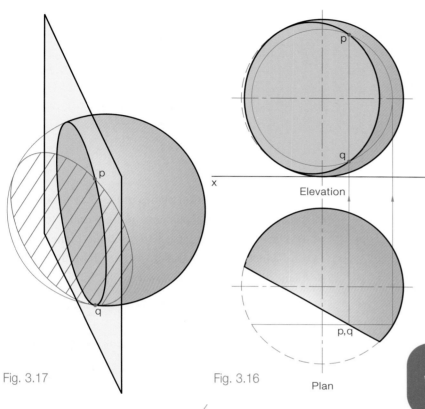

Elevation

Fig. 3.17

Fig. 3.16

Plan

An oblique cylinder is shown, Fig. 3.18, which is to be cut by the plane VTH. Draw the plan and elevation of the cut solid.

In this example vertical sections were used. The construction should be clear from Fig. 3.19.

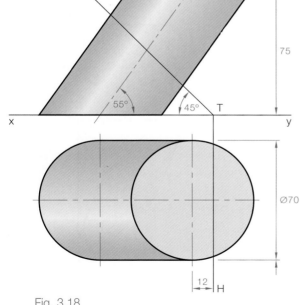

Fig. 3.18

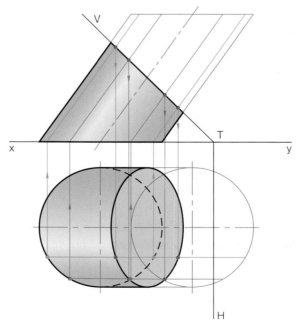

Fig. 3.19

Projection of Solids Cut by Oblique Planes

> The rectangular prism shown in Fig. 3.20 is to be cut by the oblique plane VTH. Draw the plan and elevation of the cut solid.

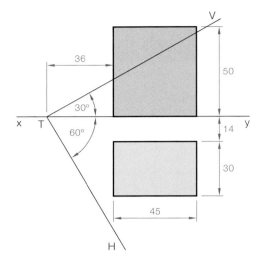

Fig. 3.20

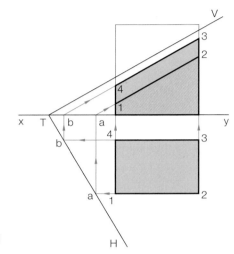

Fig. 3.21

We use vertical section planes in Fig. 3.21 to solve this problem. A vertical plane, running parallel to the xy line in plan, will intersect the oblique plane along a line which will be parallel to the VT of the oblique plane. Construction as shown in Fig. 3.21.

> A regular rectangular prism is to be cut by the oblique plane VTH, Fig. 3.22. Project the plan and elevation of the cut solid.

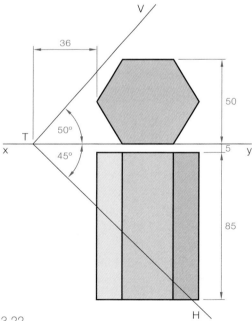

Fig. 3.22

Horizontal section planes are used which produce lines of intersection with the oblique plane which are parallel to the horizontal trace. Construction as shown in Fig. 3.23.

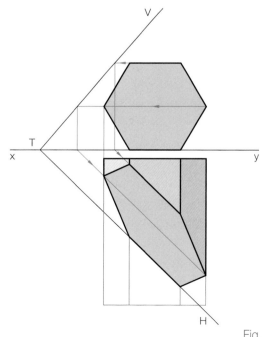

Fig. 3.23

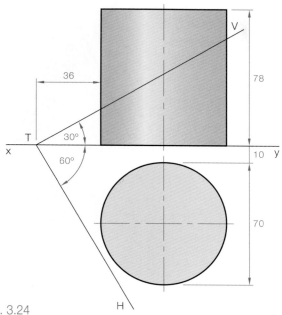

Fig. 3.24

The plan and elevation of a cylinder are shown in Fig. 3.24. Show the projections of this cylinder when it has been cut by the oblique plane VTH.

In this example the problem is solved using a series of vertical planes.

(1) A vertical plane is drawn to cut the cylinder in plan giving points 1 and 7.

(2) This vertical plane will intersect the oblique plane along a straight line which will run on the cut surface (see Fig. 3.25).

(3) This line of intersection is parallel to the vertical trace.

(4) Draw the line in elevation and project points 1 and 7 onto it. Repeat as necessary.

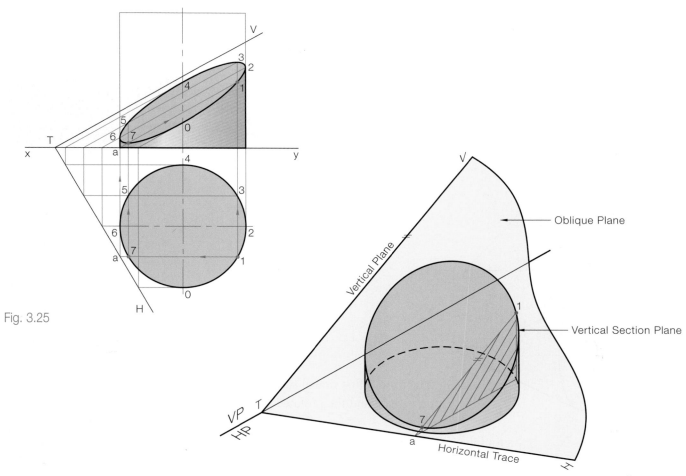

Fig. 3.25

Oblique Plane

Vertical Section Plane

Horizontal Trace

Fig. 3.26

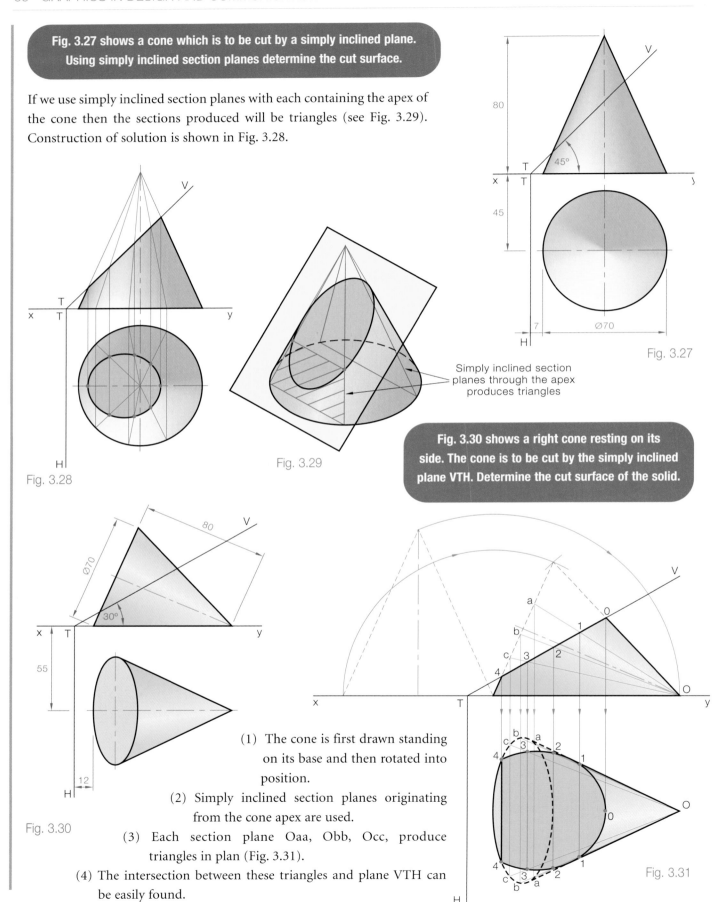

Fig. 3.27 shows a cone which is to be cut by a simply inclined plane. Using simply inclined section planes determine the cut surface.

If we use simply inclined section planes with each containing the apex of the cone then the sections produced will be triangles (see Fig. 3.29). Construction of solution is shown in Fig. 3.28.

Fig. 3.27

Fig. 3.28

Simply inclined section planes through the apex produces triangles

Fig. 3.29

Fig. 3.30 shows a right cone resting on its side. The cone is to be cut by the simply inclined plane VTH. Determine the cut surface of the solid.

Fig. 3.30

(1) The cone is first drawn standing on its base and then rotated into position.

(2) Simply inclined section planes originating from the cone apex are used.

(3) Each section plane Oaa, Obb, Occ, produce triangles in plan (Fig. 3.31).

(4) The intersection between these triangles and plane VTH can be easily found.

Fig. 3.31

HIGHER LEVEL

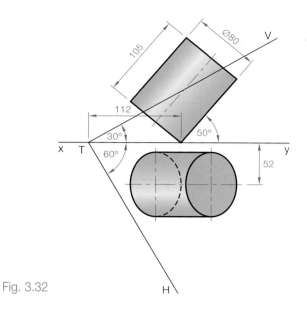

Fig. 3.32

Fig. 3.32 shows a right cylinder with its base inclined to the horizontal plane. Determine the cut surface of the solid.

(1) The line of intersection between the simply inclined plane containing the base of the cylinder and the oblique plane VTH is found. This gives the straight-line cut edge on the base.

(2) The cut line on the top of the cylinder will be parallel to the cut line on the cylinder base.

(3) Points on the curved surface of the cylinder are found by using simply inclined planes parallel to the cylinder axis.

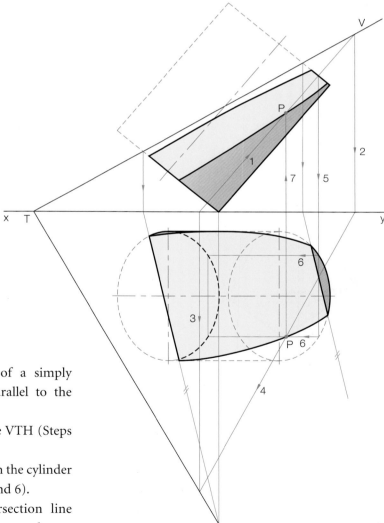

(4) Draw the vertical trace/edge view of a simply inclined plane (Step 1) which is parallel to the cylinder axis.

(5) Find its line of intersection with plane VTH (Steps 2, 3 and 4).

(6) This simply inclined plane cuts through the cylinder forming a rectangle in plan (Steps 5 and 6).

(7) Where the rectangle and the intersection line between the planes cross, gives a point p on the cut surface. Repeat as necessary.

Fig. 3.33

Cube and Tetrahedron
The Cube

This is by far the most familiar of the regular polyhedra of which there are five:

- Tetrahedron
- Cube
- Octahedron
- Dodecahedron
- Icosahedron.

A cube has six faces, eight vertices and twelve edges. Each face is a square, three of which come together at each vertex. It is the only regular polyhedron that can be tiled by itself to fill three-dimensional space. A cube of unit edge is defined as the unit of volume and all other volumes are measured by the number of unit cubes they can contain. Another name for the cube is the **regular hexahedron**.

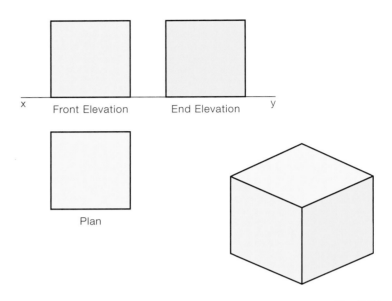

Front Elevation   End Elevation

Plan

Fig. 3.34

Duality

For every polyhedron there exists a dual polyhedron. Just looking at the regular polyhedra it will be shown that the tetrahedron is self-dual and the cube and the octahedron are a dual pair. The icosahedron and the dodecahedron are another dual pair but will not be looked at here.

Find the centre of each face by joining the diagonals. This gives the six vertices of the octahedron. Join each corner to its four neighbours, Fig. 3.35.

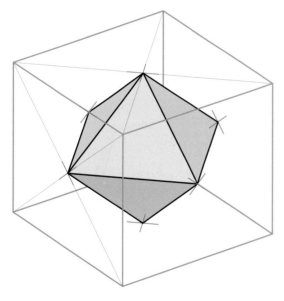

Fig. 3.35   **Dual of a cube is an octahedron.**

What is even more interesting is that the dual of a regular octahedron is a cube. Finding the dual of the dual will give back the original solid.

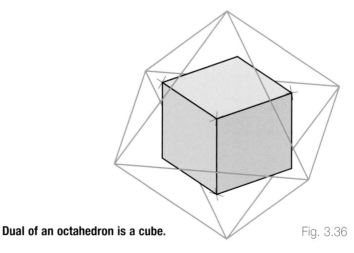

Dual of an octahedron is a cube.   Fig. 3.36

Sectioning a cube to produce a regular hexagon

If a cube is cut by a section plane so that it passes through the centre points of the edges, as shown in Fig. 3.37, a regular hexagon is produced. This section plan cuts the cube into two equal halves.

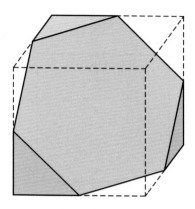

Fig. 3.37

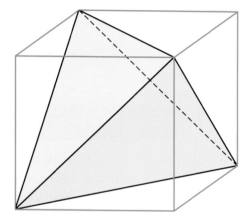

Fig. 3.38

Tetrahedron inside a cube

All the faces of a cube are squares of equal size. The diagonals of each square are therefore also equal. The six face diagonals in the cube in Fig. 3.38 form the edges of a tetrahedron. There are two possible arrangements of such tetrahedrons inside a cube.

Diagonals and sides

There obviously is a constant relationship between the sides of a cube, its short diagonals and its long diagonals. This relationship can be seen graphically in Figures 3.40 and 3.41 and can also be worked out quite easily using trigonometry.

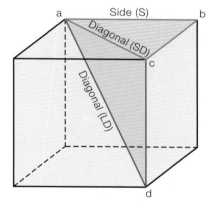

Fig. 3.39

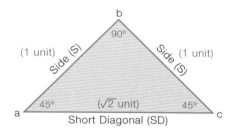

Fig. 3.40

Taking the side of the cube to be one unit in length it can be seen that the short diagonal equals $\sqrt{2}$ units in length (Pythagoras's Theorem). The long diagonal equals $\sqrt{3}$ units in length (Pythagoras's Theorem). Trigonometry can prove that angle dac equals 35° 15′ 51.8″ and angle cda equals 54° 44′ 8.2″.

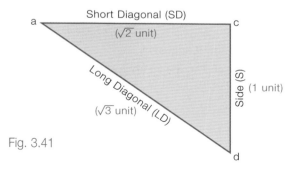

Fig. 3.41

Front Elevation

End Elevation

Plan

y^1

Side

Long Diagonal

Diameter of circumscribing sphere

x^1

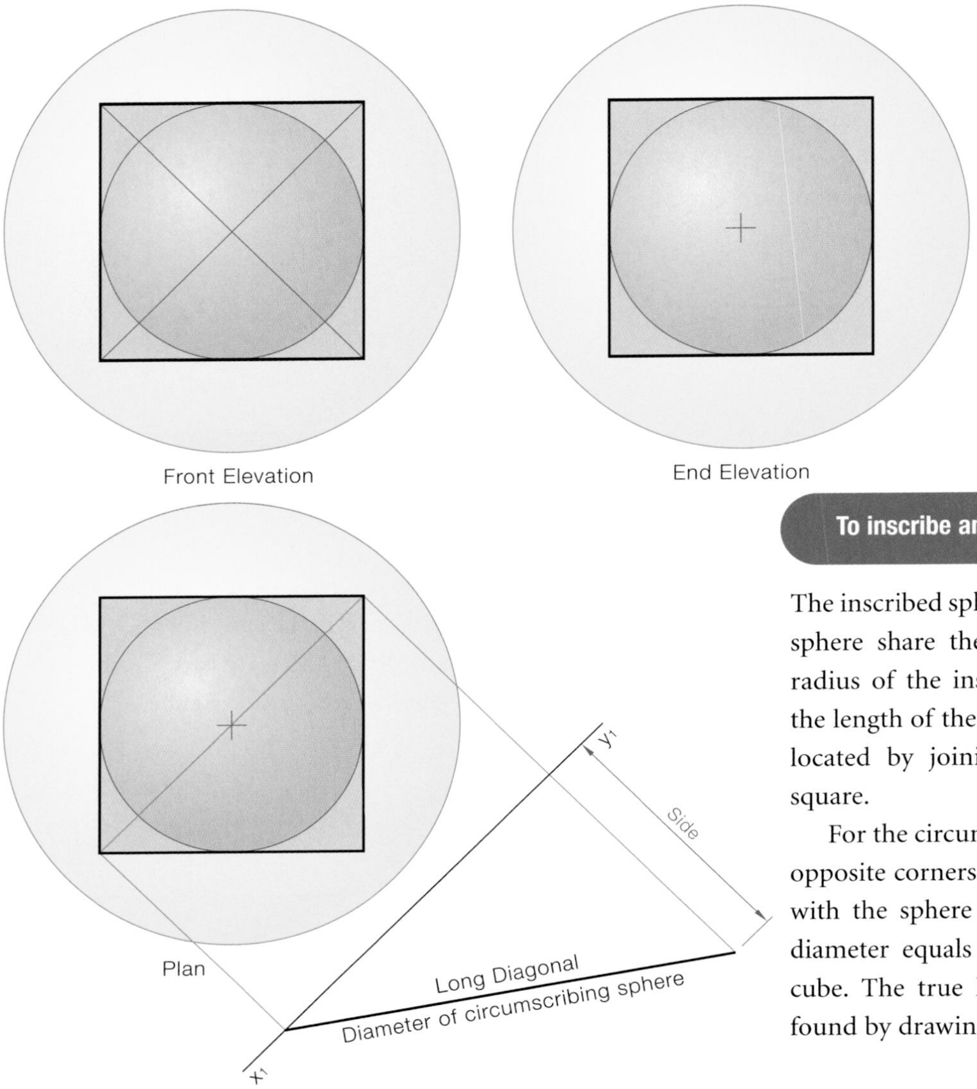

Fig. 3.42

To inscribe and circumscribe a cube

The inscribed sphere and the circumscribed sphere share the same centre point. The radius of the inscribed sphere equals half the length of the square's sides. Its centre is located by joining the diagonals of the square.

For the circumscribed sphere diagonally opposite corners of the cube are in contact with the sphere so therefore this sphere's diameter equals the long diagonal of the cube. The true length of this diagonal is found by drawing an auxiliary.

The Tetrahedron

A tetrahedron is the simplest possible polyhedron. It has four faces, four vertices and six edges. Each face is an equilateral triangle for a regular tetrahedron.

Construction
(1) Draw the plan which is an equilateral triangle and bisect each angle to locate point 0, Fig. 3.43.
(2) Edge 2,0 will be seen as a true length in end view. Project vertex 2 to the xy line and scribe an arc, centre at vertex 2, to intersect the line projected for the apex 0.
(3) Complete the end view and front elevation.

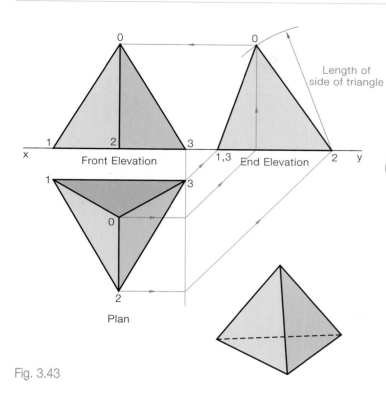

Fig. 3.43

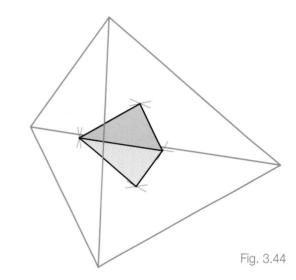

Duality

The tetrahedron stands alone as a self-dual polyhedron. When the centroid of each face is found and joined to its neighbours another tetrahedron is formed, Fig. 3.44.

Fig. 3.44

Sectioning a tetrahedron

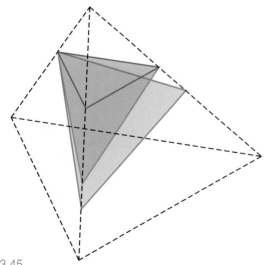

Fig. 3.45

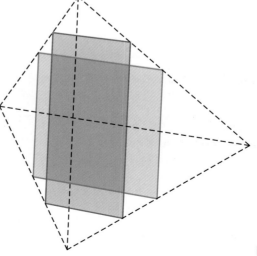

Fig. 3.46

The tetrahedron can be sectioned to give an equilateral triangle, an isosceles triangle or a scalene triangle as shown in Fig. 3.45. It can also be sectioned to produce rectangles and squares as well as other quadrilaterals, Fig. 3.46.

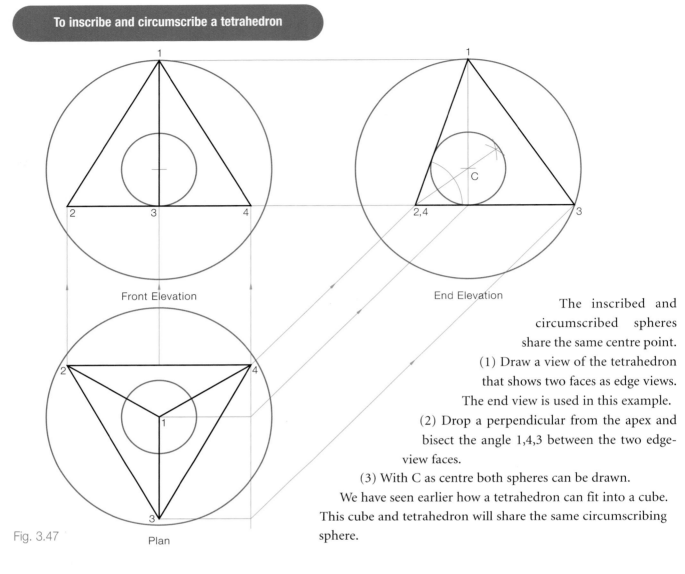

To inscribe and circumscribe a tetrahedron

Front Elevation

End Elevation

Plan

Fig. 3.47

The inscribed and circumscribed spheres share the same centre point.

(1) Draw a view of the tetrahedron that shows two faces as edge views. The end view is used in this example.

(2) Drop a perpendicular from the apex and bisect the angle 1,4,3 between the two edge-view faces.

(3) With C as centre both spheres can be drawn.

We have seen earlier how a tetrahedron can fit into a cube. This cube and tetrahedron will share the same circumscribing sphere.

Worked Problems

The plan of a square abcd which is inclined at 40° to the HP is shown in Fig. 3.48. The edge ab rests on the horizontal plane. The square is the base of a cube. Draw the plan and elevation of the solid.

(1) Line ab rests on the horizontal plane and is therefore a true length.

(2) Complete the square abc_1d_1. This represents the cube base resting on the horizontal plane.

(3) Project an auxiliary view showing ab as a point view. Project d_1c.

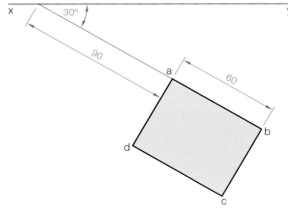

Fig. 3.48

(4) Rotate the base in the auxiliary, about ab to make a 40° angle with the x_1y_1.

(5) Complete the cube in auxiliary by rotating d_1c_1 onto the 40° line and completing a square.

(6) Project the corners back to plan. The points in plan move perpendicular to the hinge line ab.

(7) Heights for the elevation are found from the auxiliary.

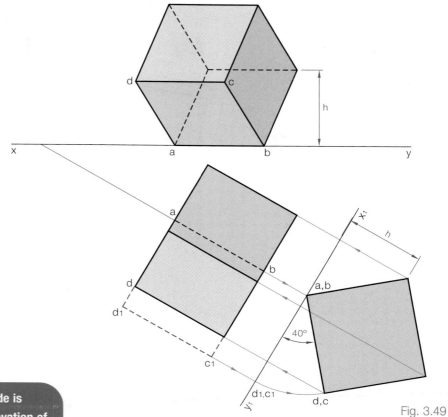

Fig. 3.49

The elevation of a cube of 50 mm side is shown in Fig. 3.50. Draw the plan and elevation of the cube.

(1) Set up line ac in elevation. Project an auxiliary plan from this with x_1y_1 parallel to ac. This view will show the true shape of abcd.

(2) Construct a square of correct size, and find the length of its diagonal. Start with a point c in auxiliary plan. Swing an arc, centre c, radius equal to the diagonal, to locate point a. Complete the square in auxiliary.

(3) Project back to the front elevation and plan similar to the previous example.

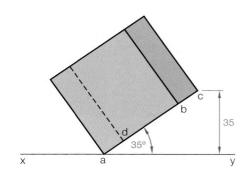

Fig. 3.50

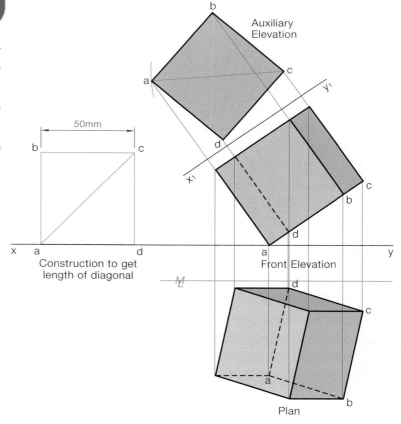

Fig. 3.51

H I G H E R   L E V E L

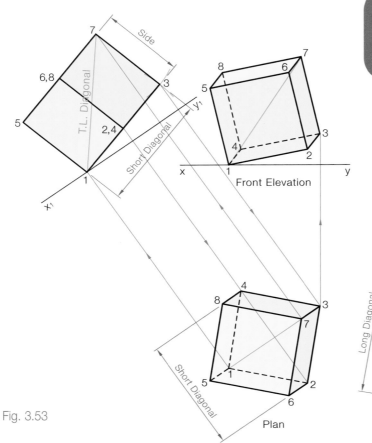

Fig. 3.53

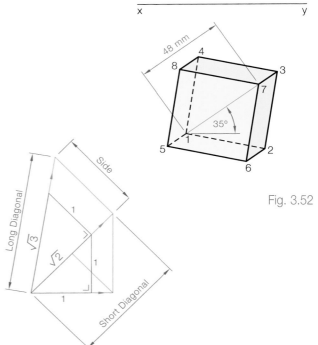

Given the plan of a cube. Line 1,7 is the long diagonal. Draw the plan and elevation of the cube when corner 1 rests on the HP and corner 7 is 60 mm above the HP.

Fig. 3.52

(1) Draw the diagonal 1,7 in plan and elevation.

(2) Project an auxiliary to show the true length of diagonal 1,7.

(3) Set up a 1,1,$\sqrt{2}$ triangle and a $\sqrt{2}$,1,$\sqrt{3}$ triangle using any unit length. These triangles show the constant relationship between the edges, short diagonals and long diagonals of a cube.

(4) Using the true length of the long diagonal, found in the auxiliary, the length of the short diagonals and sides can be found as shown.

(5) Points 2 and 4 will be halfway between 1 and 3.

(6) Complete the plan. Short diagonal 2,4 will be a true length in plan.

(7) Complete the elevation.

Shown in the diagram is the plan and elevation of a regular hexagon. This hexagon is the cut surface of a sectioned cube.

(i)   Draw the given plan and elevation and construct the half-cube from which the section was found.

(ii) Draw the circumscribing sphere.

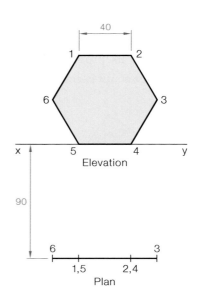

Fig. 3.54

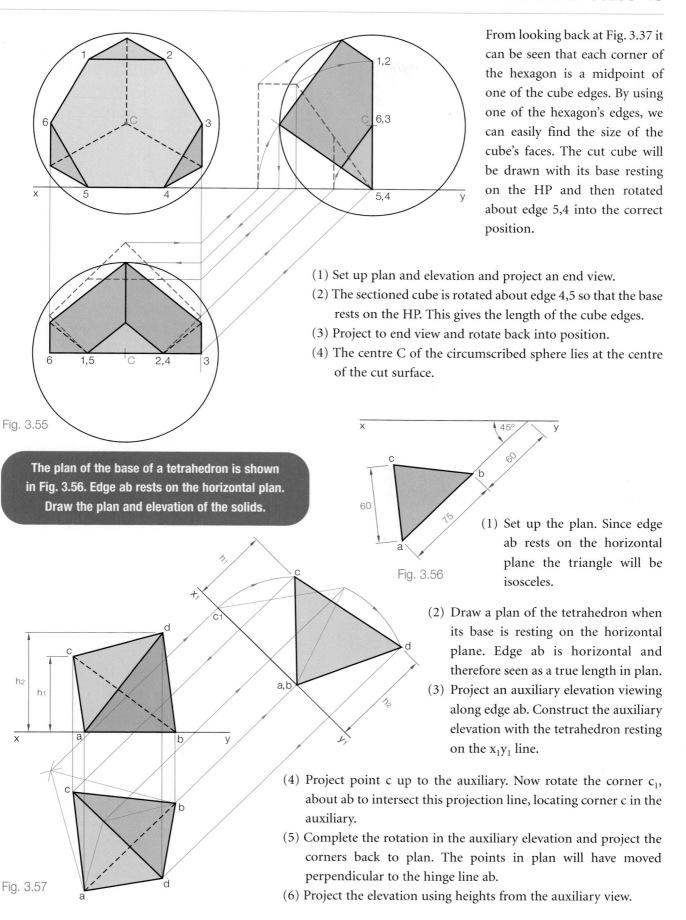

Fig. 3.55

From looking back at Fig. 3.37 it can be seen that each corner of the hexagon is a midpoint of one of the cube edges. By using one of the hexagon's edges, we can easily find the size of the cube's faces. The cut cube will be drawn with its base resting on the HP and then rotated about edge 5,4 into the correct position.

(1) Set up plan and elevation and project an end view.
(2) The sectioned cube is rotated about edge 4,5 so that the base rests on the HP. This gives the length of the cube edges.
(3) Project to end view and rotate back into position.
(4) The centre C of the circumscribed sphere lies at the centre of the cut surface.

The plan of the base of a tetrahedron is shown in Fig. 3.56. Edge ab rests on the horizontal plan. Draw the plan and elevation of the solids.

Fig. 3.56

(1) Set up the plan. Since edge ab rests on the horizontal plane the triangle will be isosceles.

(2) Draw a plan of the tetrahedron when its base is resting on the horizontal plane. Edge ab is horizontal and therefore seen as a true length in plan.

(3) Project an auxiliary elevation viewing along edge ab. Construct the auxiliary elevation with the tetrahedron resting on the $x_1 y_1$ line.

(4) Project point c up to the auxiliary. Now rotate the corner c_1, about ab to intersect this projection line, locating corner c in the auxiliary.

(5) Complete the rotation in the auxiliary elevation and project the corners back to plan. The points in plan will have moved perpendicular to the hinge line ab.

(6) Project the elevation using heights from the auxiliary view.

Fig. 3.57

The cut surface of a tetrahedron is shown in Fig. 3.58. It is a square, 40 mm side. Construct the remaining part of the solid.

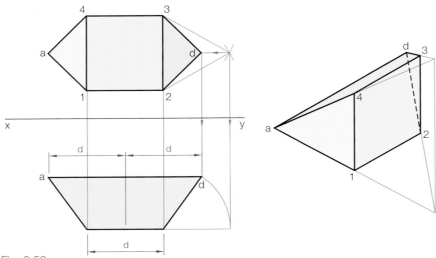

Fig. 3.59

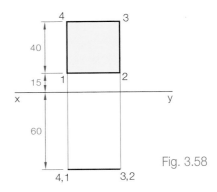

Fig. 3.58

The cut surface 1,2,3,4 divides the edges ab, ac, cd and bd in half. The square's edges will also run parallel to the tetrahedron's edges ad and cb. The triangles a,1,4 and d,2,3 will therefore be equilateral and the sides of the square will equal half of the tetrahedron's edges. Construction as shown in Fig. 3.59.

The plan of a sphere resting on the horizontal plane is shown, Fig. 3.60. The sphere is inscribed in a regular tetrahedron. Draw the plan and elevation of the tetrahedron.

There is only one size of tetrahedron that will fit around this sphere, but it can be positioned in an infinite number of aspects. It is simplest to place it with one face resting on the HP and another appearing edge on in elevation.

(1) Draw the sphere in plan and elevation.
(2) Draw a tetrahedron, of any size, such that the solid's apex is above the sphere centre in plan and that two edges appear parallel in elevation.
(3) Enlarge this solid to the required size so that the two edges, seen edge on in elevation, will be tangential to the sphere.

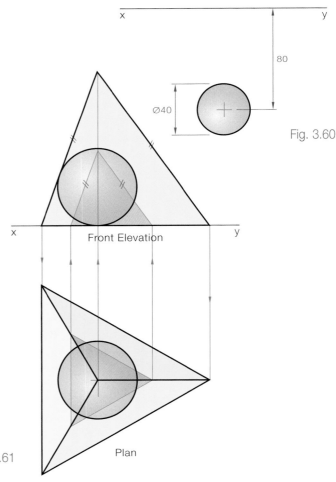

Fig. 3.60

Fig. 3.61

Given the plan and elevation of a tetrahedron. Show the projections of the smallest cube that this solid would fit into. Draw the circumscribing sphere for both solids.

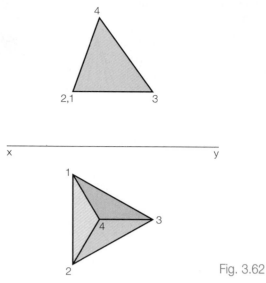

Fig. 3.62

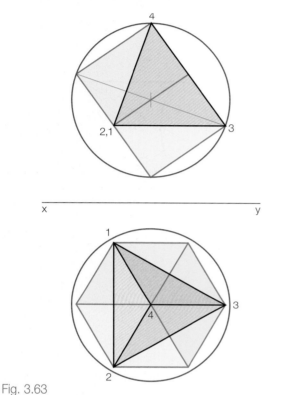

Fig. 3.63

Each edge will form the diagonal of a face of the cube. Edge 3,4 is a true length in elevation and edge 1,2 is seen as a point view in elevation. Two opposite faces of the cube will contain these two lines and will be seen as edge views in elevation. The construction is evident from the diagram.

Activities

SECTION PLANE TYPES

Q1. Make neat freehand sketches of the horizontal and vertical projection planes showing the following plane types:
- Horizontal section plane,
- Vertical section plane,
- Simply inclined section plane,
- Oblique section plane.

Draw a separate diagram for each plane type.

Q2. Explain the terms, horizontal trace and vertical trace of a plane using neat pictorial sketches accompanied by brief notes.

USING HORIZONTAL SECTION PLANES

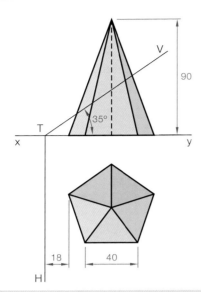

Fig. 3.64

Q3. The pentagonal right pyramid, shown in Fig. 3.64, is cut by the simply inclined plane VTH. Find the cut surface with the aid of horizontal section planes.

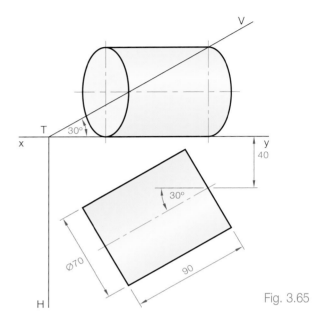

Fig. 3.65

Q4. A cylinder resting on its side is shown in Fig. 3.65. This cylinder is to be cut by the simply inclined plane VTH. Find the cut surface using horizontal section planes.

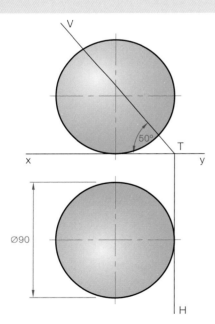

Fig. 3.66

Q5. A sphere resting on the horizontal plane is to be cut by the simply inclined plane VTH, Fig. 3.66. Find the cut surface using horizontal section planes.

USING VERTICAL SECTION PLANES

Q6. A right cylinder whose base is inclined to the HP is shown in Fig. 3.67. This cylinder is to be cut by the simply inclined plane VTH. Using vertical section planes find the cut surface.

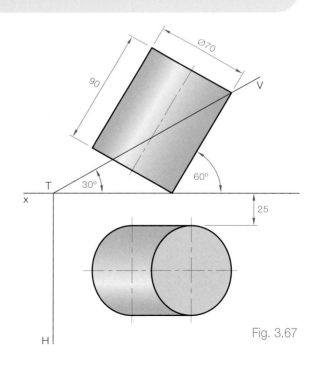

Fig. 3.67

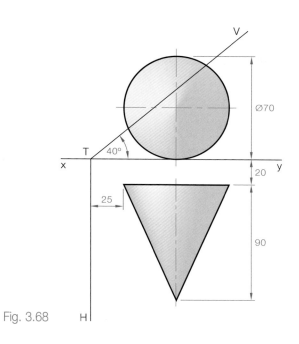

Fig. 3.68

Q7. The projections of a right cone are shown in Fig. 3.68. The cone is to be cut by the simply inclined plane VTH. Find the cut surface of the cone using vertical section planes.

SOLVING PROBLEMS OF SOLIDS CUT BY OBLIQUE PLANES USING HORIZONTAL AND VERTICAL SECTION PLANES

Q8. Using horizontal or vertical section planes find the cut surface of the hexagonal prism shown in Fig. 3.69.

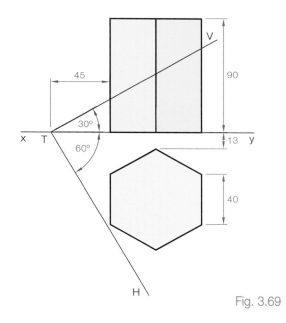

Fig. 3.69

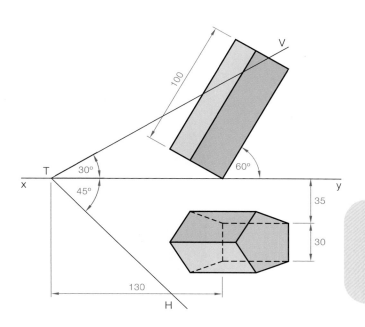

Fig. 3.70

Q9. A regular, right, pentagonal prism has been tilted onto one edge as shown in Fig. 3.70. The prism is to be cut by the oblique plane VTH. Using vertical section planes find the cut surface of the solid.

Q10. A right cylinder has been tilted to the horizontal plane as shown in Fig. 3.71. This cylinder is to be cut by the oblique plane VTH. Using vertical section planes find the cut surface of the cylinder.

USING SIMPLY INCLINED SECTION PLANES

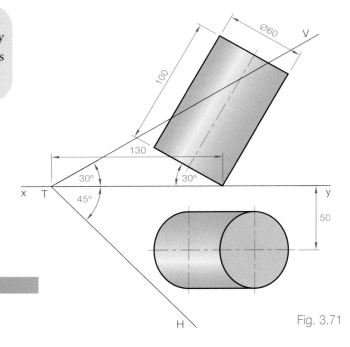

Fig. 3.71

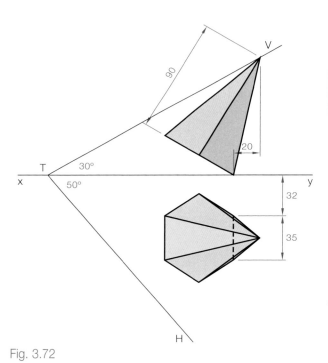

Fig. 3.72

Q11. A right hexagonal-based pyramid has been tilted at an angle to the HP as shown in Fig. 3.72. This pyramid is to be cut by the oblique plane VTH. Using simply inclined planes find the cut surface.

Q12. A right cone rests on its side as shown in Fig. 3.73. The cone is to be cut by the oblique plane VTH. Using simply inclined planes find the cut surface of the solid.

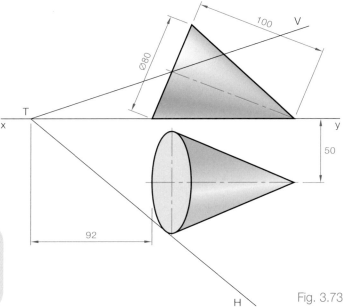

Fig. 3.73

HIGHER LEVEL

Q13. Make a neat pictorial diagram of a cube with its dual solid, the octahedron, inside it.

Q14. Make a neat pictorial diagram of an octahedron showing its dual, the cube, inside it.

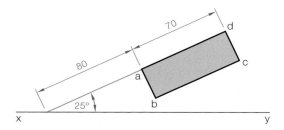

Fig. 3.74

Q15. The elevation of one face of a cube, abcd is shown in Fig. 3.74. Edge ad rests against the vertical plane and the surface abcd makes an angle of 70° to the vertical plane. Draw the plan and elevation of the cube.

Q16. One face of a cube, seen as an edge view, is shown in Fig. 3.75. This cube has edges of length 76 mm and has one edge resting on the horizontal plane. Draw the plan and elevation of the cube.

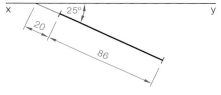

Fig. 3.75

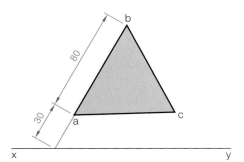

Fig. 3.76

Q17. The elevation of an equilateral triangle inclined at 20° to the VP and having edge ab in the vertical plan is shown in Fig. 3.76. The triangle is one face of a tetrahedron. Draw the plan and elevation of the solid.

Q18. The plan of a tetrahedron is shown in Fig. 3.77. Corner a rests on the horizontal plan and corner b is 14 mm above the horizontal plane. The tetrahedron has sides 70 mm long and edge bc is parallel to the xy line in plan. Draw the tetrahedron in plan and elevation.

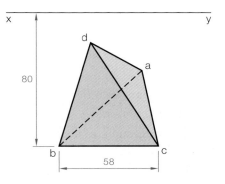

Fig. 3.77

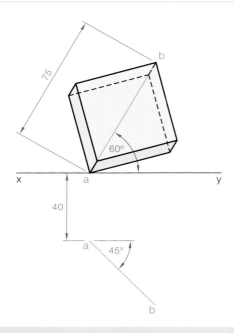

Fig. 3.78

H I G H E R   L E V E L

Q19. Given the elevation of a cube in Fig. 3.78. The long diagonal ab is shown in plan and elevation.
(i) Find the size of the cube and draw its plan and elevation.
(ii) Inscribe a sphere.

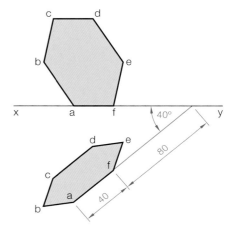

Fig. 3.79

Q20. Shown in Fig. 3.79 is the plan and elevation of a regular hexagon which is inclined at 75° to the HP.
(i) This hexagon is the section of a cube. Draw the plan and elevation of the cube.
(ii) Draw the circumscribing sphere.

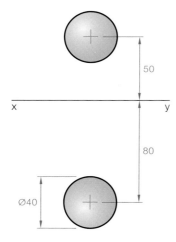

Fig. 3.80

Q21. The plan and elevation of a sphere is shown in Fig. 3.80. The sphere is inscribed in a tetrahedron. The base of the tetrahedron makes an angle of 20° with the HP. Draw the plan and elevation of the tetrahedron.

Q22. The plan of the base of a tetrahedron, which is inclined at 50° to the HP, is shown in Fig. 3.81. The edge ab of this face is horizontal and is shown in elevation.
(i)   Draw the plan and elevation of the complete tetrahedron.
(ii) Show the projections of the smallest cube that will contain this solid.
(iii) Draw the circumscribing sphere for both sides.

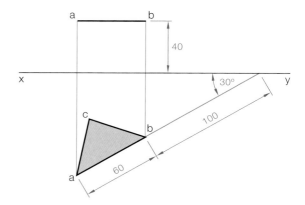

Fig. 3.81

Orthographic Projection of Solids in Contact

4

SYLLABUS OUTLINE

Areas to be studied:

• Right solids in contact.

Learning outcomes
Students should be able to:

Higher and Ordinary levels
- Construct views of up to three solids having curved surfaces and/or plane surfaces in mutual contact.
- Determine point of contact for surfaces in mutual contact.
- Construct views of solids given the point of contact.
- Depict the solutions of two-dimensional problems in three-dimensional format.

Higher Level only
- *Model various problems involving solids in contact, planes of reference and auxiliary planes.*

Solids in Contact

In this chapter you will draw the orthographic views of spheres, cones, cylinders, pyramids and prisms in contact with each other. Before this, we must examine how to find points on the surface of cylinders, cones and spheres.

> The elevation of a cylinder is shown in Fig. 4.1 and the position of a point P on its surface. Draw the plan of the cylinder and point P.

By using an end view the location of point P in the plan can be easily found, see Fig. 4.2.

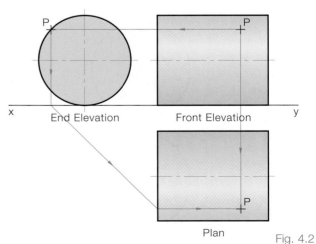

Fig. 4.2

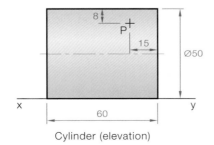

Fig. 4.1

Cylinder (elevation)

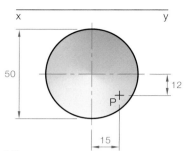

Fig. 4.3

The plan of a cone of altitude 60 mm is shown in Fig. 4.3. Also shown is a point P on its surface. Draw the elevation and locate point P.

There are two methods shown to solve this problem.

Method 1 (Fig. 4.4a)

Rotate point P in plan onto the horizontal axis. Project to the side of the cone in elevation giving the height of point P. Project the height horizontally and bring point P up from plan onto it.

Method 2 (Fig. 4.4b)

Draw the generator through point P in plan. Project this generator to elevation. Point P is projected onto this generator in elevation.

The horizontal section method is the preferred method.

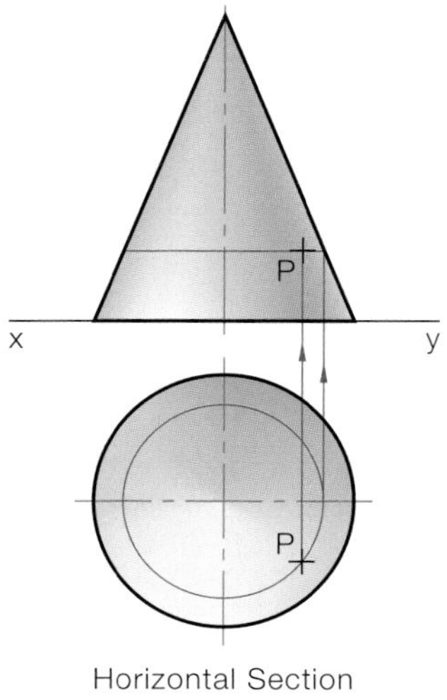

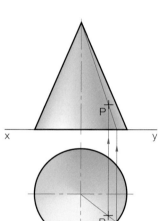

Fig. 4.4b

Generator

Horizontal Section

Fig. 4.4a

The elevation of a sphere with a point P on its surface is shown in Fig. 4.5. Draw the plan and locate point P on it.

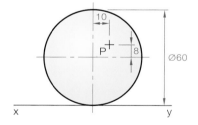

Fig. 4.5

As in the previous example, a horizontal section is used. Project P horizontally to touch the side of the sphere. Project down to the horizontal axis of the plan and rotate round. Drop point P from elevation, Fig. 4.6.

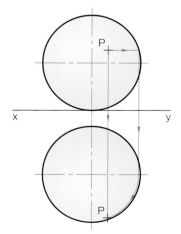

Fig. 4.6

The plan of a cone of altitude 70 mm is shown in Fig. 4.7. Also shown is a point P on the cone's surface. A sphere which rests on the horizontal plane touches the cone at point P. Draw the plan and elevation of the two solids in contact.

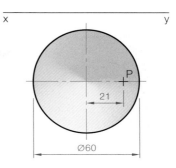

x   y

21

Ø60

Fig. 4.7

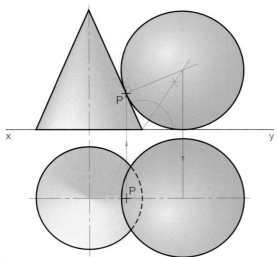

Fig. 4.8

(1) Draw the plan and project the elevation. Locate point P in elevation.

(2) Since the cone is tangential to the sphere, its edge will form a tangent to the sphere in elevation. A perpendicular to the side of the cone from point P will therefore pass through the sphere's centre.

(3) Since the sphere touches the horizontal plane and the cone edge, its centre will be on the bisector of the angle between the two, in elevation, Fig. 4.8.

(4) Draw the sphere in elevation and plan.

The plan of a cone of 70 mm altitude is shown in Fig. 4.9. Also shown is a point P on the cone's surface.

(i) Draw the plan and elevation of the cone and the point P.

(ii) Draw the plan and elevation of a sphere that rests on the horizontal plane and touches the cone at point P.

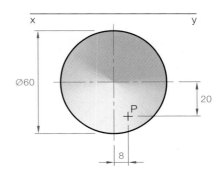

x   y

Ø60

20

P

8

Fig. 4.9

(1) Draw the plan and elevation of the cone.

(2) Rotate point P in plan about the cone centre onto the axis. Project up to the side of the cone in elevation and then project across horizontally. Locate point P on this horizontal.

(3) The sphere required to touch the cone at point P and touch the horizontal plane is constructed at the side of the cone. The construction is the same as in the previous example.

(4) Once the sphere centre is located, it is dropped to plan and rotated onto a line drawn from the cone centre through point P.

> **The centre of the cone, the point of contact and the sphere centre will form a straight line.**

(5) Draw the sphere in position in plan. Project the sphere centre to elevation and draw the sphere, Fig. 4.10.

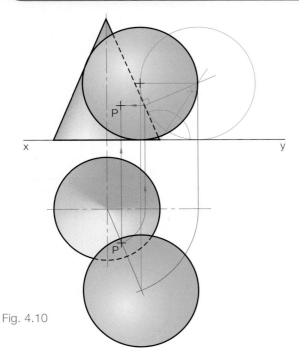

Fig. 4.10

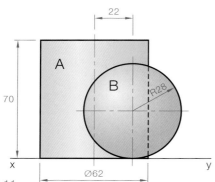

Fig. 4.11

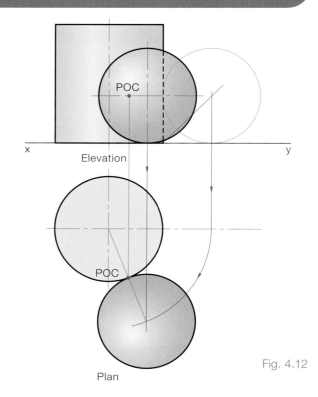

Shown in Fig. 4.11 is the elevation of a cylinder A and a sphere B. Both solids are in contact with each other and rest on the horizontal plane. Draw the elevation and plan of the solids and the point of contact.

(1) Draw the given elevation of both solids and project the plan of the cylinder.
(2) The sphere is drawn at the side of the cylinder. The point of contact (POC) can be clearly seen.
(3) Drop the centre of the sphere to the plan's horizontal axis and rotate it into the correct position. Draw the sphere in plan.
(4) Join the centres of the solid in plan thus locating the point of contact.
(5) Project the point of contact up from the plan and across from the constructional sphere, Fig. 4.12.

When a sphere and cylinder are in contact the point of contact will be level with the sphere centre.

Fig. 4.12

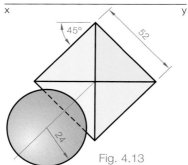

Fig. 4.13

(1) Draw the plan and elevation of the pyramid.
(2) Project an auxiliary elevation to show the face that is in contact with the sphere as an edge view.
(3) Construct the sphere in the auxiliary. The radius is 24 mm so the centre is 24 mm above the x_1y_1 line. Also bisect the angle between the x_1y_1 and the side of the pyramid.
(4) Once the sphere is located in auxiliary it is projected back to plan and elevation.
(5) The point of contact is first found in the auxiliary by drawing a line from the sphere centre, perpendicular to the face of the pyramid. It is projected to plan and then elevation. The height of the POC in elevation equals the height of the POC in the auxiliary elevation, Fig. 4.14.

The plan of a square-based pyramid and a sphere, resting on the horizontal plane, are shown in Fig. 4.13. They are in contact with each other. Draw the plan and elevation of the solids showing the point of contact. The pyramid has an altitude of 58 mm.

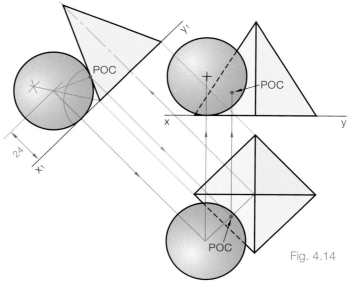

Fig. 4.14

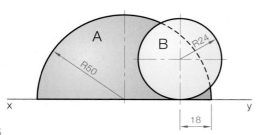

Fig. 4.15

The elevation of a hemisphere A and a sphere B resting on the horizontal plane is shown in Fig. 4.15. The solids are in contact. Draw the plan and elevation of the solids and show the point of contact in both views.

(1) Draw the given elevation and draw the plan of the hemisphere A.

(2) Sphere B is drawn to the side of the hemisphere in elevation. The centre is located by projecting the centre of sphere B horizontally. This horizontal line is then cut by an arc drawn from the centre of the hemisphere and equal to the two radii added together, i.e. 50 mm + 24 mm = 74 mm.

(3) The point of contact is located between the hemisphere and the constructional sphere by joining their centres.

(4) Both point of contact and sphere centre are dropped to plan and rotated into position.

(5) The point of contact is located in elevation, Fig. 4.16.

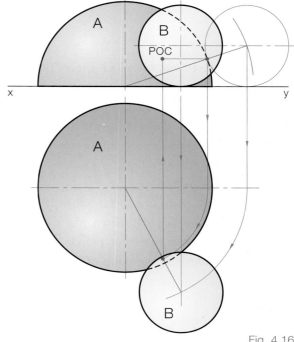

Fig. 4.16

Fig. 4.17 shows the plan of a cone, resting on the horizontal plane, having an altitude of 60 mm. Also shown is a point P on the cone's surface. Draw the plan and elevation of the cone. Draw the plan and elevation of a sphere that will touch point P and also rest on the horizontal plane.

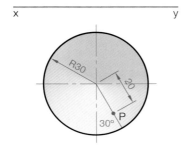

Fig. 4.17

(1) Draw the given plan and project the elevation. Point P is rotated in plan onto the horizontal axis, projected to the side of the cone and then horizontally.

(2) The sphere is constructed to the side of the cone in elevation. Point P is brought horizontally to the side of the cone and a perpendicular constructed to the cone edge. The angle between the xy and the cone side is bisected. The intersection between the perpendicular and the bisector gives the sphere centre.

(3) The sphere is rolled into position and drawn in both views, Fig. 4.18.

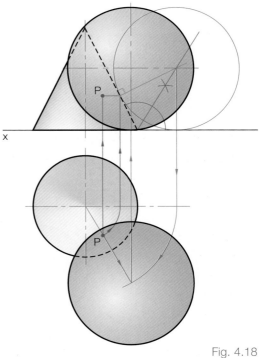

Fig. 4.18

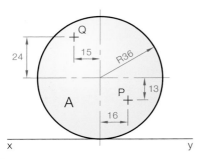

Fig. 4.19

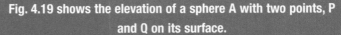

Fig. 4.19 shows the elevation of a sphere A with two points, P and Q on its surface.

(i)   **Draw the given elevation and project a plan showing points P and Q in both views.**

(ii) **Show the projections of a sphere of radius 15 mm that will be in contact with the sphere A at point P.**

(iii) **Show the projections of a sphere of radius 28 mm that will be in contact with sphere A at point Q.**

(1) Draw the given elevation and project the plan of the sphere.

(2) Project point P horizontally in elevation to the side of the sphere. Project down to the plan's horizontal axis and rotate into position, vertically below point P in elevation.

(3) Similar construction for point Q.

(4) Point P is the point of contact. When it is moved horizontally to the circumference of sphere A we can construct the sphere of radius 15 mm. The centre of sphere A, the point of contact and the centre of the required sphere will be in line. The distance between the centres will be equal to the sum of the radii.

(5) Draw the sphere and project through the views.

(6) Similar construction for the sphere touching at point Q, Fig. 4.20.

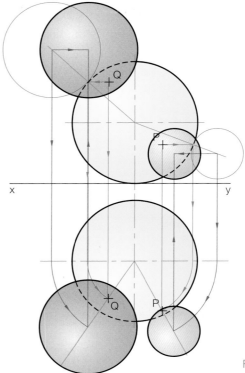

Fig. 4.20

Fig. 4.21 shows the plan of a cylinder A and a cone B. Both solids rest on the horizontal plane. The cylinder has an altitude of 80 mm and the cone has an altitude of 50 mm. A sphere C of radius 20 mm is placed so that it touches both these solids and rests on the horizontal plane. Draw the plan and elevation of the solids and show the points of contact.

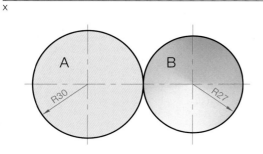

Fig. 4.21

(1) Draw the elevation and plan of the cone and cylinder.

(2) Draw the sphere C touching the side of the cylinder. Project the centre to the plan and rotate it about the cylinder. Similarly for the cone, draw the sphere C touching its side in elevation.

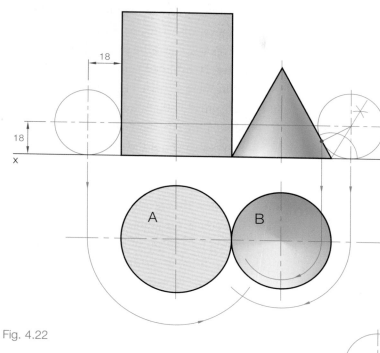

Fig. 4.22

(3) The required sphere has its centre where these two arcs cross in plan, Fig. 4.22.

(4) The point of contact between the sphere and cone is found at the side of the cone in elevation, dropped to the plan and rotated into position. the construction is evident from Fig. 4.23.

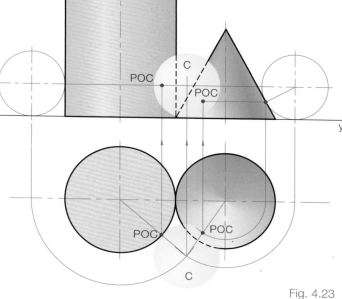

Fig. 4.23

Shown in Fig. 4.24 is the elevation of a cylinder A and a hemisphere B in contact with each other and resting on the horizontal plane. A sphere of 50 mm diameter is placed in position C. The sphere is to be in contact with the other two solids and the horizontal plane. Draw the plan and elevation of the solids showing all points of contact.

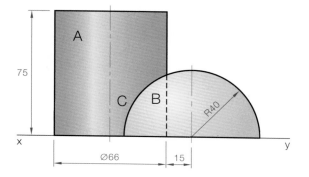

Fig. 4.24

(1) Draw the given elevation and project the plan of the cylinder.

(2) The centre of hemisphere B is projected to plan. The distance between the centres of A and B in plan will equal the sum of their radii.

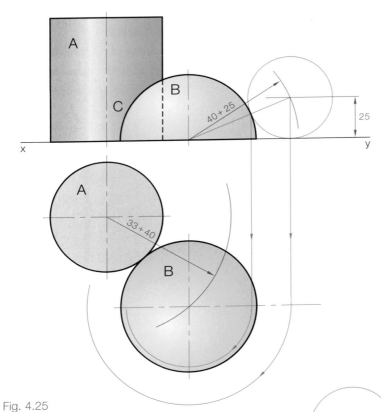

Fig. 4.25

(3) Draw the sphere to the side of hemisphere B in elevation. The distance between their centres will equal the sum of their radii. The centre is dropped and rotated about the hemisphere in plan, Fig. 4.25.

(4) The sphere is then drawn to the side of the cylinder in elevation, dropped to the plan and rotated about the cylinder.

(5) The centre of the sphere is located where the arcs from steps 3 and 4 cross.

(6) Complete the elevation.

(7) The points of contact are located on lines joining the centres of the solids in plan.

(8) The points of contact are projected to elevation, Fig. 4.26.

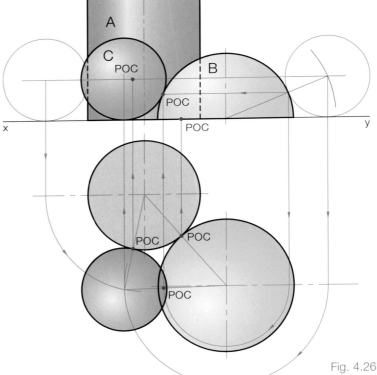

Fig. 4.26

Fig. 4.27 shows the elevation of a cone A and a sphere B resting on the horizontal plane and in contact with each other.

(i) Draw the elevation and plan of the two solids.

(ii) Draw the projections of another sphere C, of 40 mm diameter, which is in contact with the sphere and cone in position S. The centre of the sphere is to be 50 mm above the horizontal plane.

(iii) Show all points of contact.

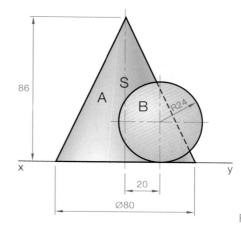

Fig. 4.27

(1) Draw the given elevation and project the plan of the cone.

(2) Sphere B must be drawn to the side of the cone, touching it, projected to plan and rolled into position, Fig. 4.28.

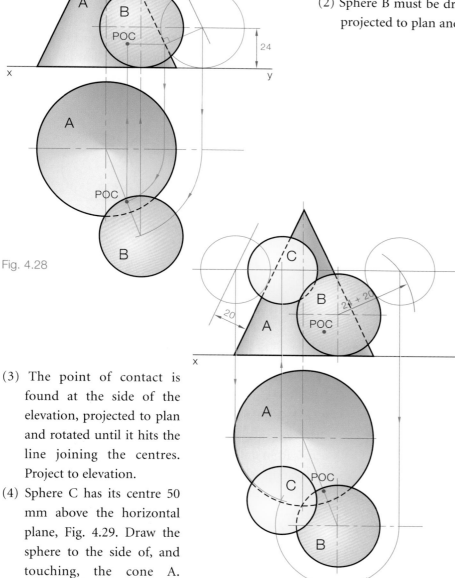

Fig. 4.28

Fig. 4.29

Fig. 4.30

(3) The point of contact is found at the side of the elevation, projected to plan and rotated until it hits the line joining the centres. Project to elevation.

(4) Sphere C has its centre 50 mm above the horizontal plane, Fig. 4.29. Draw the sphere to the side of, and touching, the cone A. Project to plan and rotate about the cone.

(5) Draw the sphere C to the side of, and touching, sphere B. Project to plan and rotate about sphere B.

(6) Draw the sphere C on its correct position in both views.

(7) The points of contact between the solids are found in the usual way as can be seen in Fig. 4.30.

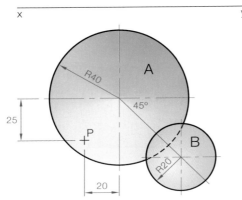

Fig. 4.31

Fig. 4.31 shows the plan of a right cone A in contact with a sphere B. The cone's altitude is 55 mm. Both solids rest on the horizontal plane. The position of a point P on the cone's surface is also given.

(i) Draw the cone A and sphere B in plan and elevation showing the point of contact.

(ii) Locate point P in elevation.

(iii) Another sphere C is placed on the horizontal plane and is in contact with cone A at the point P. Draw this sphere in plan and elevation.

(1) Draw the plan and elevation of the cone.

(2) Construct a 20 mm radius sphere to the side of the cone and in contact with it. Drop the centre down and rotate it onto the 45° line in plan. Project the sphere to elevation.

(3) The point of contact is found at the side of the elevation. Draw a line from the centre of the constructional sphere, perpendicular to the cone side. Project down to plan and rotate onto the line joining the centres, Fig. 4.32.

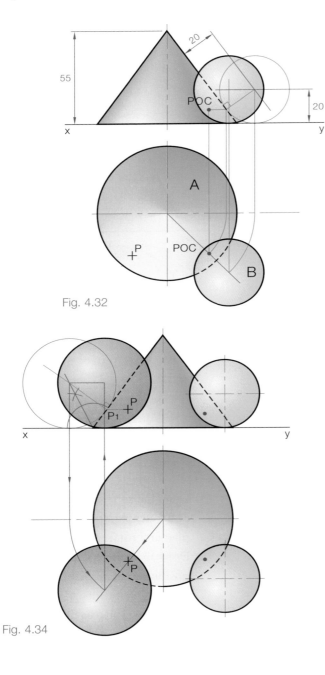

Fig. 4.32

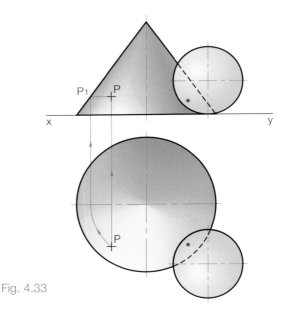

Fig. 4.33

(4) Point P is rotated to the side of the cone, then projected to the cone side in elevation, P_1. A horizontal is brought across from this point. Point P is on this line, Fig. 4.33.

(5) In elevation, where the horizontal from point P hits the side of the cone, P_1, construct a sphere that will touch this point and the horizontal plane. Bisect the angle between the cone side and the horizontal plane. Draw a perpendicular to the cone side from point P_1. The perpendicular and the bisector cross giving the sphere centre.

(6) Find the final position of this sphere in the usual way, Fig. 4.34.

Fig. 4.34

Fig. 4.35 shows the plan of a rectangular-based pyramid of 55 mm height. A sphere of 20 mm radius is in contact with the horizontal plane and the pyramid. Also shown is a point P on the surface of the pyramid.

(i) Draw the elevation and plan of the two solids showing the point of contact.

(ii) Show the plan and elevation of a sphere that rests on the horizontal plan and is in contact with the pyramid at point P.

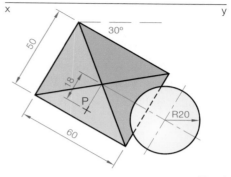

Fig. 4.35

(1) Draw the plan and elevation of the pyramid.

(2) Project an auxiliary elevation that will show the surface in contact with the sphere as an edge view.

(3) Construct the sphere in the auxiliary. Bisect the angle between the pyramid face and the xy line. Draw a horizontal line 20 mm above the xy line. These two lines cross giving the required sphere's centre point. Draw the sphere.

(4) Find the point of contact and project both centre and POC back to plan and elevation, Fig. 4.36.

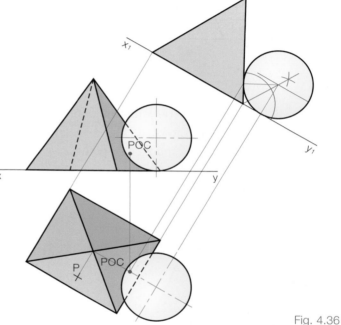

Fig. 4.36

(5) To find the sphere that touches point P. Project an auxiliary that will show the surface containing point P as an edge view. Find the sphere centre in the auxiliary by drawing a perpendicular to the pyramid side from point P and bisecting the angle the pyramid surface makes with the xy line, Fig. 4.37.

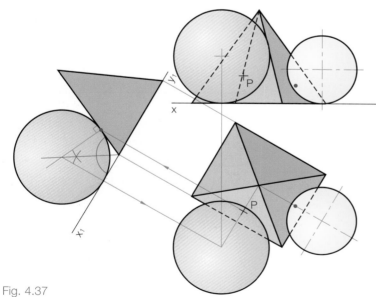

Fig. 4.37

Activities

Q1. The plan of a cylinder is shown in Fig. 4.38. A and B are points on its surface. Project an elevation of the cylinder and locate points A and B.

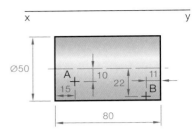

Fig. 4.38

Q2. The elevation of a cone is shown in Fig. 4.39. Two points C and D are shown on the surface. Project a plan showing clearly how the two points are located.

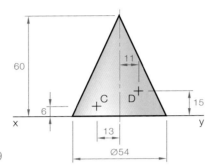

Fig. 4.39

Q3. The plan of a sphere with two points on its surface, E and F, is shown in Fig. 4.40. Project the elevation of the sphere and the two points.

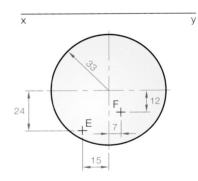

Fig. 4.40

Q4. The elevation of a sphere and cone are shown in Fig. 4.41. The two solids are in contact. Draw the given view and project the plan. Show the point of contact in both views.

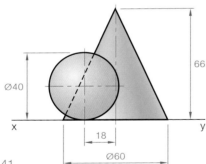

Fig. 4.41

Q5. The plan of a cone A and a sphere B are shown in Fig. 4.42. The two solids are in contact and rest on the horizontal plane. Draw the plan and elevation of the solids and show the point of contact in both views. The cone has an altitude of 60 mm.

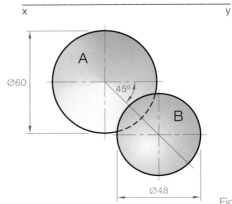

Fig. 4.42

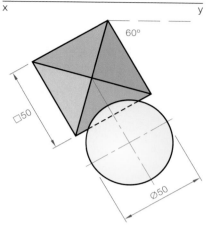

Fig. 4.43

Q6. Fig. 4.43 shows the plan of a square-based pyramid of altitude 70 mm. Also shown is a sphere which is in contact with the pyramid. Both solids rest on the horizontal plane. Draw the given plan and project the elevation. The point of contact should be clearly shown in both views.

Q7. The elevation of a hemisphere is shown in Fig. 4.44. A sphere S is in contact with the hemisphere. Draw the plan and elevation of the two solids showing the point of contact clearly in both views.

Also shown is a point P on the surface of the hemisphere. Draw the plan and elevation of point P.

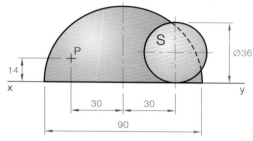

Fig. 4.44

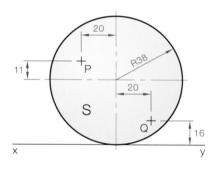

Fig. 4.45

Q8. The elevation of a sphere S is shown in Fig. 4.45 with two points on its surface, points P and Q.
(i) Draw the plan and elevation of the sphere and points.
(ii) Draw the plan and elevation of a sphere of radius 25 mm that has point P as its point of contact with sphere S.
(iii) Draw the plan and elevation of a sphere of radius 8 mm that has point Q as its point of contact with sphere S.

Q9. The plan of a cylinder A and a cone B are shown in Fig. 4.46. Both solids rest on the horizontal plane and are in mutual contact.
(i) Draw the plan and elevation of the two solids and show the point of contact.
(ii) A sphere C rests on the horizontal plane and is in contact with the cone B and the cylinder A. Sphere C has a radius of 12 mm. Project the views of this solid and show all points of contact.

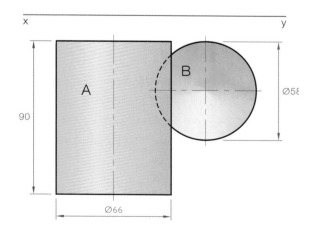

Fig. 4.46

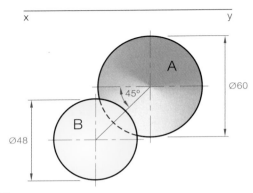

Fig. 4.47

Q10. The plan of a cone A of 50 mm altitude and a sphere B are shown in Fig. 4.47. Both solids rest on the horizontal plane and are in contact with each other.
(i) Draw the plan and project the elevation of the solids.
(ii) Draw the projections of another sphere C diameter 30 mm, whose centre is 36 mm above the horizontal plane. The sphere C is to touch the cone A and the other sphere B.
(iii) Show the points of contact in all views.

Q11. Shown in Fig. 4.48 is the elevation of a hemisphere A and a sphere B in contact with each other and resting on the horizontal plane.
(i) Draw the elevation and project the plan of the solids.
(ii) Draw the projections of a diameter 40 mm sphere which rests on the horizontal plane and touches the hemisphere A and sphere B.
(iii) Show all points of contact.

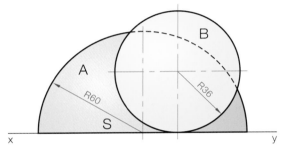

Fig. 4.48

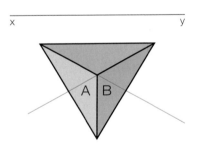

Fig. 4.49

Q12. The diagram in Fig. 4.49 shows the plan of a tetrahedron of 66 mm side resting on the horizontal plane.
(i) Draw the given plan and project the elevation.
(ii) Draw the projection of a 40 mm diameter sphere that rests on the horizontal plane and is in contact with surface A.
(iii) Draw the projections of a 50 mm diameter sphere that rests on the horizontal plane and is in contact with surface B. Show all points of contact.

Q13. Fig. 4.50 shows the elevation of a cone A and two spheres B and C. The three solids are in contact.
(i) Draw the given elevation and project a plan.
(ii) Show the points of contact in both views.

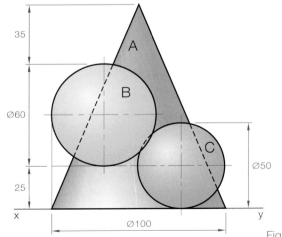

Fig. 4.50

Problems

H I G H E R   L E V E L

PROBLEM 1

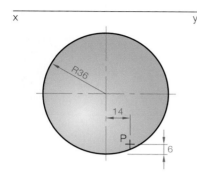

Fig. 4.51

Fig. 4.51 shows the plan of a sphere with a point P on its underside.

(i) **Draw the plan and elevation of the sphere and find the projections of point P.**

(ii) **Find the projections of the sphere which rests on the horizontal plane and has point P as its point of contact.**

(1) Draw the sphere in plan and elevation.

(2) Find point P in elevation in the usual way. Rotate point P onto the horizontal axis in plan and project to the sphere's circumference in elevation giving P₁.

(3) Draw a line from C through P₁ and extend.

(4) Draw a locus of points equidistant from the circumference and the xy line.

(5) The locus and CP₁ extended cross giving the sphere centre, Fig. 4.52.

(6) Draw the sphere and roll it into position, Fig 4.53.

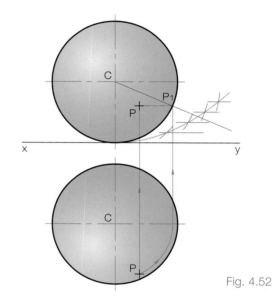

Fig. 4.52

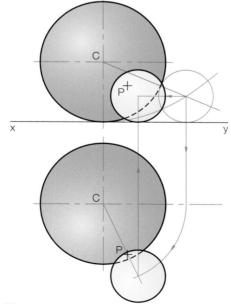

Fig. 4.53

HIGHER LEVEL

PROBLEM 2

> The diagram in Fig. 4.54 shows the elevation of two spheres and a cone in contact with one another. Draw the elevation and plan of the solids showing all points of contact.

(1) Draw the plan and elevation of the cone. The elevation of sphere A can also be drawn.

(2) The location of sphere A in plan is found by rolling the sphere to the side of the cone, dropping it to the side of the plan and rotating it into position. The centre point is brought across in elevation and intersects with the bisector of the angle formed by the cone side and the horizontal plane, Fig. 4.55.

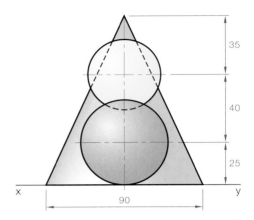

Fig. 4.54

(3) The radius of sphere B is not given. It too must be brought to the side of the cone. Project the given centre point across to the side. This line intersects with the locus of points which are equidistant from the cone side and the circumference of sphere A rotated.

(4) Project the sphere centres back to the elevation and plan, Fig. 4.55.

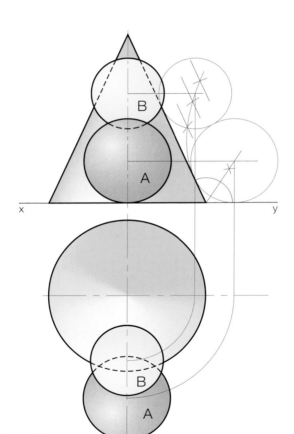

Fig. 4.55

(5) The points of contact must now be found. Join the centres of the two rotated spheres giving P_1. Draw a perpendicular from the rotated spheres centres to the cone side, as shown in Fig. 4.56, thus locating P_2 and P_3. The three points of contact may then be projected back onto the plan and elevation.

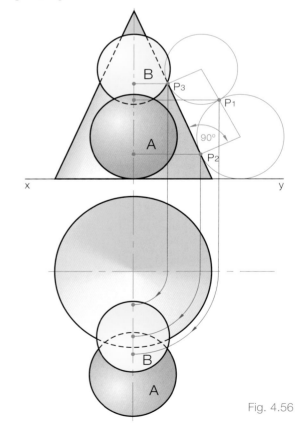

Fig. 4.56

H I G H E R   L E V E L

PROBLEM 3

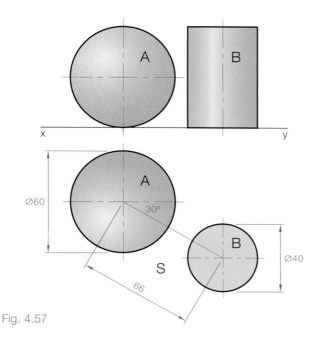

Fig. 4.57

Fig. 4.57 shows the plan and elevation of a sphere A and a cylinder B.

(i) Draw the elevation and plan of the solids.
(ii) Draw the elevation and plan of a cone of 60 mm base diameter and 60 mm height, which rests on the horizontal plane in position S and is in contact with the given solids. Show all points of contact.

(1) Draw the required cone to the side of the elevation and slide it across to come into contact with sphere A.
(2) The point of contact is located.
(3) Drop the cone centre and point of contact down to plan and rotate about the plan of sphere A, Fig. 4.58.

(4) The cone and cylinder will make contact on the horizontal plane and their circular plans will make contact but not overlap. Add their radii in plan and scribe an arc.
(5) Where the arcs cross from Step 3 and Step 4 gives the centre of the required cone.
(6) Complete the views in the usual way.

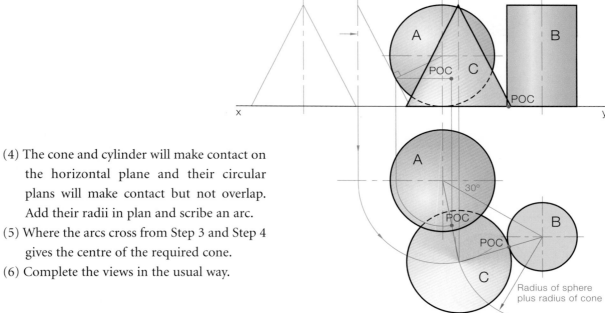

Fig. 4.58

H I G H E R   L E V E L

PROBLEM 4

The diagram shows the projection of a sphere A which rests on the horizontal plane, Fig. 4.59.

(i) Draw the sphere in plan and elevation.

(ii) Draw the projections of a sphere of 50 mm diameter which touches the sphere A at a point 60 mm above the horizontal plane and also touches the vertical plane. Show the point of contact in both views.

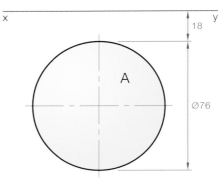

Fig. 4.59

(1) Draw the plan and elevation of sphere A.

(2) Mark the height of the point of contact, 60 mm above the xy line.

(3) Where this height line intersects the circumference gives point P_1. Construct the new sphere to touch P_1 as shown in Fig. 4.60.

(4) Drop this sphere's centre to plan and rotate about the plan until it crosses a line 25 mm (the radius of the new sphere) from the xy line, the vertical plane.

(5) Draw the elevation of this sphere and find the point of contact in the usual way, Fig. 4.60.

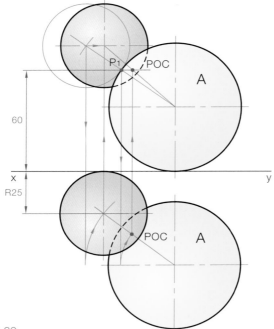

Fig. 4.60

PROBLEM 5

Fig. 4.61 shows the plan of two spheres A and B resting on the horizontal plane.

(i) Draw the plan and elevation of the two spheres and show the projections of the smallest sphere which rests on the horizontal plane and touches both sphere A and sphere B.

(ii) Show the points of contact in all views.

(1) Draw the plan and elevation of the solids.

(2) The smallest sphere to touch both existing solids will have its centre in line with the centres of sphere A and sphere B in plan. Project an auxiliary elevation with the x_1y_1 line parallel to the line joining the centres of sphere A and B. This auxiliary will show the space between the spheres.

(3) Locate the centre of the new sphere by the use of locii. Draw the locus of points which are equidistant from the circumference of sphere A and the x_1y_1 line.

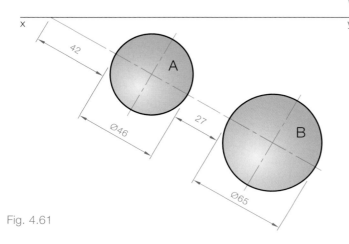

Fig. 4.61

(4) Similarly for sphere B and the x_1y_1 line.

(5) The locii intersect giving a point which is equidistant from the sphere A, the sphere B and the x_1y_1 line.

(6) Draw the sphere and project back through the views.

(7) The points of contact are also found in the auxiliary and projected back through the views, Fig. 4.62.

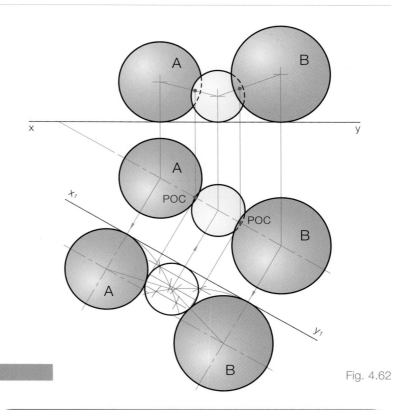

Fig. 4.62

PROBLEM 6

The diagram Fig. 4.63 shows the plan of a right cone A having an altitude of 90 mm, resting on the horizontal plane.

(i) Draw the plan and elevation of the cone and show the projections of a sphere B which rests on the horizontal plane and makes contact with the cone at point P.

(ii) Show the projections of another right cone C resting on the horizontal plane. This cone is to make contact with sphere B, 15 mm above the horizontal plane, and to touch cone A at the point Q.

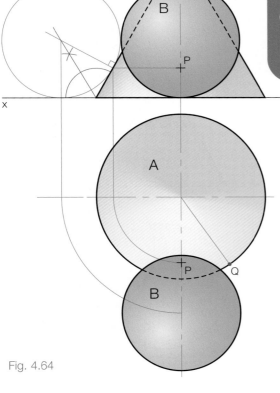

Fig. 4.64

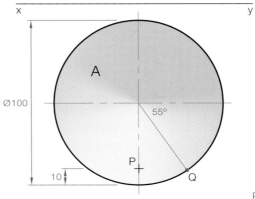

Fig. 4.63

(1) Draw the plan and elevation of the cone.
(2) Find sphere B in the usual way, Fig. 4.64.

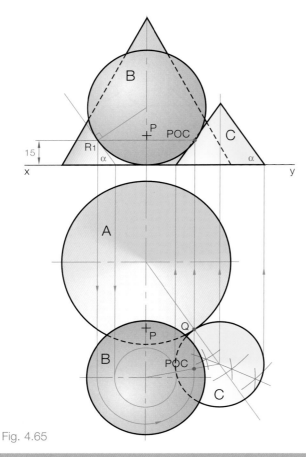

Fig. 4.65

PROBLEM 7

(3) The angle of the cone C can be found by constructing a tangent at the height of the point of contact, on the circumference of sphere B, at point R_1.

(4) The base of cone C projects underneath sphere B and is rotated.

(5) The base circle of cone C must touch this rotated point and point Q and is found by using a locus as shown in Fig. 4.65.

(6) Once the base circle is found, the point of contact is obtained by joining the centres in plan and by dropping point R_1 from elevation and rotating.

(7) The elevation of cone C is found by projection, having its base angle matching that of the tangent at R_1.

> The plan of a right cone is shown in Fig. 4.66.
> The cone has an altitude of 70 mm. Also shown is a point P on the cone's surface.
> (i)   Draw the projections of the cone and point P.
> (ii) Draw the elevation and plan of a sphere that makes contact with the cone at point P and also touches the vertical plane.

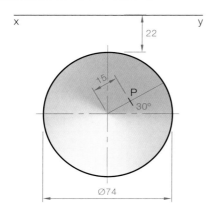

Fig. 4.66

(1) Point P is rotated to the side of the cone.

(2) A perpendicular to the cone side is constructed. A possible radius D is stepped out on this perpendicular to point d. This point d is dropped to plan and rotated about the cone.

(3) A line is drawn parallel to the xy line in plan the same distance D away. The arc and line intersect giving a point on the locus.

(4) Repeat for larger distances forming the locus.

(5) The centre of the required sphere will be on this locus and the line extended from the cone centre through P, Fig. 4.67.

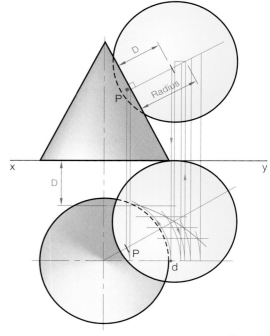

Fig. 4.67

Tangent Planes to Solids

PROBLEM 1

(1) In plan join the sphere centre to P.
(2) Project an auxiliary view having x_1y_1 parallel to cP.
(3) Locate point P in the auxiliary. It will be on the circumference.
(4) Draw the edge view of the tangent plane in auxiliary.
(5) Find the traces.

To draw a plane tangential to a sphere at a given point P on its surface.

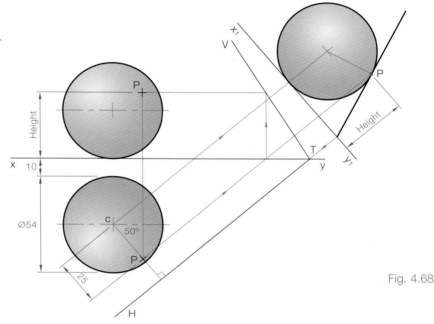

Fig. 4.68

To draw the traces of a plane tangential to a cone at a given point P on its surface.

PROBLEM 2

(1) In plan, draw the generator from the cone apex through point P to the base of the cone. The horizontal trace will be perpendicular to this.
(2) Find P in elevation and the vertical trace in the usual way.

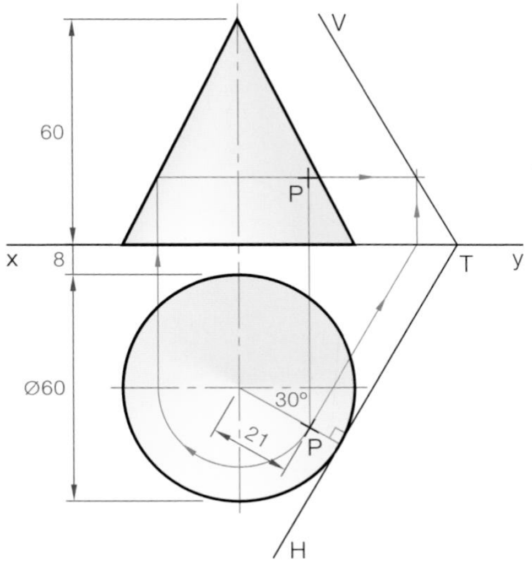

Fig. 4.69

PROBLEM 3

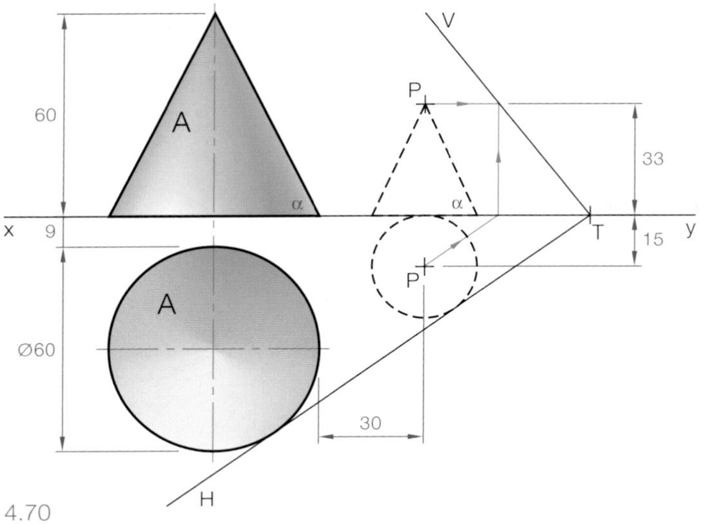

To draw the traces of a plane that is tangential to the cone A and that contains point P.

(1) Set up the question.

(2) Draw the plan and elevation of a cone, having the same base angle as cone A and having point P as its apex.

(3) The horizontal trace will be tangential to the two base circles. The vertical trace is found as before.

The tangent plane's horizontal trace will be tangential to the base circles of the cones. It can also be seen from the pictorial that the plane makes contact with the cones along a whole generator, Fig. 4.71.

Fig. 4.70

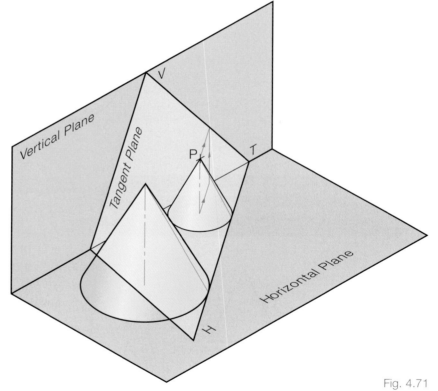

Fig. 4.71

HIGHER LEVEL

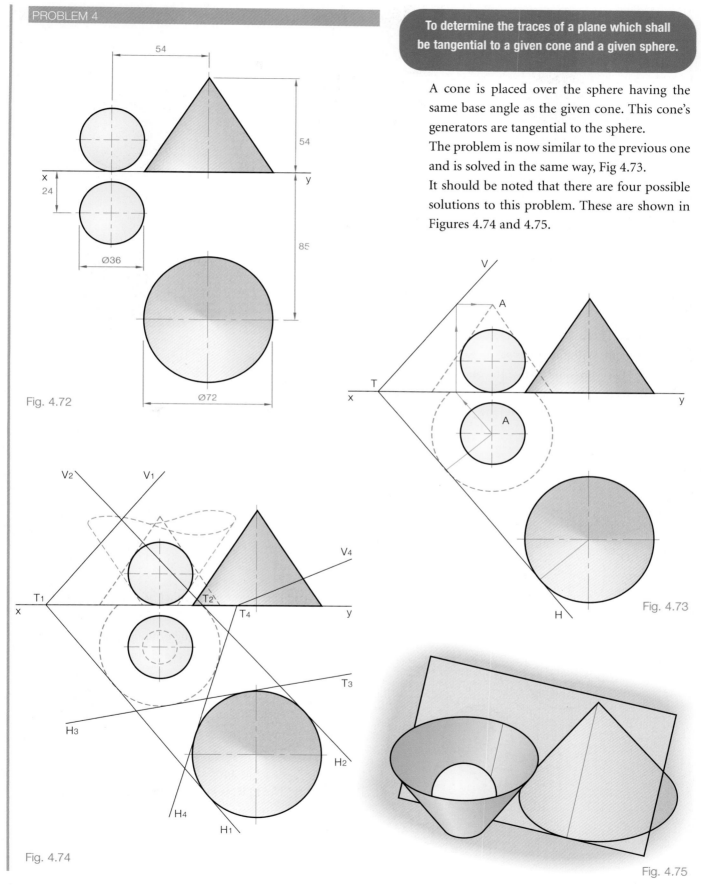

PROBLEM 4

To determine the traces of a plane which shall be tangential to a given cone and a given sphere.

A cone is placed over the sphere having the same base angle as the given cone. This cone's generators are tangential to the sphere.

The problem is now similar to the previous one and is solved in the same way, Fig 4.73.

It should be noted that there are four possible solutions to this problem. These are shown in Figures 4.74 and 4.75.

Fig. 4.72

Fig. 4.73

Fig. 4.74

Fig. 4.75

Given the plan and elevation of two spheres A and B. Determine the traces of a plane that is tangential to both solids, makes an angle of 60° to the horizontal plane and passes between the spheres. Find the points of contact.

(1) Construct a 60° base angle cone over one of the spheres. Now place an inverted 60° base angle cone to envelop the other sphere.

(2) Find the circles in plan where these cones make contact with the horizontal plane.

(3) Construct the horizontal trace (HT) as a tangent to these two circles.

(4) The vertical trace is constructed as before.

Note: There are four possible solutions to this problem. With the cones set up as in Fig. 4.77 there are two possible tangents (horizontal traces) between the cones. The inverted cone could be drawn around sphere B and the upright cone around sphere A, giving two other traces.

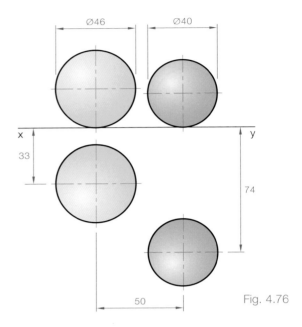

Fig. 4.76

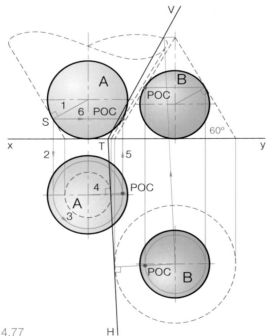

Fig. 4.77

(i) The point of contact is located by drawing a perpendicular to the side of the cone from the sphere centre giving point S. This gives the height of the POC above the xy line.

(ii) Drop S to the plan and rotate.

(iii) Draw a perpendicular to the HT from the cone apex in plan. This is the line of contact between the inverted cone and the plane.

(iv) The point of contact is the intersection between Step (ii) and Step (iii).

(v) The POC is projected to elevation.

Activities

Q1. Fig. 4.78 shows the elevation of a cone and a sphere. The cone is in contact with the sphere A at point P.
Draw the elevation and plan of the solids in contact and determine the exact position of point P.

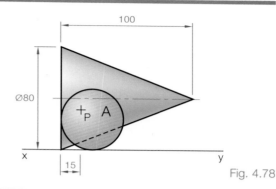

Fig. 4.78

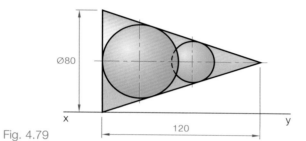

Fig. 4.79

Q2. Fig. 4.79 shows the elevation of a square-based pyramid and two spheres. The solids are in contact with each other.
Draw the elevation and plan of the solids showing all points of contact.

Q3. Fig. 4.80 shows the elevation of a sphere A and a cone B. The two solids are in contact.
(i) Draw the plan and elevation of the sphere and cone in contact.
(ii) Draw the projections of another sphere C of 40 mm diameter that is in contact with the cone and sphere and has its centre on line S–S.

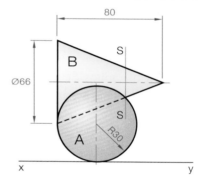

Fig. 4.80

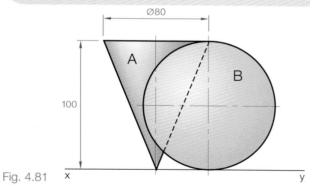

Fig. 4.81

Q4. Fig. 4.81 shows the elevation of a right cone A and a sphere B. Both solids are in contact.
(i) Draw the plan and elevation of the solids.
(ii) Draw the projections of the smallest possible sphere that touches the cone A, the sphere B and the horizontal plane.

Q5. Fig. 4.82 shows the elevation of a sphere A in contact with a cone B.
(i) Draw the plan and elevation of the two solids showing the point of contact clearly.
(ii) Draw the projections of a second sphere C of diameter 30 mm which touches both solids. Sphere C makes contact with sphere A at a point 44 mm above the horizontal plane.

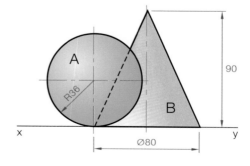

Fig. 4.82

HIGHER LEVEL

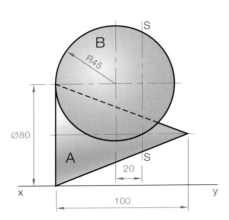

Fig. 4.83

Q6. The diagram Fig. 4.83 shows a right cone A and a sphere B, which are in contact with each other.
(i)   Draw the front elevation, end elevation and plan of the solids showing the point of contact in all views.
(ii) Draw the projections of another sphere C of 36 mm diameter and having its centre on line S–S. Sphere C must make contact with the other two solids. Show all points of contact.
(iii) Draw the traces of a plane that passes through the centre of sphere B and the apex of cone A. The plane is to make an angle of 75° to the horizontal plane.

Q7. Fig. 4.84 shows the elevation of a right cone A in contact with a sphere B.
(i)   Draw the elevation and plan of the two solids showing the point of contact in both views.
(ii) Draw the projections of another sphere C of 30 mm diameter is position S. Sphere C must make contact with the other two solids. Show all points of contact.
(iii) Draw the traces of a plane that is tangential to cone A and sphere C.

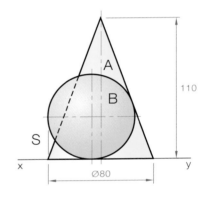

Fig. 4.84

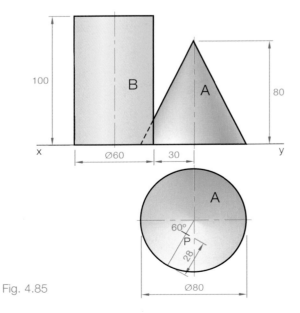

Fig. 4.85

Q8. Fig. 4.85 shows the elevation of a cone A and a cylinder B in contact with each other. The plan of the cone is also shown with a point P on its surface.
(i)   Draw the plan and elevation of both solids.
(ii) Draw the projections of a sphere C which makes contact with the cone A at point P and which also makes contact with the cylinder.
(iii) Draw the traces of the plane that passes through the lowest point of sphere C and is tangential to cone A.

5 Rotation and Inclination of Solids

SYLLABUS OUTLINE

Areas to be studied:

• Projection of right and oblique solids.

Learning outcomes

Students should be able to:

Higher and Ordinary levels

• Project views of right solids such that any face or edge of the solid may be on one of the principal planes of reference.

Higher level only

• *Project views of oblique solids (axis inclined to one of the principal reference planes only) such that any face or edge of the solid may be on one of the planes of reference or inclined to one of both planes of reference.*

Rotation and Inclination of Right Solids

> The plan of a cube is shown in Fig. 5.1. Draw a front elevation, end elevation and plan of the cube when the bottom face is inclined at 25° to the horizontal plane and the edge bc rests on the horizontal plane.

(1) Draw the given plan.

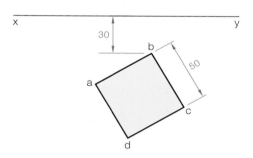

Fig. 5.1

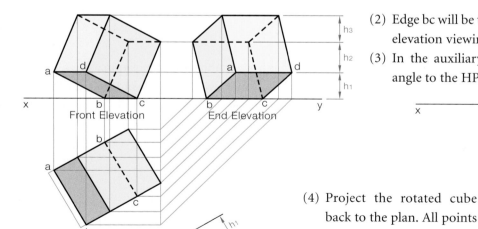

Front Elevation   End Elevation

Plan

Auxiliary Elevation

Fig. 5.3

(2) Edge bc will be the axis of rotation. Project an auxiliary elevation viewing along bc.

(3) In the auxiliary the cube is rotated to the required angle to the HP, Fig. 5.2.

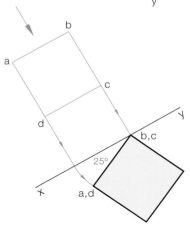

(4) Project the rotated cube back to the plan. All points will move perpendicular to the axis in plan.

(5) Project both sets of elevations. The heights for the corners are found in the auxiliary elevation, Fig. 5.3.

Fig. 5.2

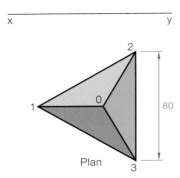

Fig. 5.4

Fig. 5.4 shows the plan of a tetrahedron. Draw the front elevation, end elevation and plan of the solid when the base is rotated at 30° to the HP about the edge 1,3.

(1) The construction is the same as the previous problem. View in the direction of edge 1,3.

(2) The edge 2,0 will be a true length in the auxiliary.

(3) Project the views back from the auxiliary and the heights are taken from the auxiliary, Fig. 5.5.

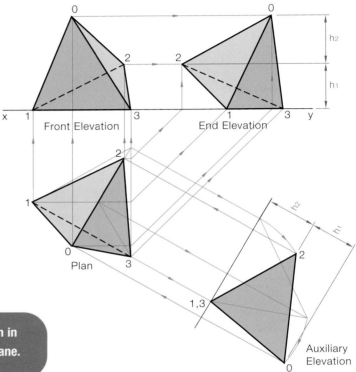

Fig. 5.5

(1) The solid is drawn in its normal position.

(2) Edge ab is a point view in elevation and will act as the axis of rotation. Rotate the apex about ab in elevation until point o intersects the xy line.

Project views of the square-based pyramid shown in Fig. 5.6 such that surface A is on the horizontal plane.

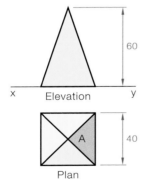

Fig. 5.6

(3) Rotate points c and d about ab in elevation.

(4) The length from o to cd in the original elevation is used in the new elevation to locate c and d in the new elevation, Fig. 5.7.

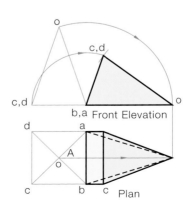

Fig. 5.7

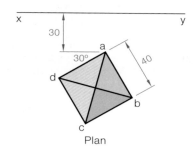

Fig. 5.8

Shown in Fig. 5.8 is the plan of a square-based pyramid of altitude 60 mm. Draw the front elevation and end elevation of the pyramid when its base is inclined at 45° to the horizontal plane and edge ad remains touching the horizontal plane.

(1) Draw the given plan. Edge ad will form the axis of rotation for the solid.
(2) Draw an auxiliary view of the pyramid looking along the line ad. Rotate the pyramid in this view about ad which is a point of view.
(3) Project the rotated pyramid to plan. Remember the points more perpendicular to the axis of rotation in plan.
(4) The front elevation is projected, with the heights being taken from the auxiliary, Fig. 5.9.

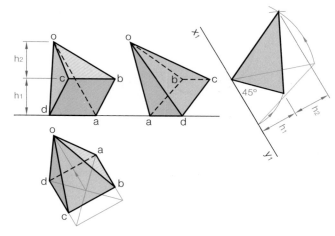

Fig. 5.9

Shown in Fig. 5.10 is the elevation of a right regular hexagonal-based pyramid which is inclined at an angle of 40° to the horizontal plane. Draw the given view, project a plan and an end elevation of the pyramid.

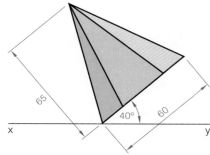

Fig. 5.10

(1) Draw the given elevation.
(2) Project an auxiliary plan to show the base as a true shape – a regular hexagon.
(3) The plan is projected down from the elevation with the widths being taken from the auxiliary plan.
(4) The end elevation is projected in the normal way, Fig. 5.11.

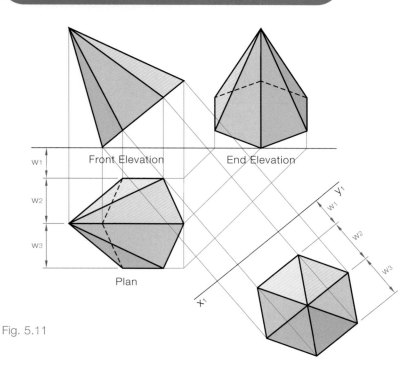

Fig. 5.11

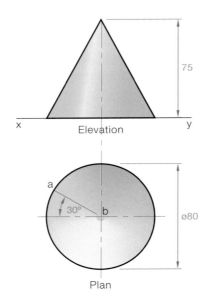

Fig. 5.12

Shown in Fig. 5.12 is a right cone. Draw the front elevation, end elevation and plan of the cone when the generator ab rests on the horizontal plane.

(1) Draw the plan of the cone with the base on the horizontal plane.
(2) Draw an auxiliary elevation of the cone with x₁y₁ parallel to the generator ab.
(3) Rotate the cone in the auxiliary.
(4) The circular base is divided into parts and the points are projected through the views to locate the ellipses in all three views, Fig. 5.13.

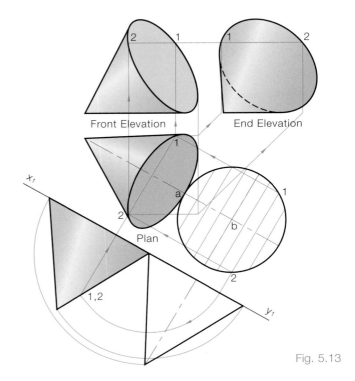

Fig. 5.13

The plan and elevation of a pentagonal-based right pyramid are shown in Fig. 5.14. Draw new views of the object when the surface abc is parallel to the vertical plane.

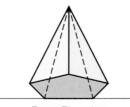

Fig. 5.14

Fig. 5.15

(1) Draw the given plan and project the end view.
(2) In the end view, surface abc appears as an edge view.
(3) Rotate the pyramid until surface abc is vertical.
(4) Project the remaining views from the end view, Fig. 5.15.

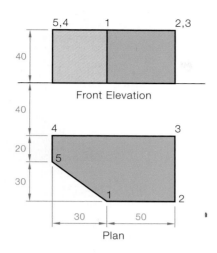

Fig. 5.16

Given in Fig. 5.16 are the plan and elevation of a block which has a section removed. Rotate the block so that the cut surface is parallel to the vertical plane.

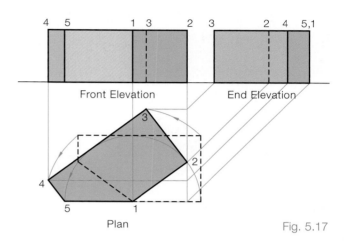

Fig. 5.17

(1) Draw the given plan.
(2) The plan may be rotated about any of its corners. The solution Fig. 5.17 is rotated about corner 1. Rotate 5 first until line 1,5 is parallel to the xy line.
(3) All subsequent points are found by triangulation. For example, point 2 is rotated about point 1. The distancee from 5 to 2 is taken on the plan. Place the compass on the new point 5 and scribe an arc to cut the arc from point 2.
(4) When the plan is complete, project the other views, Fig. 5.17.

The diagram, Fig. 5.18, shows the elevation of a cylinder which has been cut by a simply inclined plane. Draw the elevation and plan when the cylinder has been rotated so that the cut surface is parallel to the horizontal plane.

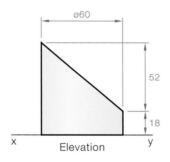

Fig. 5.18

(1) Draw the elevation and plan.
(2) Rotate the top surface until it is level.
(3) Build up the elevation by rotating the rest of the corners.
(4) Choose any point on the original circular plan, e.g. points 1 and 2.
   Project points 1 and 2 to the cut surface of the original elevation.
(5) Rotate points 1 and 2 onto the horizontal surface.
(6) Project down and then across from the plan.
(7) Repeat with other points on the original circle to build up the shape of the cut surface, Fig. 5.19.

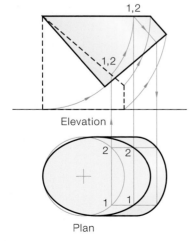

Fig. 5.19

Rotation and Inclination of Oblique Solids

Fig. 5.20 shows a rectangular-based oblique pyramid. Draw three views of this object when surface A is on the horizontal plane.

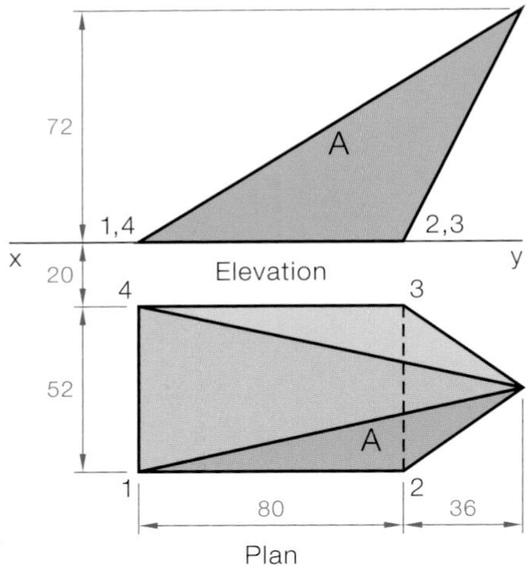

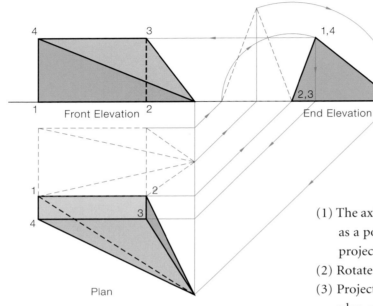

Fig. 5.20

Fig. 5.21

(1) The axis of rotation will be edge 1,2. This edge can be seen as a point view in the end view. Draw the given plan and project an end view.

(2) Rotate the solid in end view, about edge 1,2.

(3) Project the solid back through the views thus finding the plan and front elevation, Fig. 5.21.

Fig. 5. 22 shows an oblique rectangular prism having one face on the VP. Draw views of the object when the prism is rotated about edge ad until edge bc touches the horizontal plane.

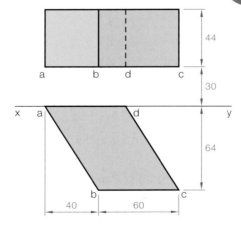

Fig. 5.22

The construction of the solution should be clear from the diagram Fig. 5.23.

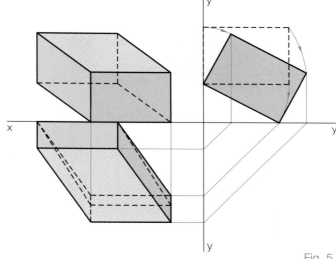

Fig. 5.23

An oblique regular hexagonal-based pyramid is shown in Fig. 5.24. Draw a new front elevation, end elevation and plan of the object when the base is rotated about edge ab until it makes an angle of 30° to the horizontal plane.

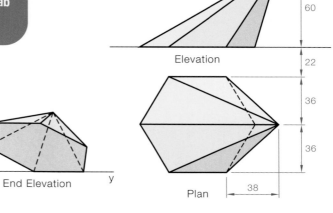

Fig. 5.24

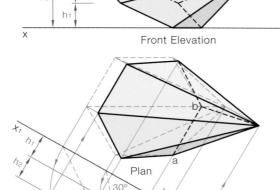

Fig. 5.25

(1) Draw the plan as given.

(2) Since the solid is being rotated about ab we take an auxiliary elevation viewing along edge ab.

(3) We can rotate the solid in the auxiliary.

(4) Points are projected back to the plan from the auxiliary. Points on the original plan move perpendicular to the axis line ab.

(5) Once the plan is completed the elevations are found. Heights are taken from the auxiliary elevation as shown, Fig. 5.25.

HIGHER LEVEL

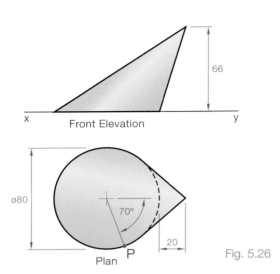

Front Elevation

ø80

70°

20

P

Plan

Fig. 5.26

Fig. 5.26 shows an oblique cone. Draw the projections of the solid when the base is tilted to an angle of 45° to the horizontal plane and point P rests on the horizontal plane.

(1) Draw the given plan.
(2) Join P to the centre of the base circle. Draw the x_1y_1 line parallel to this line.
(3) The solid is rotated in the auxiliary.
(4) Project the views in the usual way, Fig. 5.27.

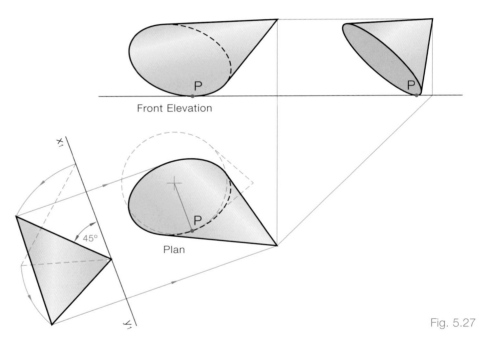

Front Elevation

Plan

45°

Fig. 5.27

Activities

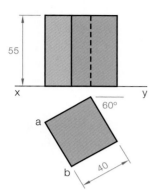

Fig. 5.28

Q1. The plan and elevation of a square-based prism is shown in Fig. 5.28. Draw a front elevation, end elevation and plan of the prism when the bottom face is inclined at 20° to the horizontal plane and edge ab rests on the horizontal plan.

Q2. The plan and elevation of a rectangular-based pyramid are shown in Fig. 5.29. Draw the front elevation, end elevation and plan of the pyramid when the edge co is vertical and corner c rests on the horizontal plane.

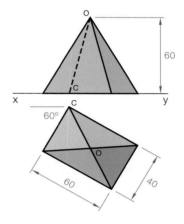

Fig. 5.29

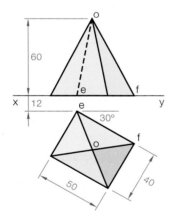

Fig. 5.30

Q3. The pyramid in Fig. 5.30 is to be rotated about edge ef until the apex o touches the vertical plane. Draw the front elevation, end elevation and plan of the pyramid in its new position.

Q4. Fig. 5.31 shows the plan and elevation of a hexagonal-based prism. The prism is to be rotated about edge 1,2 until edge 3,4 is directly above edge 1,2. Draw the plan, front elevation and end view of the prism in its new position.

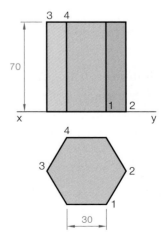

Fig. 5.31

Q5. A pentagonal-based pyramid rests on the vertical plane. The pyramid is rotated about edge 1,2 until surface 1,2,3 rests on the vertical plane. Draw the front elevation, end elevation and plan of the solid in its new position, Fig. 5.32.

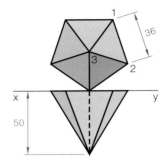

Fig. 5.32

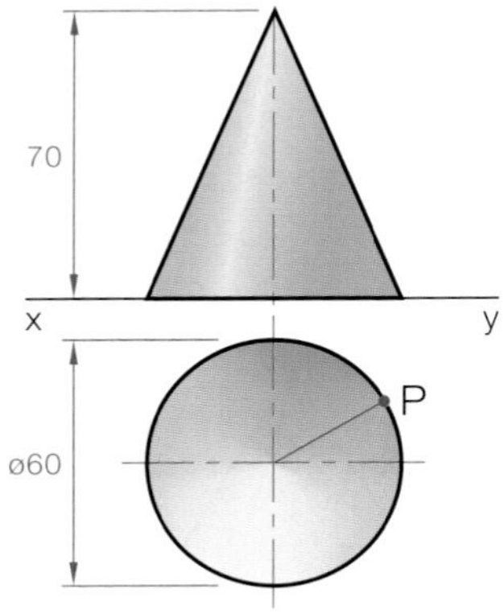

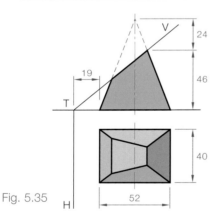

Fig. 5.33

Q6. Fig. 5.33 shows the plan and elevation of a cone. The cone is to be tilted on point P so that the base makes an angle of 20° with the horizontal plane. Draw the front elevation, end elevation and plan of the solid when it is tilted.

Q7. The plan and elevation of a cylinder are shown in Fig. 5.34. The cylinder is to be tilted on point P until the base makes an angle of 60° with the horizontal plane. Draw the front elevation, end elevation and plan of the tilted solid.

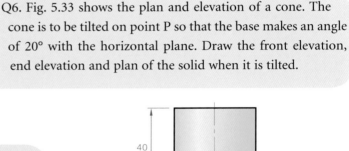

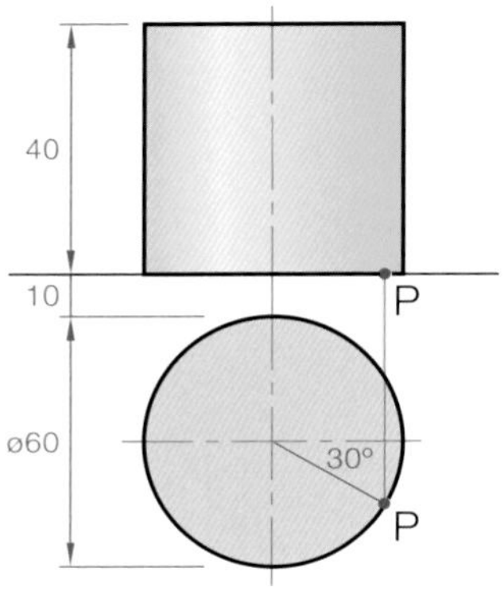

Fig. 5.34

Q8. A rectangular-based pyramid has been cut by the simply inclined plane VTH. Draw the front elevation, end elevation and plan of the solid when the pyramid has been rotated so that the cut surface is parallel to the horizontal plane.

Fig. 5.35

Q9. A tetrahedron of 70 mm side is shown in Fig. 5.36. It is to be cut by the simply inclined plane VTH. Draw the front elevation, end elevation and plan of the cut tetrahedron after it has been rotated about edge 1,2 until the cut surface is horizontal.

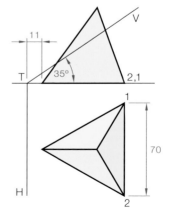

Fig. 5.36

ROTATION AND INCLINATION OF OBLIQUE SOLIDS

Fig. 5.37

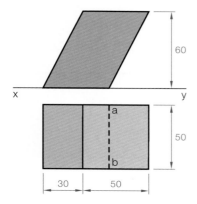

Q10. A square-based oblique prism is shown in Fig. 5.37. Draw the front elevation, end elevation and plan of the solid when the base makes an angle of 20° to the horizontal plane, and edge ab remains on the horizontal plane.

Q11. An oblique pyramid is shown in Fig. 5.38. Draw the front elevation, end elevation and plan of the solid when surface A is inclined at 30° to the horizontal and edge pq remains on the horizontal plane.

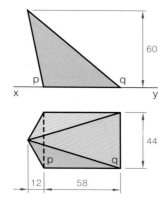

Fig. 5.38

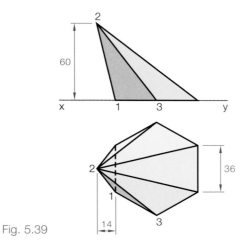

Q12. Draw the front elevation, end elevation and plan of the oblique, hexagonal-based pyramid, when surface 1,2,3 is on the horizontal plane, Fig. 5.39.

Fig. 5.39

Q13. An oblique cylinder is shown in Fig. 5.40. The cylinder is to be rotated keeping P on the horizontal plane until the base makes an angle of 40° with the horizontal plane. Draw the front elevation, end elevation and plan of the object after it is rotated.

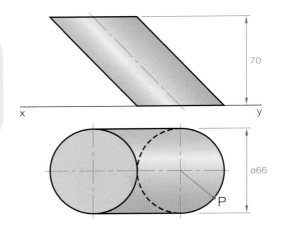

Fig. 5.40

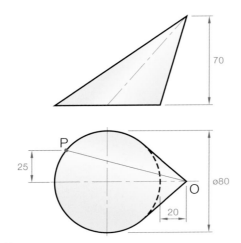

Fig. 5.41

Q14. Draw the front elevation, end elevation and plan of the oblique cone when point P is on the horizontal plane and generator OP is vertical, Fig. 41.

6 Pictorial Projection 1

SYLLABUS OUTLINE

Areas to be studied:

• Isometric drawing of solids. • *Derivation*, construction and application of the isometric scale.
• The axonometric plane and axes. • Principles of orthogonal axonometric projection.

Learning outcomes

Students should be able to:

Higher and Ordinary levels

- Complete isometric drawings of solids containing plane and/or curved surfaces.
- Complete a portion of the axonometric plane given the projection of the axes of the planes of reference.
- Determine the true shape of the planes of reference, showing the axonometric plane.
- Determine the isometric projections of solids, including the sphere, using the isometric scale.
- Determine the axonometric projections of solids, including the sphere, using the axes method.
- Project a two-dimensional view of an object from its axonometric view on to one of the principal planes of reference.
- Demonstrate a knowledge of the principles involved in the isometric scale.

Higher level only

- *Project orthogonal axonometric views of objects when the axes are inclined in isometric, dimetric or trimetric positions.*

Isometric

In isometric drawings, measurements are transferred onto isometric lines. These isometric lines are parallel to the isometric axes. It is a pictorial view and will often show a solid more clearly than an orthographic can.

Sloping lines do not maintain their true length in isometric, circular curves become elliptical and angles do not show their true angle. Care must be taken when producing isometrics and they can often be slow to produce.

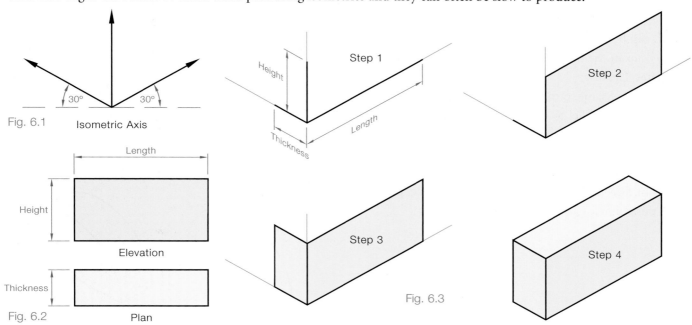

Fig. 6.1   Isometric Axis   30°   30°

Height   Step 1   Length   Thickness

Step 2

Length   Height   Elevation   Thickness   Plan

Fig. 6.2

Step 3   Step 4

Fig. 6.3

Sloping Lines and Surfaces

Sloping lines do not maintain their true length in isometric drawing and angles do not measure as true angles. No angular measurements can therefore be used in these drawings. Angular measurements must be changed into linear measurements along the isometric axes.

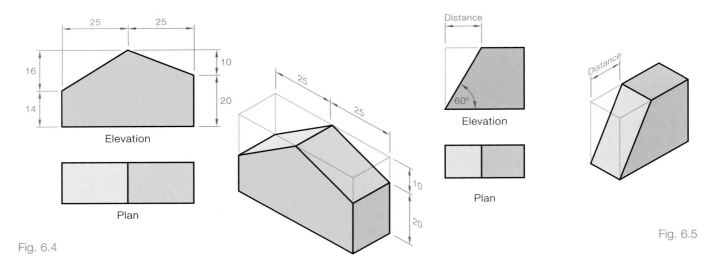

Fig. 6.4

Fig. 6.5

Circles in Isometric

Circles will appear elliptical in isometric, and depending on the size of the circle and the accuracy needed we have the choice of several methods of construction.

COORDINATE METHOD

This is the most accurate method, as the number of points which can be found on the curve are limitless. The curve is divided up in the orthographic view by using a number of ordinates, Fig. 6.6.

Draw the same ordinates in the isometric. Since the ordinates are parallel to one of the isometric axes they will appear as true lengths. Transfer the height of each ordinate from the orthographic to the isometric, Fig. 6.7a.

Join the plotted points on the curve, freehand, to produce the front face. The thickness of the object is stepped back from this curve to give the back curve, Fig. 6.7b.

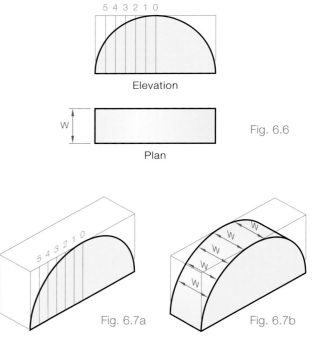

Fig. 6.6

Fig. 6.7a

Fig. 6.7b

The coordinate method is ideal for irregular curves, as can be seen in Fig. 6.8.

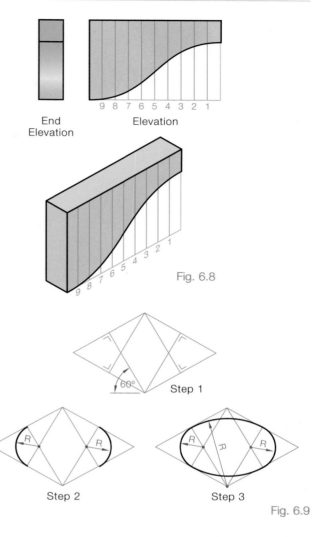

Fig. 6.8

FOUR-CENTRE ELLIPSE

For most isometric drawings which contain circles, an approximate ellipse is perfectly satisfactory, as exact measurements are rarely taken from isometrics. They are used more for explanatory purposes. For this reason an ellipse which can be constructed quickly with the aid of a compass is very useful, Fig 6.9.

(1) Draw the isometric box to contain the circle.
(2) Draw lines from the corners perpendicular to the opposite sides. These will be 60° lines.
(3) Where these lines cross gives the centres for the small arcs.
(4) The top and bottom corners are the centres for the large arcs.

When drawing an object having concentric circles (Fig. 6.10) it should be noted that each ellipse has its own parallelogram and centres (Fig. 6.11).

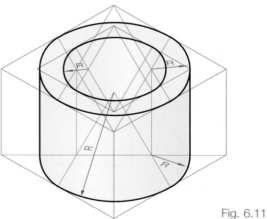

Fig. 6.9

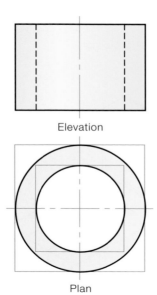

Elevation

Fig. 6.10

Plan

Fig. 6.11

It should be noted again that this construction of ellipses is not accurate, but it is sufficient for most isometrics.

A closer approximation to a true ellipse can be found by the following method.

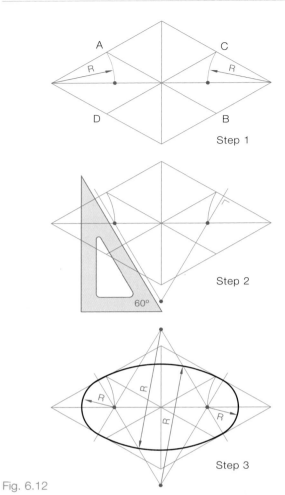

Fig. 6.12

(1) Draw the isometric of the square which will contain the isometric circle. The sides of the square will equal the length of the diameter.
(2) Join the diagonals and the bisectors of the sides AB and CD.
(3) Swing the ends of the bisectors onto the diagonal as shown. This gives the centre of the small arcs.
(4) Draw perpendiculars to the sides, through these centre points locating the centres for the large arcs.
(5) Complete the drawing with the compass.

Crating or Boxing

Objects can be more easily constructed in isometric by the use of crating. This involves constructing a box around the whole object or parts of the object in the orthographic, Fig. 6.13.

These boxes can then be drawn in isometric giving a good starting point for the rest of the drawing details to be filled in, Fig. 6.14.

Hidden lines and centre lines should only be drawn if they are needed to make the drawing clearer or for dimensioning.

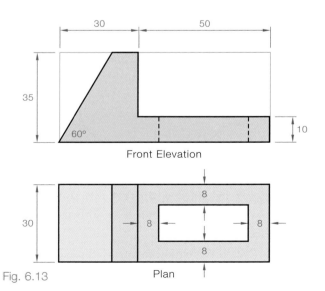

Fig. 6.13

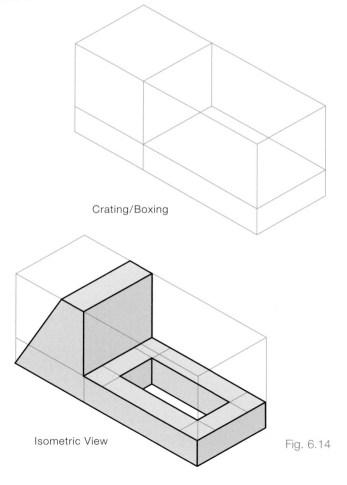

Crating/Boxing

Isometric View   Fig. 6.14

Worked Examples

Given the front elevation, end elevation and plan of a shaped solid. Draw the given views and produce an isometric view of the object.

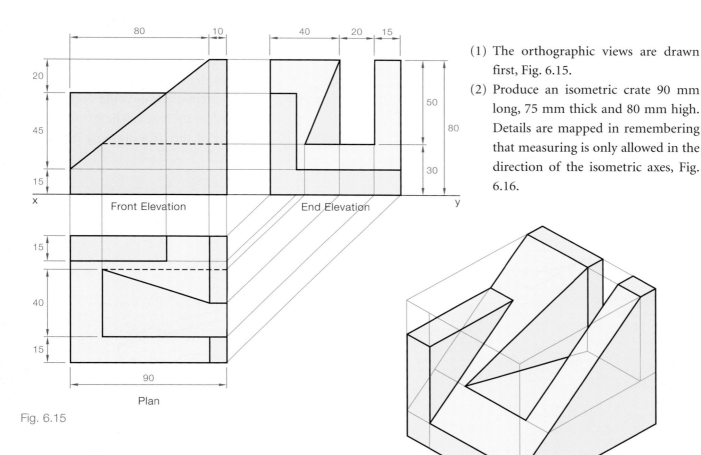

(1) The orthographic views are drawn first, Fig. 6.15.

(2) Produce an isometric crate 90 mm long, 75 mm thick and 80 mm high. Details are mapped in remembering that measuring is only allowed in the direction of the isometric axes, Fig. 6.16.

Front Elevation

End Elevation

Plan

Fig. 6.15

Isometric View

Fig. 6.16

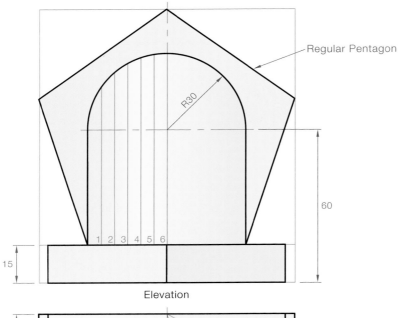

Regular Pentagon

R30

60

1 2 3 4 5 6

15

Elevation

15

R45

Semi-hexagon   Plan

Fig. 6.17a

Fig. 6.17a shows the plan and elevation of a solid. Draw the given views and draw an isometric of the solid.

(1) Draw the elevation of the central portion.
(2) From this draw the regular pentagon using a protractor. Pentagon sides will be 60 mm long.
(3) The semi-hexagon in plan will be tangential to the radius 45 mm curve in plan. The length of the sides of the hexagon can be found by drawing a 30° line from the circle centre. Alternatively we could work out that the width of the base will be 90 mm, i.e. the diameter of the circle forming the central portion.

(4) The best way to approach the isometric is by crating.
(5) The curved central portion must be constructed using ordinates as shown. The fact that the front is doubly curved means that the four-centre ellipse will not work. For the sake of clarity some of the ordinates have not been shown in the isometric, Fig. 6.17b.

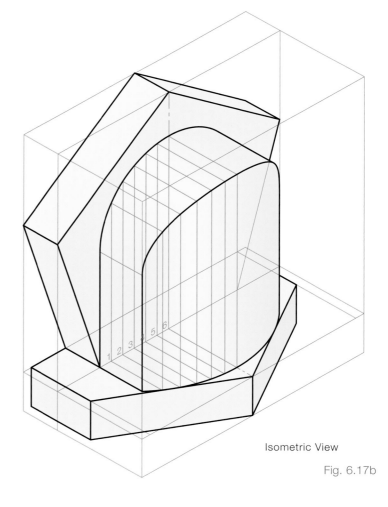

1 2 3 5 6

Isometric View

Fig. 6.17b

Fig. 6.18a shows the plan and elevation of a shaped solid. Draw the given views and draw an isometric of the solid.

(1) Start with the plan of the square prism.
(2) Draw the hexagonal prism having sides of the same length as the square.
(3) Draw the R44 arc and build up the right-hand side of the base.
(4) The centre of the R24 arc must be located by adding the two radii, 44 + 24 = 68 mm. Scribe an arc. Another arc of 24 mm radius is drawn from the corner, 40 mm in from the right.
(5) The isometric is produced by caging each element of the solid separately.
(6) Start with the base. The curve is drawn by using ordinates.
(7) Draw the upper curve and step the lower curve 28 mm below it.

The step will be stepped down 14 mm, Fig. 6.18b.

Elevation

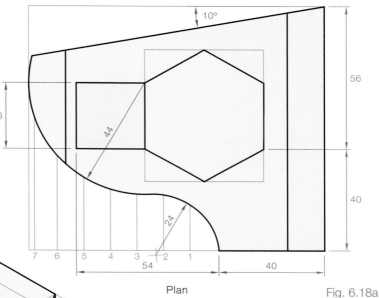

Plan

Fig. 6.18a

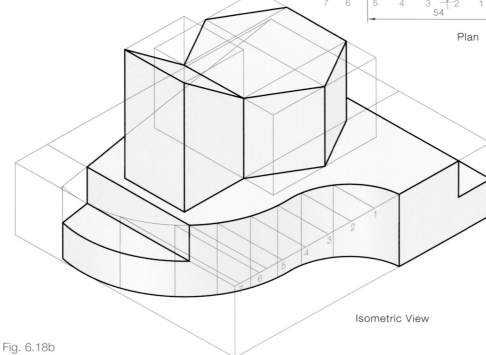

Isometric View

Fig. 6.18b

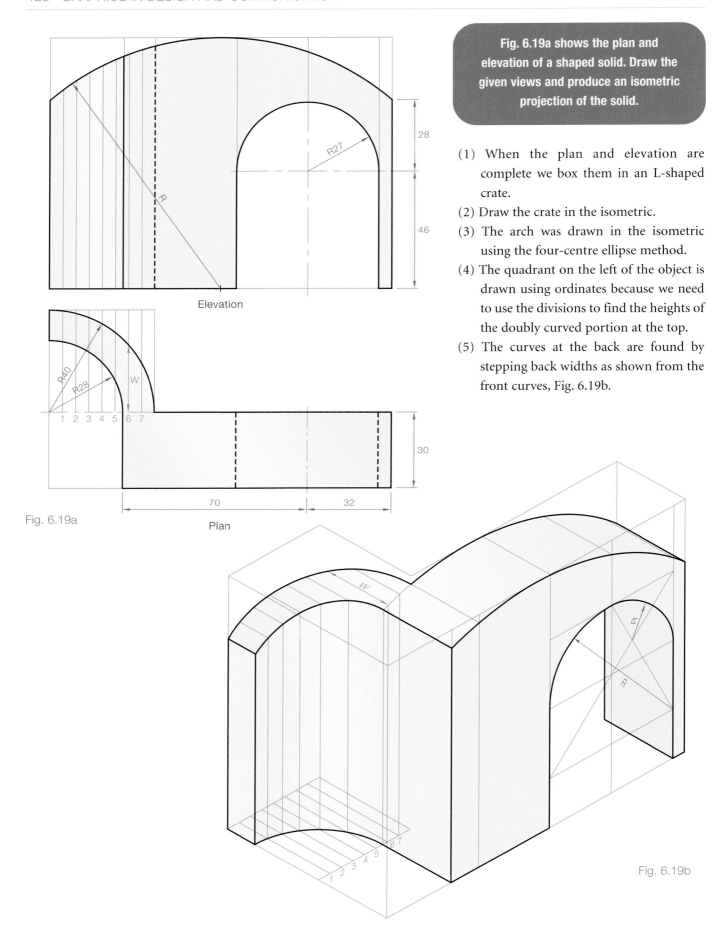

Elevation

Fig. 6.19a

Plan

Fig. 6.19a shows the plan and elevation of a shaped solid. Draw the given views and produce an isometric projection of the solid.

(1) When the plan and elevation are complete we box them in an L-shaped crate.

(2) Draw the crate in the isometric.

(3) The arch was drawn in the isometric using the four-centre ellipse method.

(4) The quadrant on the left of the object is drawn using ordinates because we need to use the divisions to find the heights of the doubly curved portion at the top.

(5) The curves at the back are found by stepping back widths as shown from the front curves, Fig. 6.19b.

Fig. 6.19b

Activities

Q1., Q2. and Q3.
Draw the given plan and elevation and draw an isometric view of the solid, Figures 6.20, 6.21 and 6.22.

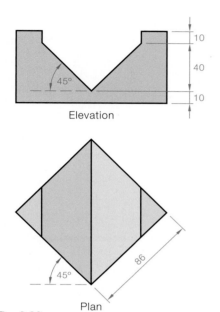

Fig. 6.20

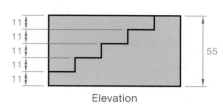

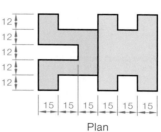

Fig. 6.21

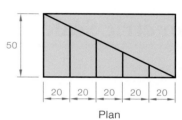

Fig. 6.22

Q4., Q5. and Q6.
Draw the given plan and elevation. Produce an isometric of the solid. Curves should be found with ordinates, Figures 6.23, 6.24 and 6.25.

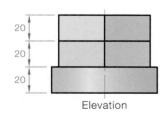

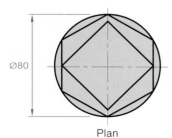

Fig. 6.23

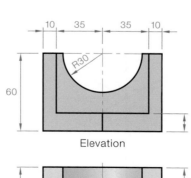

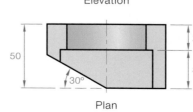

Fig. 6.24

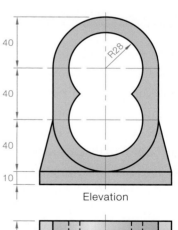

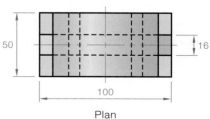

Fig. 6.25

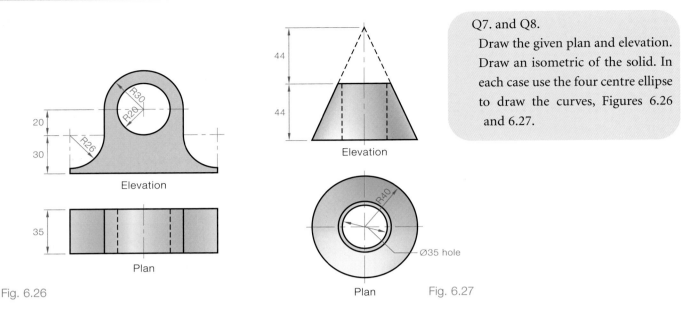

Q7. and Q8.
Draw the given plan and elevation. Draw an isometric of the solid. In each case use the four centre ellipse to draw the curves, Figures 6.26 and 6.27.

Fig. 6.26

Fig. 6.27

Isometric Scale

When we make a visual comparison between the orthographic projections of the solids in Figures 6.17a, 6.18a and 6.19a with their corresponding isometric projections, it can be seen that the isometric appears and actually is larger. The reason for this is that the solid drawn in isometric is inclined to the horizontal plane, tilted up on one of its corners. This means that all edges are sloping and therefore do not show their true length. When we draw an isometric we ignore this fact and measure the full measurement along the axes, thus making the isometric larger than the orthographic. In order to give the correct proportions between the two types of drawing we must use an **isometric scale**.

EXAMPLE OF HOW ISOMETRIC GIVES A DISTORTED VIEW.

We will take the example of a cube of 30 mm sides. The isometric of the cube shows corners 3 and 8 on the same point, so therefore the diagonal 3,8 will be a horizontal line. It can be proved that in order to get this diagonal horizontal, we must tilt the cube by 35°16′ (35 degrees 16 minutes). We may now draw an end view of the cube, from the isometric, having its base on the inclined plane as shown in Fig. 6.28. All edges of the cube will be inclined to the vertical plane and will not show true lengths in the isometric.

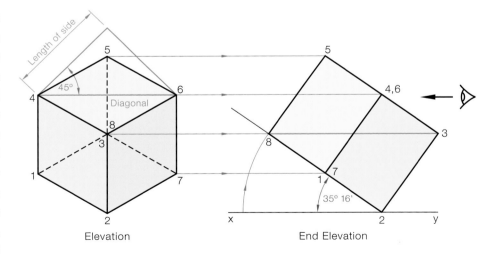

Fig. 6.28

Getting back to the isometric (elevation). The diagonal 4,6 will be seen as a true length in this view. If we have the diagonal of a square we can easily find the length of the side of that square (the sides of a square make an angle of 45° to the diagonal). When we do this we find that the length of the side is much more than 30 mm, as was required. The isometric cube is too big and does not represent a cube of 30 mm side. To rectify this we need a reducing scale.

ISOMETRIC SCALE

The scaling factor needed for isometric is a constant for all isometrics and can be derived from the cube example given previously. The 45° line shows the true length of the cube side and the 30° line shows the isometric representation of that length, Fig. 6.29.

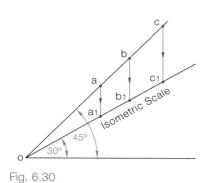

Fig. 6.30

We set up a 45° line (Fig. 6.30) to show true lengths and a 30° line to show their isometric equivalents. Lengths oa, ob and oc are drawn on the 45° line. These are projected vertically to give oa, ob and oc as the isometrical scaled distances. An isometric scale measurement is 0.816 of the true length distance.

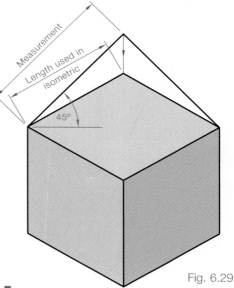

Fig. 6.29

Worked Example Using Isometric Scale

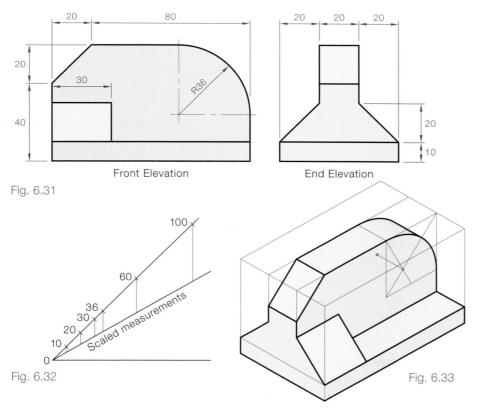

Front Elevation

Fig. 6.31

End Elevation

Fig. 6.32

Fig. 6.33

(1) Draw the front and end elevation of the shaped solid using full measurements, Fig. 6.31.

(2) Set up the isometric scale using a 45° line and a 30° line as explained earlier.

(3) Any measurement needed for the isometric is set out from the corner, along the 45° line, e.g. 10, 20, 30, 36 etc., Fig 6.32.

(4) Drop each measurement vertically to give the scaled measurements used in the isometric. Draw the isometric, Fig. 6.33.

(5) If you are constructing a circle or curve using ordinates, the length of each ordinate would have to be scaled also.

The Sphere in Isometric

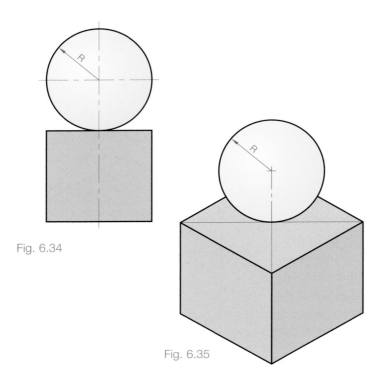

Fig. 6.34

Fig. 6.35

When drawing a sphere in isometric we must first consider what type of isometric we are producing. Are we drawing an isometric using full sizes or with scaled sizes? It should be noted that a sphere looks the same regardless of which way it is viewed or which plane it is projected onto. Having said that, it must also be noted that an unscaled isometric gives a distorted view, an enlarged view of objects. It stands to reason therefore that an unscaled drawing of an object containing a sphere, or part of a sphere, should give an enlarged view of that sphere. When drawing a sphere in isometric we must lengthen the radius unless we are producing a scaled isometric.

Fig. 6.34 shows the elevation of a pedestal with a sphere on top having a diameter equal to the pedestal width. Fig. 6.35 shows the isometric and it can be seen that the sphere appears too small even though the radius is the same as in Fig. 6.34.

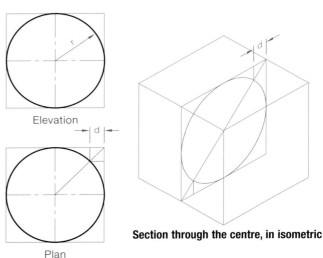

Elevation

Plan

Fig. 6.36a

Section through the centre, in isometric

Fig. 6.36b

Fig. 6.36 shows how to find the radius for an unscaled isometric sphere. The radius of the sphere will equal half the major axis of the ellipse. The sectional ellipse need not be drawn. The length of the major is all that is needed.

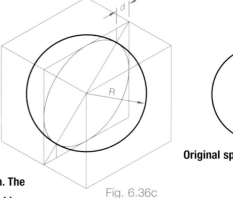

**Isometric drawing of a sphere.
The sphere surrounds the section. The
sphere is larger than in orthographic.**

Fig. 6.36c

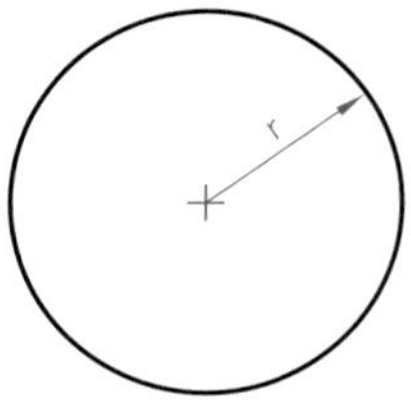

Original sphere as comparison

Fig. 6.36d

Scaled Isometric of a Sphere

When drawing an isometric using the isometric scale the size of the sphere will not be distorted and its radius remains unchanged, Fig. 6.37.

(1) Draw the elevation.
(2) Set up the isometric scale.
(3) The width of the pedestal changes from W to W_1 for the isometric.
(4) The height changes from h to h_1 for the isometric.
(5) The point of contact between the two solids is found by joining the diagonals.
(6) The centre of the ellipse is stepped up. The distance used is R_1 the scaled radius. The sphere is drawn with radius R.

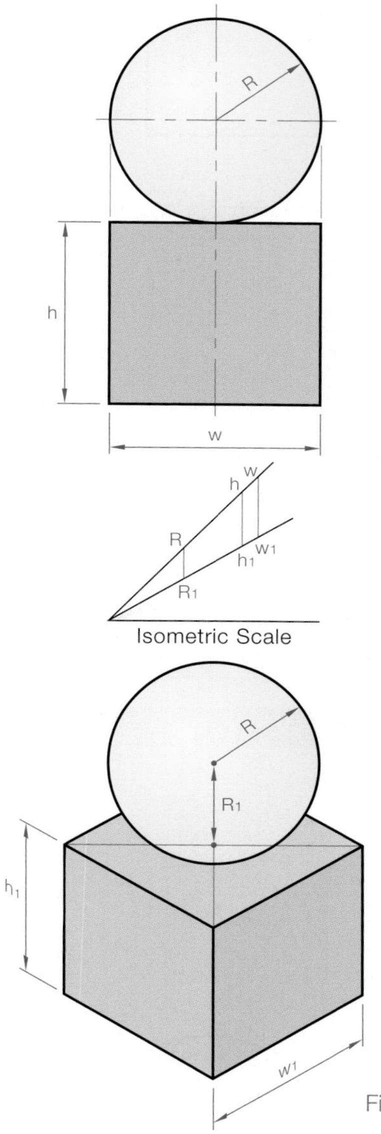

Isometric Scale

Fig. 6.37

Cone in Isometric

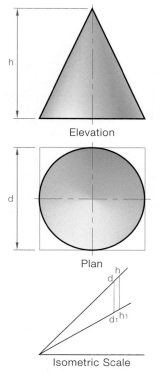

Elevation

Plan

Isometric Scale

Fig. 6.38a

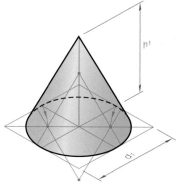

Fig. 6.38b

When drawing a cone we start with the base, Fig. 6.38a. The width d changes to d_1 using the isometric scale. The ellipse is constructed here using the ortho four-centre ellipse. The height h becomes h_1, Fig. 6.38b.

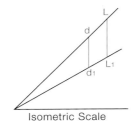

Cylinder in Isometric

If using ordinates to construct an ellipse the length of each ordinate must be scaled before using it in the isometric.

L
d
Elevation
End Elevation

Fig. 6.39a

L
d
L1
d1
Isometric Scale

Fig. 6.39b

L1

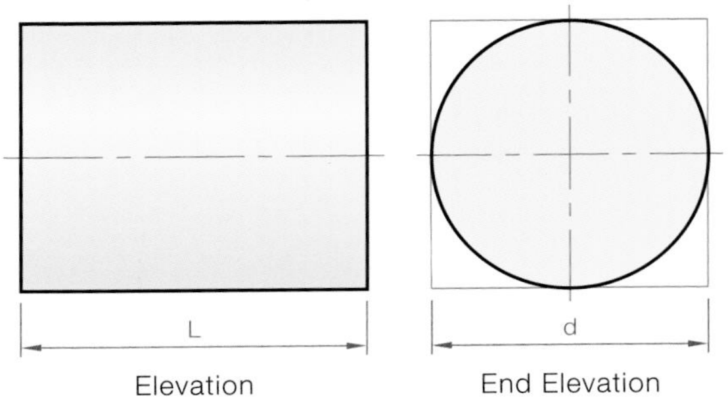

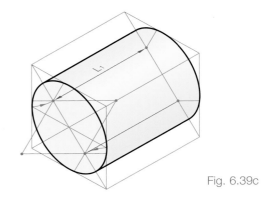

Fig. 6.39c

Activities

Q1. TO Q6. DRAW A TRUE ISOMETRIC OF THE FOLLOWING OBJECTS USING AN ISOMETRIC SCALE.

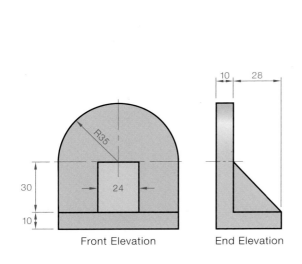

R35
24
30
10
10
28
Front Elevation
End Elevation

Fig. 6.40

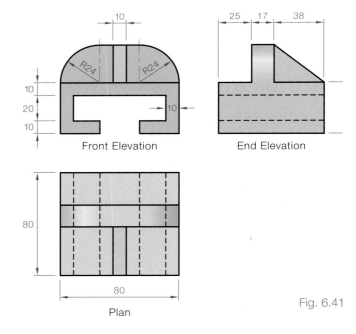

10
R24
R24
10
20
10
10
25
17
38
80
80
Front Elevation
End Elevation
Plan

Fig. 6.41

Q1. Fig. 6.40.

Q2. Fig. 6.41.

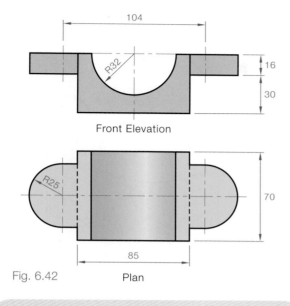

Front Elevation

Plan

Fig. 6.42

Q3. Fig. 6.42

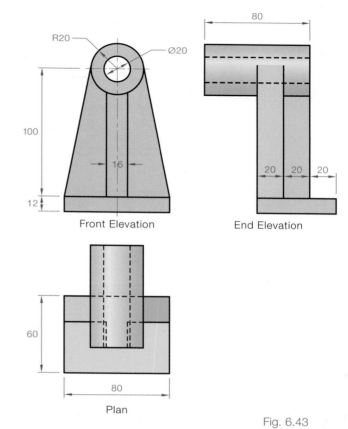

Front Elevation   End Elevation

Plan

Fig. 6.43

Q4. Fig. 6.43

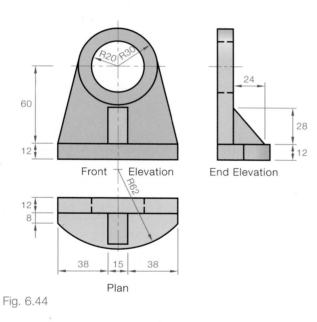

Front   Elevation   End Elevation

Plan

Fig. 6.44

Q5. Fig. 6.44

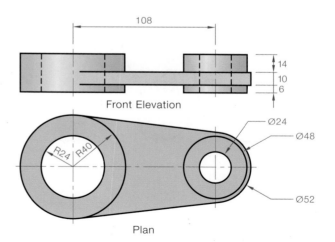

Front Elevation

Plan

Fig. 6.45

Q6. Fig. 6.45

Q7. TO Q.10. DRAW A TRUE ISOMETRIC OF THE OBJECTS USING THE ISOMETRIC SCALE.

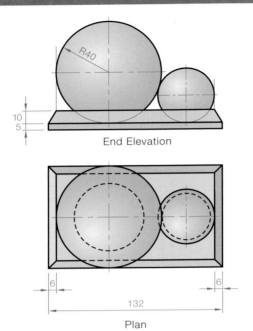

End Elevation

Plan

Fig. 6.46

Q7. Fig. 6.46

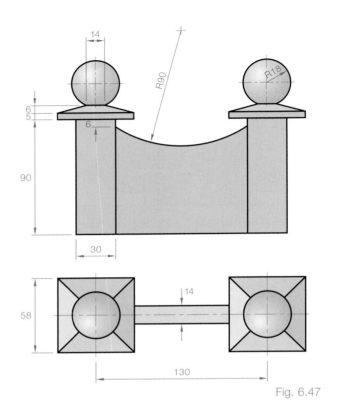

Fig. 6.47

Q8. Fig. 6.47

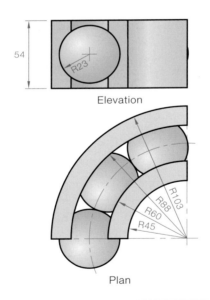

Elevation

Plan

Fig. 6.48

Q9. Fig. 6.48

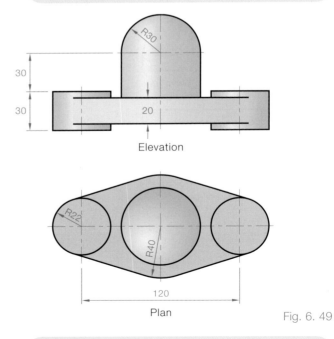

Elevation

Plan

Fig. 6. 49

Q10. Fig. 6.49

Axonometric Plane

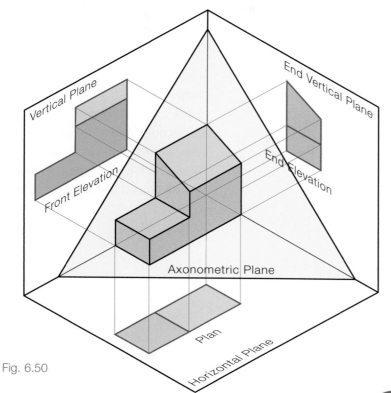

Fig. 6.50

Fig. 6.50 shows a pictorial drawing of the planes of reference and an axonometric plane. When lines are projected from an object perpendicularly onto the axonometric plane we get an isometric of that object. What is happening here is that rather than tilting the object, as in Fig. 6.28 on a plane at 35°16′, we are tilting the plane onto which the object is projected. For isometric, this plane must make equal angles with the horizontal, vertical and end vertical plane. The plane itself will be an equilateral triangle. The axonometric plane is seen as a true shape in the pictorial. The isometric will be a scaled isometric.

True Isometric

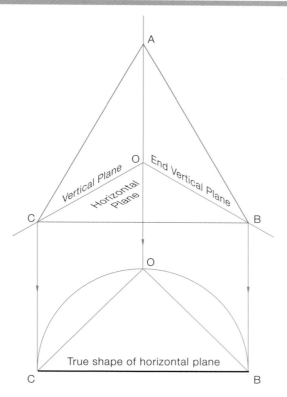

Fig. 6.52

Draw a true isometric of the object shown in Fig. 6.51 using the axonometric plane method.

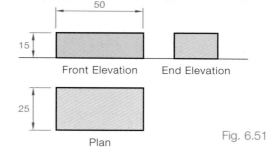

Fig. 6.51

Step 1

Draw the axonometric plane. It will be an equilateral triangle ABC. Draw the lines of intersection between the horizontal, the vertical and the end vertical planes OC, OB and OA. These lines meet in the background.

Step 2

In order to draw the isometric we need a minimum of two orthographic views. We will use the plan and end elevation. The true shape of the triangular portion of the horizontal plane OBC is found as shown in Fig. 6.52. The angle COB must be a right angle so the construction is based on the angle in a semicircle.

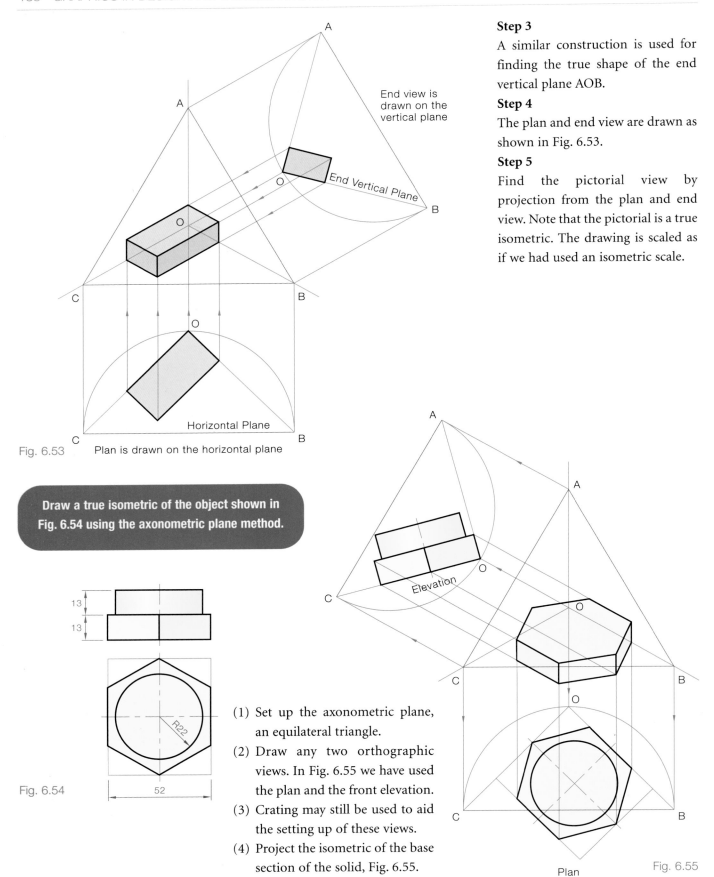

End view is drawn on the vertical plane

End Vertical Plane

Horizontal Plane

Fig. 6.53   Plan is drawn on the horizontal plane

Draw a true isometric of the object shown in Fig. 6.54 using the axonometric plane method.

Fig. 6.54

R22

13

13

52

Elevation

Plan

Fig. 6.55

Step 3

A similar construction is used for finding the true shape of the end vertical plane AOB.

Step 4

The plan and end view are drawn as shown in Fig. 6.53.

Step 5

Find the pictorial view by projection from the plan and end view. Note that the pictorial is a true isometric. The drawing is scaled as if we had used an isometric scale.

(1) Set up the axonometric plane, an equilateral triangle.

(2) Draw any two orthographic views. In Fig. 6.55 we have used the plan and the front elevation.

(3) Crating may still be used to aid the setting up of these views.

(4) Project the isometric of the base section of the solid, Fig. 6.55.

(5) The top of the circular section is constructed using the ortho four-centre ellipse but could easily be constructed using ordinates. The following example will be done using ordinates.

The circle is crated in the plan. The crate is constructed in the isometric, Fig. 6.56. The centre lines are found.

(6) The centre points for the four curves are found as shown earlier in the chapter in Fig. 6.12.

(7) The lower curve is found by drawing the bottom of the crate. Draw in the diagonal.

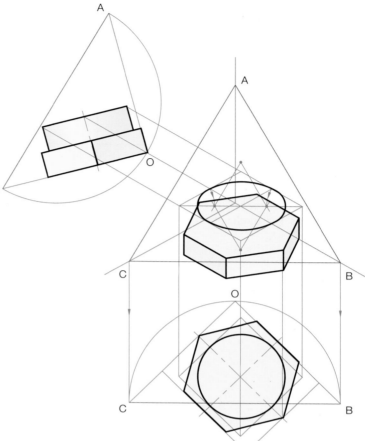

Fig. 6.56

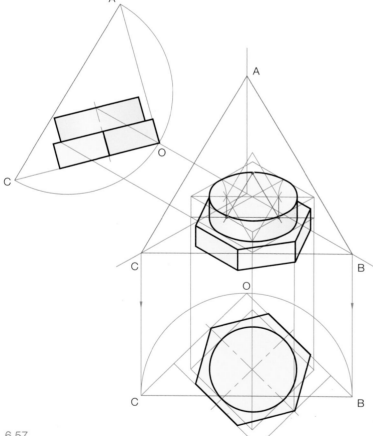

Fig. 6.57

(8) Drop down the centres for the small arcs onto this diagonal, Fig. 6.57.

(9) The centre for the large arc can be found by dropping down the centre from the top ellipse or by drawing 60° lines as we did here.

(10) Complete the isometric. Hidden detail is not shown in isometric unless essential for dimensioning or to clarify some detail.

Draw a true isometric of the given solid, Fig. 6.58, using the axonometric plane method.

(1) Set up the axonometric plane and draw the plan, Fig. 6.59.
(2) Draw the elevation.
(3) Divide the quarter-circles in plan, giving points 1–8.
(4) Find points 1–8 in elevation, Fig. 6.60.
(5) Project isometric.
(6) Similar approach for points a–f, Fig. 6.61.

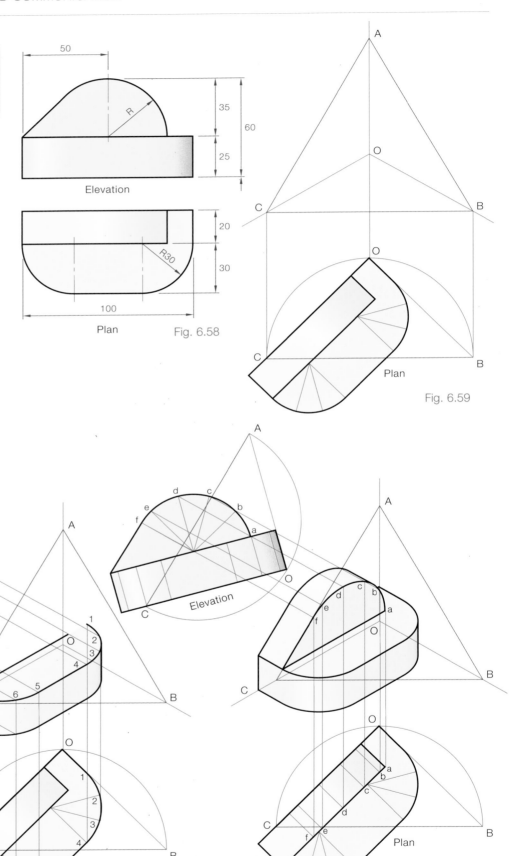

Elevation

Plan

Fig. 6.58

Plan

Fig. 6.59

Elevation

Plan

Fig. 6.60

Elevation

Plan

Fig. 6.61

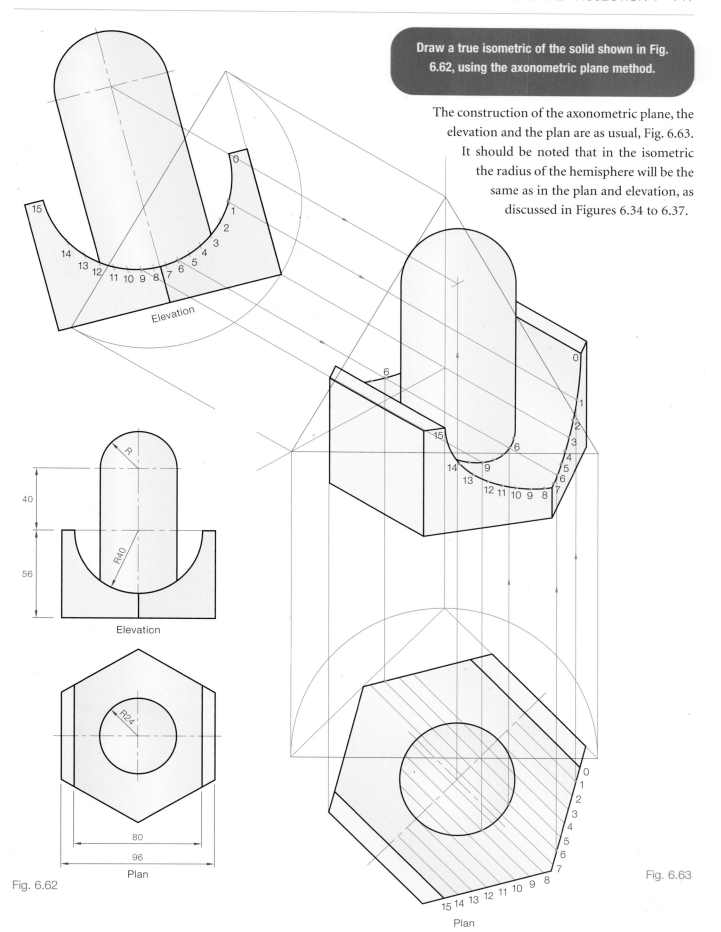

Draw a true isometric of the solid shown in Fig. 6.62, using the axonometric plane method.

The construction of the axonometric plane, the elevation and the plan are as usual, Fig. 6.63. It should be noted that in the isometric the radius of the hemisphere will be the same as in the plan and elevation, as discussed in Figures 6.34 to 6.37.

Elevation

Fig. 6.62

Fig. 6.63

Plan

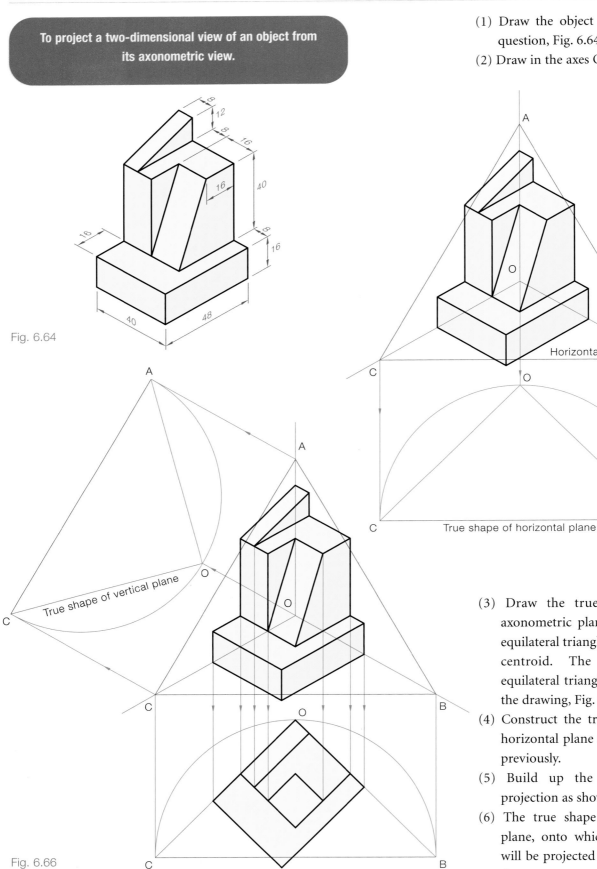

To project a two-dimensional view of an object from its axonometric view.

Fig. 6.64

Axonometric Plane

Horizontal Plane

True shape of horizontal plane

Fig. 6.65

True shape of vertical plane

Fig. 6.66

(1) Draw the object as given in the question, Fig. 6.64.

(2) Draw in the axes OA, OB and OC.

(3) Draw the true shape of the axonometric plane. It will be an equilateral triangle having O as its centroid. The size of the equilateral triangle will not effect the drawing, Fig. 6.65.

(4) Construct the true shape of the horizontal plane as we have done previously.

(5) Build up the plan view by projection as shown in Fig. 6.66.

(6) The true shape of the vertical plane, onto which the elevation will be projected can be found in the same way.

(7) Similar construction for the end vertical plane if it is needed.

(8) Front elevation and end view are found as shown in Fig. 6.67.

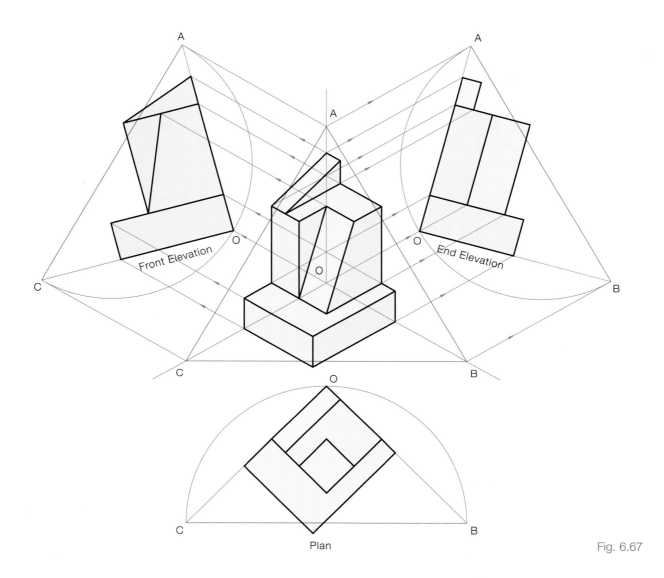

Fig. 6.67

To draw a front elevation and plan of an object given its axonometric view.

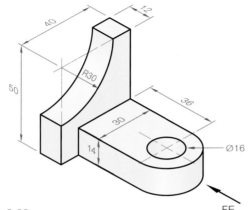

Fig. 6.68

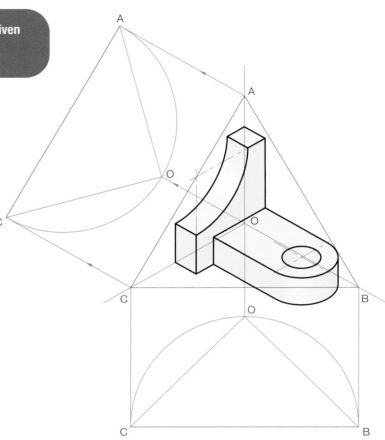

Fig. 6.69

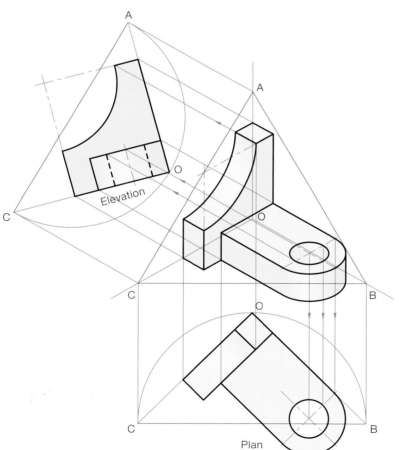

Fig. 6.70

(1) Draw the object to the given sizes, Fig. 6.68.
(2) Construct the axes OA, OB and OC. Draw the axonometric plane.
(3) Find the true shape of the horizontal and vertical planes OBC and OAC, Fig. 6.69.
(4) Project the two views as shown in Fig. 6.70.
(5) It should be noted again that the sizes of the plan and front elevation will be larger than the true isometric. The radii of the circle, semicircle and quadrant therefore must all be found by projection.

The isocircle could be crated and the crate found in the orthographic views, thus finding the centre and radius, or alternatively the centre and radius can be found as shown.

Isometric, Dimetric and Trimetric Projection – A Comparison

Isometric

So far we have only looked at isometric projection. In isometric the principal edges (axes) of an object make equal angles with the plane of projection, either by tilting the object (Figures 6.28, 6.29 and 6.30) or by using an axonometric plane (Fig. 6.50).

Isometric has only one scale as all sides are inclined equally to the projection plane.

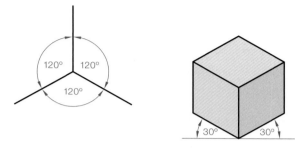

Fig. 6.71

Dimetric (Two Measures)

A dimetric projection is an axonometric projection of an object having two of its axes equally inclined to the projection plane. The third axis makes a different angle to the projection plane. Generally the object is so placed that one of its axes will be vertical when projected. Two different scales are needed in dimetric projection. The axes of similar angle will be foreshortened by the same amount. The third axis will need its own scale.

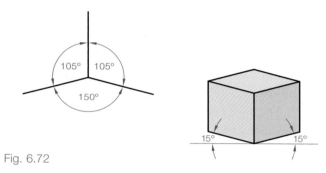

Fig. 6.72

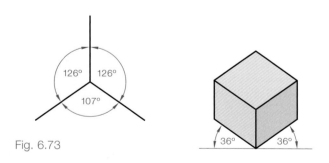

Fig. 6.73

This choice of angles shows more of the top face of the object.

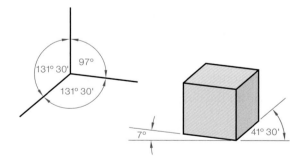

A different choice of angles shows more of the left face.

HIGHER LEVEL

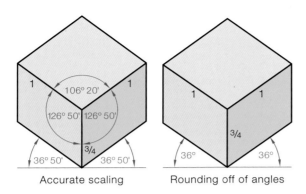

Fig. 6.74a

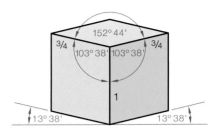

Fig. 6.74b

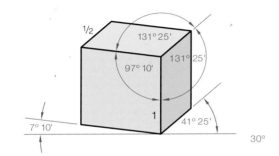

Fig. 6.74c

In order to get a realistic pictorial the measurements must be scaled. If we select our angles carefully we can do this quite easily. Fig. 6.74 shows a choice of dimetric angles which give easy scaling factors. These angles can be rounded off without much loss of accuracy.

In the first example, Fig. 6.74a, the vertical lines are scaled to three-quarters of the original size. Sloping lines parallel to the axes are left full size.

In the second example, Fig. 6.74b, the two side axes are scaled to three-quarters while the verticals are left full size.

The third example, Fig. 6.74c, shows the verticals and measurements to the left remaining full size while the measurements to the right are scaled by half.

Trimetric (Three Measures)

A trimetric projection is an axonometric projection of an object placed in such a position that none of its axes makes an angle with the projection plane equal to that made by any other axis. As with dimetric, the object is usually placed so that one of its edges will appear vertical when projected. Three different scales are needed in trimetric for the three different axes.

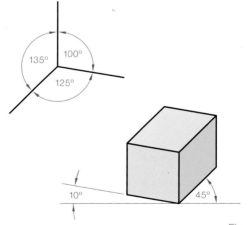

Fig. 6.75

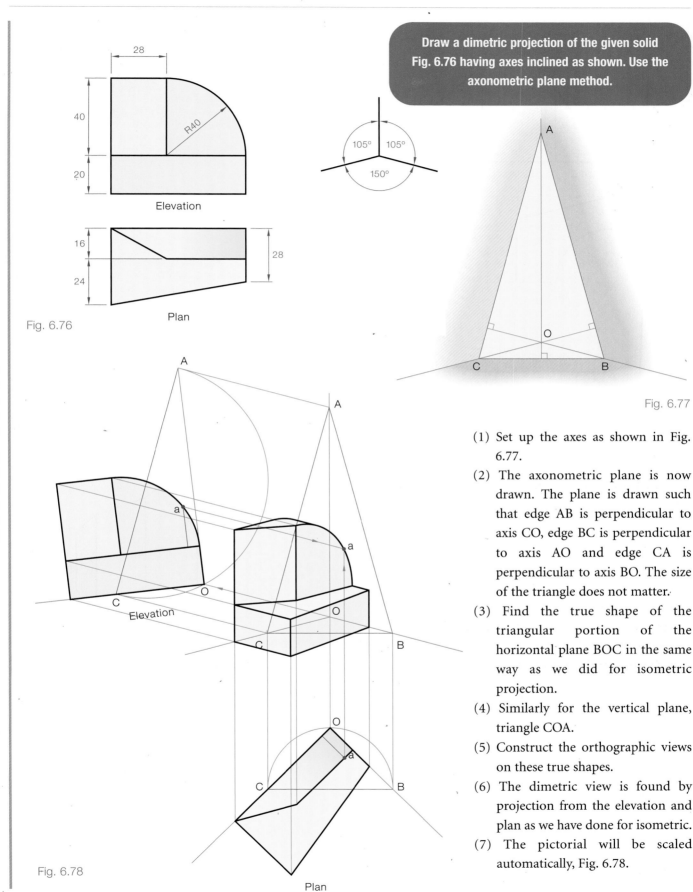

Draw a dimetric projection of the given solid Fig. 6.76 having axes inclined as shown. Use the axonometric plane method.

28

40

R40

20

Elevation

105° 105°

150°

16

28

24

Plan

Fig. 6.76

A

C   O   B

Fig. 6.77

(1) Set up the axes as shown in Fig. 6.77.

(2) The axonometric plane is now drawn. The plane is drawn such that edge AB is perpendicular to axis CO, edge BC is perpendicular to axis AO and edge CA is perpendicular to axis BO. The size of the triangle does not matter.

(3) Find the true shape of the triangular portion of the horizontal plane BOC in the same way as we did for isometric projection.

(4) Similarly for the vertical plane, triangle COA.

(5) Construct the orthographic views on these true shapes.

(6) The dimetric view is found by projection from the elevation and plan as we have done for isometric.

(7) The pictorial will be scaled automatically, Fig. 6.78.

A

A

a

a

Elevation

C   O

C   O   B

O

a

C   B

Fig. 6.78

Plan

HIGHER LEVEL

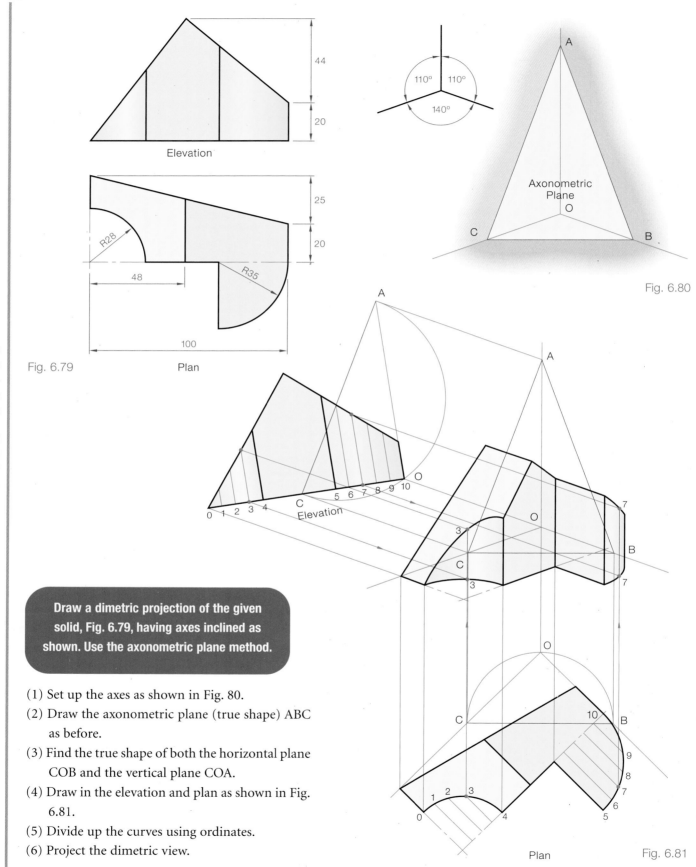

Fig. 6.80

Fig. 6.79

Elevation

Plan

Fig. 6.81

Draw a dimetric projection of the given solid, Fig. 6.79, having axes inclined as shown. Use the axonometric plane method.

(1) Set up the axes as shown in Fig. 80.
(2) Draw the axonometric plane (true shape) ABC as before.
(3) Find the true shape of both the horizontal plane COB and the vertical plane COA.
(4) Draw in the elevation and plan as shown in Fig. 6.81.
(5) Divide up the curves using ordinates.
(6) Project the dimetric view.

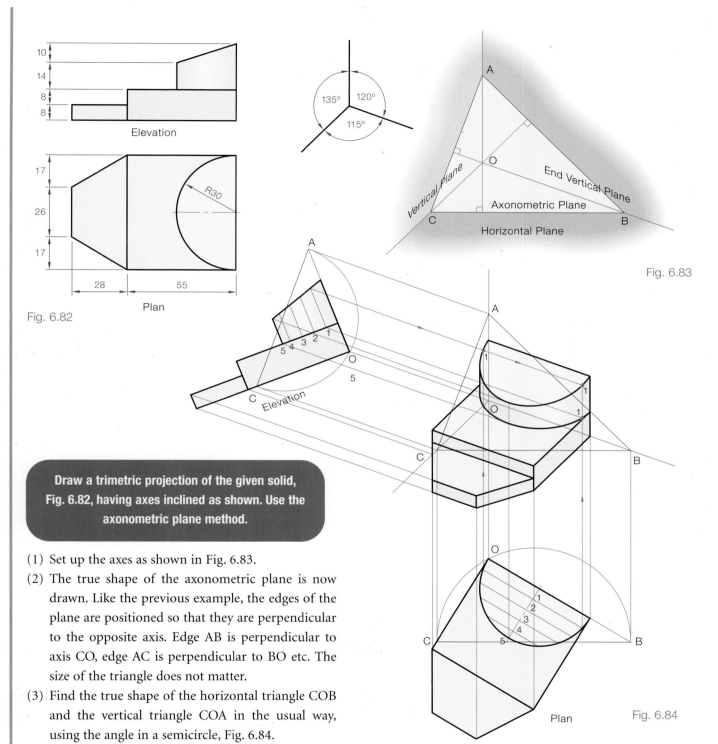

Elevation

Fig. 6.82

Plan

R30

Fig. 6.83

A

Vertical Plane

End Vertical Plane

Axonometric Plane

O

C

B

Horizontal Plane

Elevation

Plan

Fig. 6.84

HIGHER LEVEL

Draw a trimetric projection of the given solid, Fig. 6.82, having axes inclined as shown. Use the axonometric plane method.

(1) Set up the axes as shown in Fig. 6.83.

(2) The true shape of the axonometric plane is now drawn. Like the previous example, the edges of the plane are positioned so that they are perpendicular to the opposite axis. Edge AB is perpendicular to axis CO, edge AC is perpendicular to BO etc. The size of the triangle does not matter.

(3) Find the true shape of the horizontal triangle COB and the vertical triangle COA in the usual way, using the angle in a semicircle, Fig. 6.84.

(4) Construct the orthographic views in these triangles.

(5) The trimetric is found by projection from these views parallel to the axes.

(6) The cylindrical portion is found by using ordinates as shown.

(7) The lengths are scaled automatically using this method.

H I G H E R   L E V E L

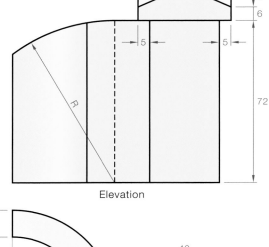

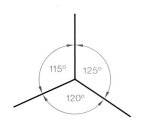

Elevation

Fig. 6.85

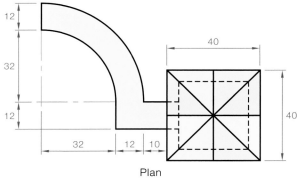

Plan

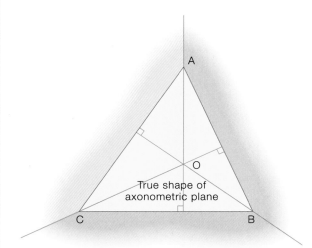

Fig. 6.86

Draw a trimetric projection of the given solid, Fig. 6.85, having axes inclined as shown. Use the axonometric plane method.

(1) Set up the axes to the given angles, Fig. 6.86.
(2) Find the true shape of the axonometric plane ABC as described before.
(3) Project the true shape of the horizontal plane COB and the vertical plane COA.
(4) Draw the plan and elevation on their respective planes, Fig. 6.87.
(5) Project the trimetric view of the solid from the two orthographic views.

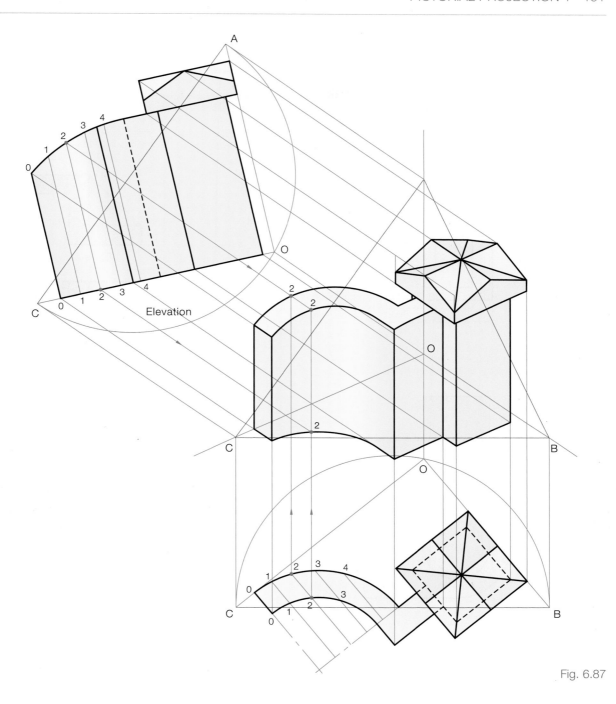

Elevation

Fig. 6.87

HIGHER LEVEL

Activities

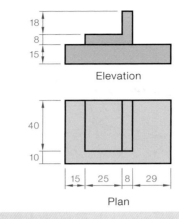

Elevation

Plan

Fig. 6.88

Q1. Fig. 6.88

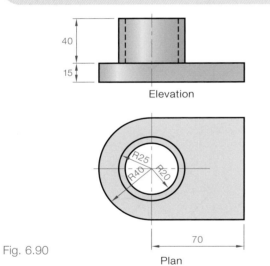

Elevation

Plan

Fig. 6.90

Q3. Fig. 6.90

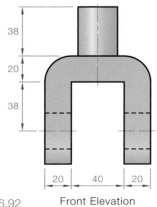

Fig. 6.92   Front Elevation

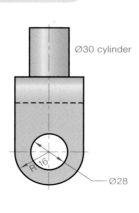

End Elevation

Ø30 cylinder

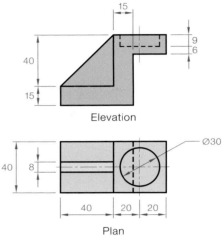

Elevation

Plan

Fig. 6.89

Q2. Fig. 6.89

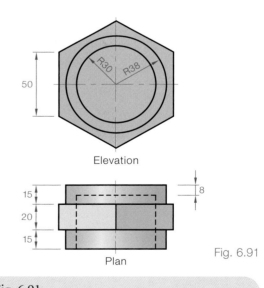

Elevation

Plan

Fig. 6.91

Q4. Fig. 6.91

Q5. Fig. 6.92

Q6., Q7. AND Q8. GIVEN THE TRUE ISOMETRIC VIEWS, FIND THE FRONT ELEVATION, END ELEVATION AND PLAN
USING THE AXONOMETRIC PLANE METHOD.

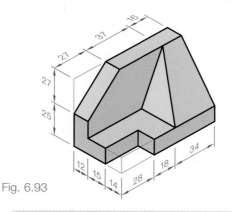

Fig. 6.93

Q6. Fig. 6.93

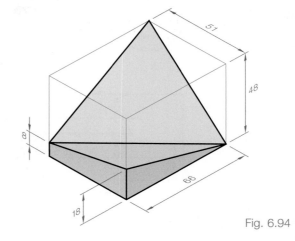

Fig. 6.94

Q7. Fig. 6.94

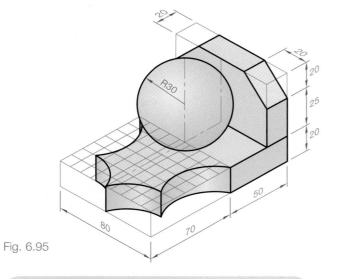

Fig. 6.95

Q8. Fig. 6.95

Q9. AND Q10. GIVEN ORTHOGRAPHIC VIEWS OF
AN OBJECT, CONSTRUCT A DIMETRIC VIEW.
THE AXES ARE AS SHOWN.

HIGHER LEVEL

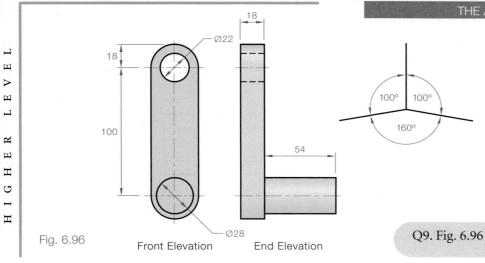

Fig. 6.96

Front Elevation   End Elevation

Q9. Fig. 6.96

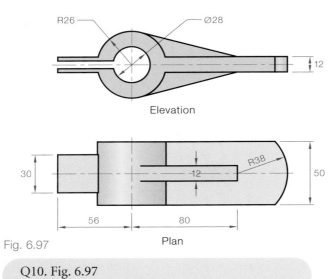

Fig. 6.97

Q10. Fig. 6.97

Q11. AND Q12. GIVEN ORTHOGRAPHIC VIEWS OF AN OBJEC. CONSTRUCT A TRIMETRIC VIEW GIVEN THE AXES.

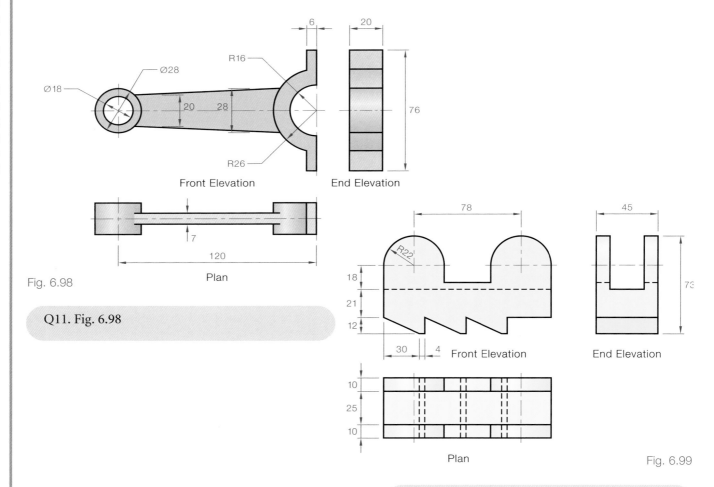

Fig. 6.98

Q11. Fig. 6.98

Fig. 6.99

Q12. Fig. 6.99

7 Pictorial Projection 2

SYLLABUS OUTLINE

Areas to be studied:

• Principles of pictorial perspective drawing. • Parallel and angular perspective. • Vanishing points for horizontal lines.
• *Derivation of vanishing points for inclined lines.*

Learning outcomes

Students should be able to:

Higher and Ordinary levels

• Demonstrate a knowledge of vanishing points, picture plane, ground line and horizon lines.
• Determine the vanishing points and height lines for horizontal lines.
• Complete perspective drawings of given objects.

Higher level only

• *Determine the vanishing points for sets of inclined lines (auxiliary vanishing points).*

Perspective

Perspective is a pictorial representation of objects which very closely matches the view from the human eye. It is different from all other projection systems because the projection rays radiate from/to a single point. In the other systems of projection the projection rays are parallel. The effect this has on the pictorial is that objects that are in the distance will appear smaller than the same objects closer to the observer. If you walk up close to an object it appears bigger than if you see the same object from a large distance away. We see everything in perspective and are therefore used to making the adjustment for size. Look down a straight street of houses. The house in the distance appears very small compared to the house nearby, yet we know that all the houses are the same size. The sides of the street appear to narrow in the distance yet we know they stay parallel, Fig. 7.1.

Fig. 7.1

Perspective gives a very realistic view of objects and is very useful for that reason but it should not be used to give sizes as it does not show true lengths.

Terms Associated with Perspective

Picture Plane

As with all projection systems the image is projected onto a plane. This plane is called the picture plane. The picture plane may be passing through the object, may be between the object and the observer or may be behind the object. Fig. 7.2 shows each of these arrangements. It can be seen that the placing of the picture plane does not effect the proportions of the perspective, only the size of the perspective.

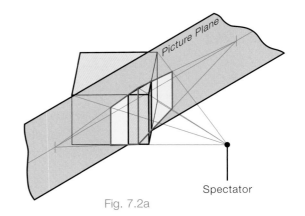

Fig. 7.2a

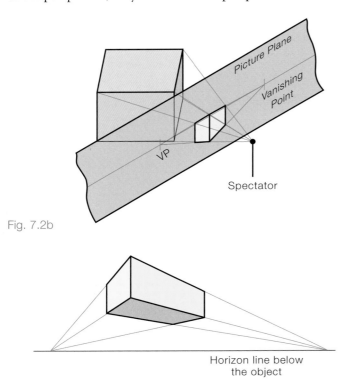

Fig. 7.2b

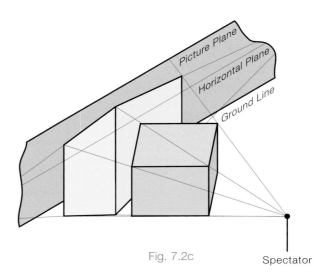

Fig. 7.2c

Horizon line below the object

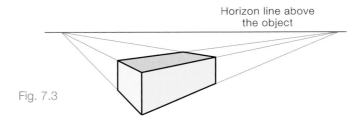

Horizon line above the object

Fig. 7.3

When the picture plane is in front of the object the perspective drawing is smaller than the object. Having the picture plane behind the object means that the perspective projects larger than the object.

Horizon Line

The horizon line is a line on the picture plane at the eye level of the spectator. The position of the horizon line will effect the final perspective view of a given object. When the horizon line is above the object it means that the spectator has a high viewpoint and can see the top surface of the solid. Having the horizon below the object results in a perspective that shows the bottom surface of the object, Fig. 7.3 demonstrates how horizon level changes the perspective.

The upper diagram shows a perspective with the spectator lower than the object, the horizon line is below the perspective of the object and therefore we see its bottom surface. The lower diagram shows the other extreme – the spectator's viewpoint is high, the horizon is therefore high and so we see the upper surface of the object.

Position of the Station Point

The position of the station point (SP) relative to the object also has a huge effect on the final perspective. When the SP is close to the object we are viewing the object from nearby and when the SP is far away we are viewing the object from a large distance away. Fig. 7.4 shows two perspective views of the same object. The upper diagram is produced by having the spectator near the object and the view we get is quite distorted. The lower diagram is produced having the spectator further away. The sides of the box are closer to being parallel. It is worth noting that the perspective produced when the spectator (S) is further from the object, the second perspective, is actually larger than the first.

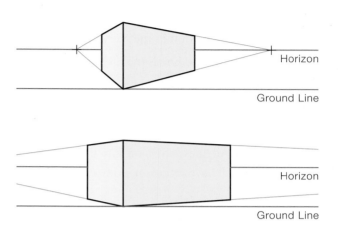

Fig. 7.4

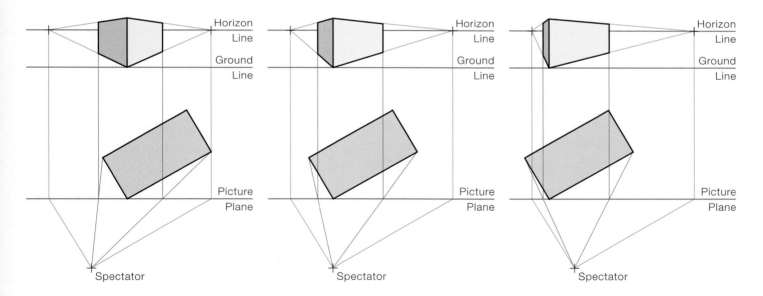

Fig. 7.5

This would appear to break the rules. Objects in the distance should appear smaller than objects nearby. It is, however, the position of the picture plane that determines the size of the perspective, not the position of the spectator.

The spectator can be moved from left to right, and again this will effect the final view. In general, the centre line of the cone of visual rays should be directed toward the centre of the object, or the centre of interest of the object, see Fig. 7.5.

Terms Used in Perspective

Just a quick recap on some of the terminology.

Picture Plane: The image is projected onto the picture plane. It is a vertical plane and can be moved. The position of the picture plane, relative to the object being viewed, affects the size of the finished perspective. Having the picture plane behind the object means an enlarged perspective, a view larger than the actual object. Having the picture plane in front of the object means a reduction in the size of the perspective.

Ground Line: The ground line is the line of intersection between the picture plane and the horizontal plane.

Horizon Line: This is a horizontal line on the picture plane that matches the height of the spectator's eyes.

Spectator: The person viewing the object.

Station Point: The position of the spectator relative to the object and the picture plane.

Vanishing Points: All lines vanish off into the distance. Sets of parallel lines vanish off to the same point, a vanishing point. Horizontal lines will have vanishing points on the horizon line.

The Three Types of Perspective

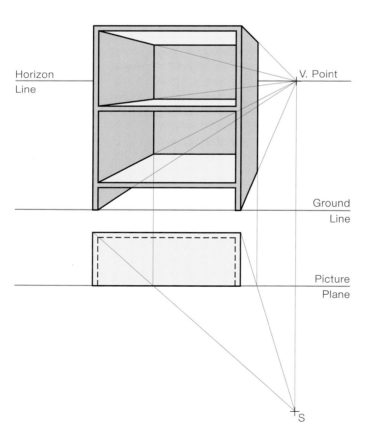

Fig. 7.6

So far we have been experimenting with the various elements of perspective to see how they affect the final drawing. We have moved the picture plane, horizon line and the spectator, each making its own changes to the perspective produced. The last variable is the object itself and its orientation to the picture plane.

Placing the object so that one of its faces is parallel to the picture plane results in a **one-point perspective** or **parallel perspective**. Tilting the object so that two faces are at an angle to the picture plane while still having vertical edges parallel to the picture plane, produces a **two-point perspective** or **angular perspective**. Finally, if the object is so placed so that none of its edges are parallel to the picture plane we get a **three-point perspective**. Three-point perspective is not on the syllabus but we will just look at it briefly to tie in with the other two.

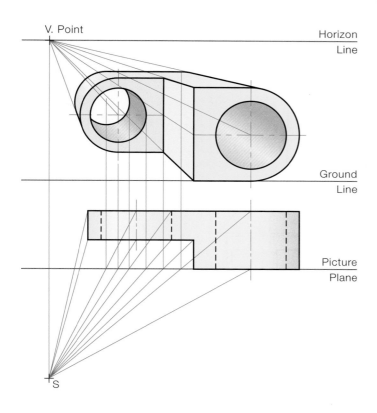

Fig. 7.7

One-point Perspective

Two of the object's principal axes must be parallel to the picture plane, leaving the third to vanish off to a single vanishing point. This is the least complicated of the perspectives and is quick to produce. Useful for presentation work and for representing the interior of a room. It is also useful for solids containing circular curves. Position the object so that the surface(s) containing the circles are parallel to the picture plane and the perspective view of these circles can be drawn with the compass, Figures 7.6, 7.7 and 7.8.

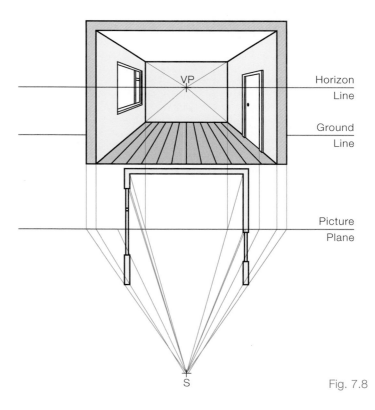

Fig. 7.8

Two-point Perspective

This is the most commonly used perspective. The object is placed so that one set of edges is vertical and therefore parallel to the picture plane and the other two sets are inclined to the picture plane, thus giving two vanishing points. It produces a very realistic view and is used extensively to represent buildings in architecture, Fig. 7.9.

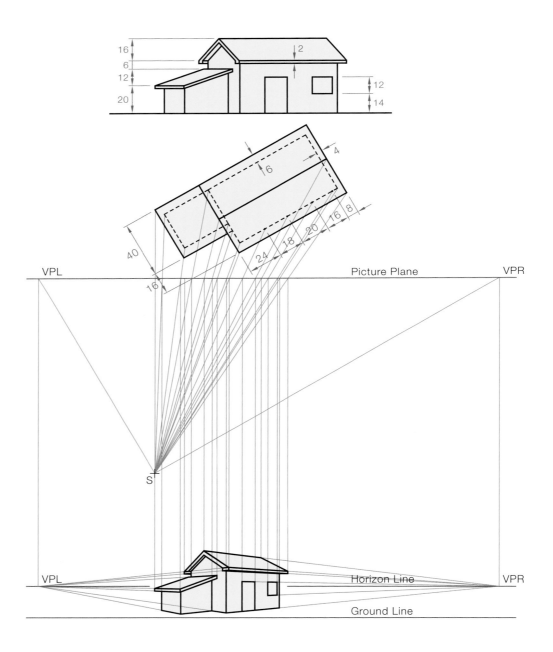

Fig. 7.9

Three-point Perspective

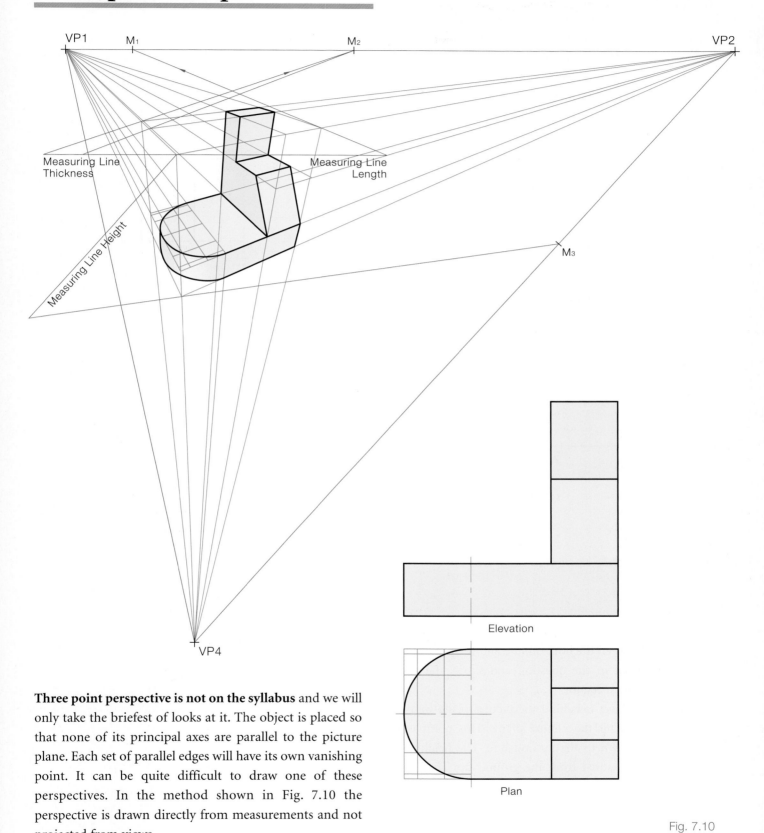

Fig. 7.10

Three point perspective is not on the syllabus and we will only take the briefest of looks at it. The object is placed so that none of its principal axes are parallel to the picture plane. Each set of parallel edges will have its own vanishing point. It can be quite difficult to draw one of these perspectives. In the method shown in Fig. 7.10 the perspective is drawn directly from measurements and not projected from views.

Method of constructing a one-point perspective.

The following series of diagrams illustrate how to set up and construct a one-point perspective of a simple object.

Given the plan and elevation of an object, the position of the spectator and the picture plane, Fig. 7.11a:

(1) Set up the problem on the page. Usually we do not need to draw the elevation. Draw the ground line as shown in Fig. 7.11b. The ground line is drawn parallel to the picture plane.

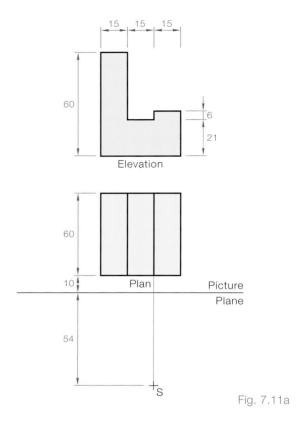

Fig. 7.11a

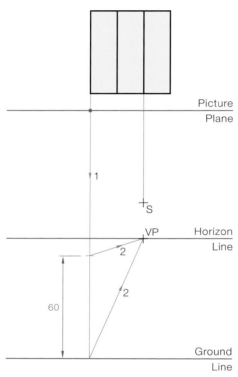

Fig. 7.11b

(2) Draw the horizon line parallel to the ground line. The spacing between the horizon line and the ground line is usually given in the question and shows the viewing height of the spectator.

(3) Since the object is behind the picture plane we extend one edge to hit the picture plane. This point is then projected down to the ground line. The height of the object is measured from the ground up. The top and bottom of the height line are vanished back to the vanishing point, which is found on the horizon line, directly below the spectator.

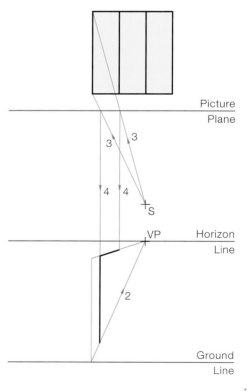

Fig. 7.11c

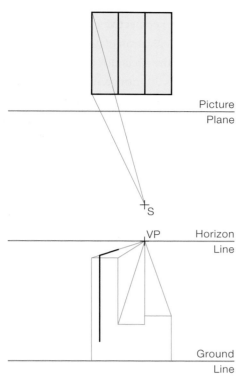

Fig. 7.11d

(4) A visual light ray is brought from the two corners of the plan to the spectator, as shown in Fig. 7.11c. Where these light rays pierce the picture plane they are dropped down to the perspective finding the front left edge and the back corner.

(5) The elevation of the object is built up using the height line as one of its edges as shown in Fig. 7.11d.

(6) What we have done is lengthened the object until it hits the picture plane. **Objects in the picture plane show their true sizes.** That is why we can draw the elevation full size on the ground line. The corners of this elevation are vanished back to the vanishing point.

(7) Corners of the perspective are located by using rays of light as in Step 4. Rays are brought from the two corners on the right. Where they pass through the picture plane they are projected into the perspective view as shown in Fig. 7.11e.

Note: In the top half of the drawing we are looking at the plan of the object, the plan of the picture plane (we are seeing it edge on) and we are seeing the plan of the spectator. In the lower half of the drawing we are seeing through the spectator's eyes and looking at the picture plane. The ground line is the line of intersection between the picture plane and the horizontal plane. The horizon line is at the spectator's eye level. The perspective itself is the projection of an image of the object, onto the picture plane, using rays of light.

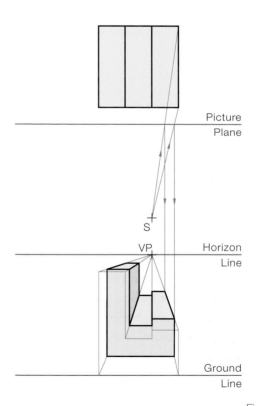

Fig. 7.11e

Method of constructing a two-point perspective.

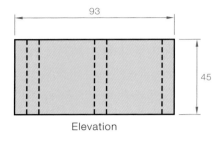

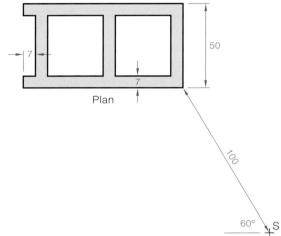

Elevation

Plan

Fig. 7.12a

The following series of diagrams illustrate the process of producing a two point perspective of an object.

Given the plan and elevation of an object (Fig. 7.12a). Also given the direction of the spectator and its distance from the corner. The spectator is 70 mm above the ground.

We have not been given the picture plane's position so our first step is to locate it in plan. **The picture plane is always perpendicular to the central line of sight.** To get a balanced perspective we will have the spectator view toward the centre of the object.

(1) The extreme corners of the plan are joined back to the spectator. The angle formed is bisected giving the centre of vision as shown in Fig. 7.12b. The picture plane is now drawn.

(2) The location of the vanishing points on the picture plane is the next step. The vanishing points are found by drawing lines from the spectator parallel to the principal axes of the object and finding their piercing points in the picture plane.

(3) The ground line and horizon line are now drawn parallel to the picture plane. The spacing between them is usually given in the question.

(4) The two vanishing points located on the picture plane are now projected onto the horizon line.

(5) To start the perspective we need a height line. One edge ab is extended to hit the picture plane at c. This point c is projected down to the ground line. The height of the object is measured on this line.

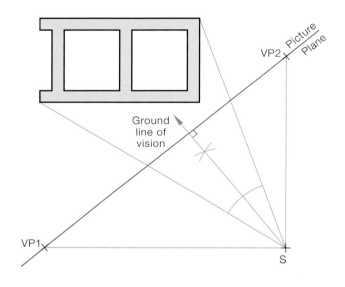

Fig. 7.12b

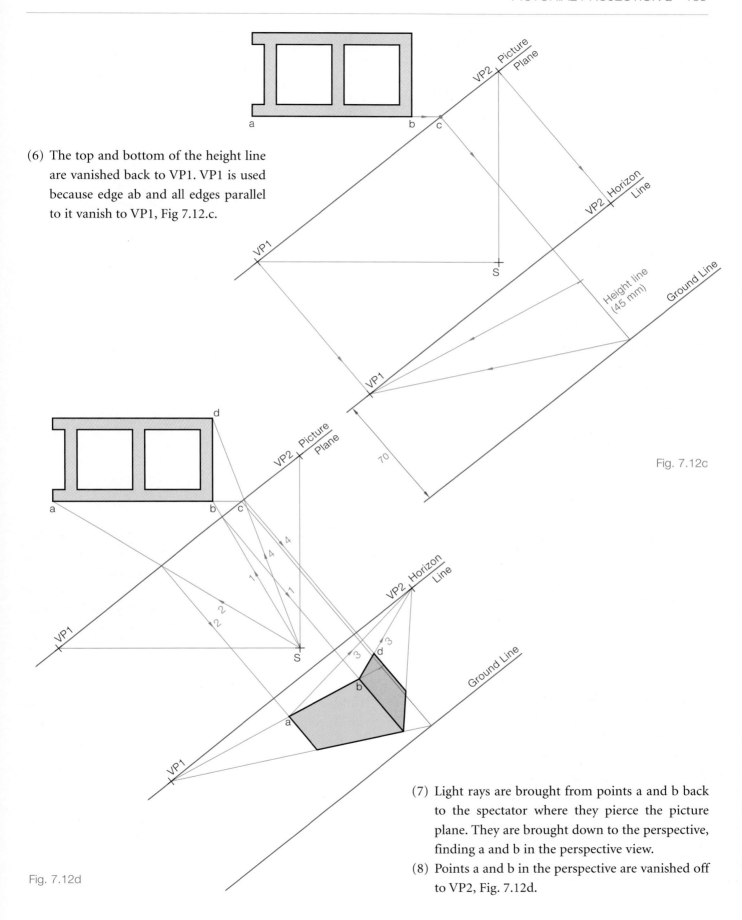

(6) The top and bottom of the height line are vanished back to VP1. VP1 is used because edge ab and all edges parallel to it vanish to VP1, Fig 7.12.c.

Fig. 7.12c

Fig. 7.12d

(7) Light rays are brought from points a and b back to the spectator where they pierce the picture plane. They are brought down to the perspective, finding a and b in the perspective view.

(8) Points a and b in the perspective are vanished off to VP2, Fig. 7.12d.

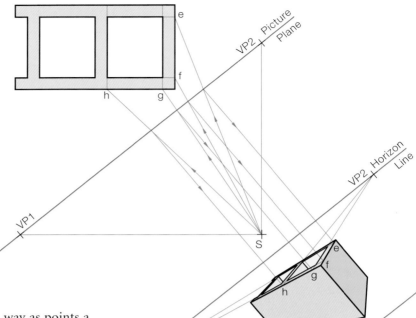

Fig. 7.12e

(9) Point d is found in the same way as points a and b.

(10) The top of the block is built up in the same way. The lines on the top surface are extended in plan to points e, f, g and h.

(11) Find these four points in the perspective as shown in Fig. 7.12e. Vanish lines off to VP1 and VP2 as appropriate. Repeat for the lines further in the distance (not shown).

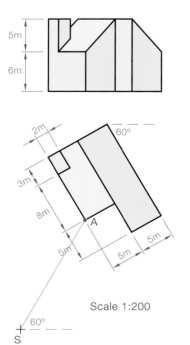

Scale 1:200

Fig. 7.13a

Given the plan and elevation of a building. Draw a perspective view of the building when the position of the spectator is 19 m from the corner A, the picture plane touches the corner A and the horizon line is 5 m above the ground line.

Step 1

Join a light ray from the extreme corners to the spectator. Bisect the angle formed. Draw the picture plane perpendicular to this central line of vision. Draw the ground line and the horizon line parallel to the picture plane and 5 m apart. Locate VP1 and VP2 as before. Corner A is in the picture plane and so will be seen as a true length in the perspective. Using corner A as a height line mark off 6 m and 11 m. Vanish to VP1 and complete the side of the building as shown in Fig. 7.13b.

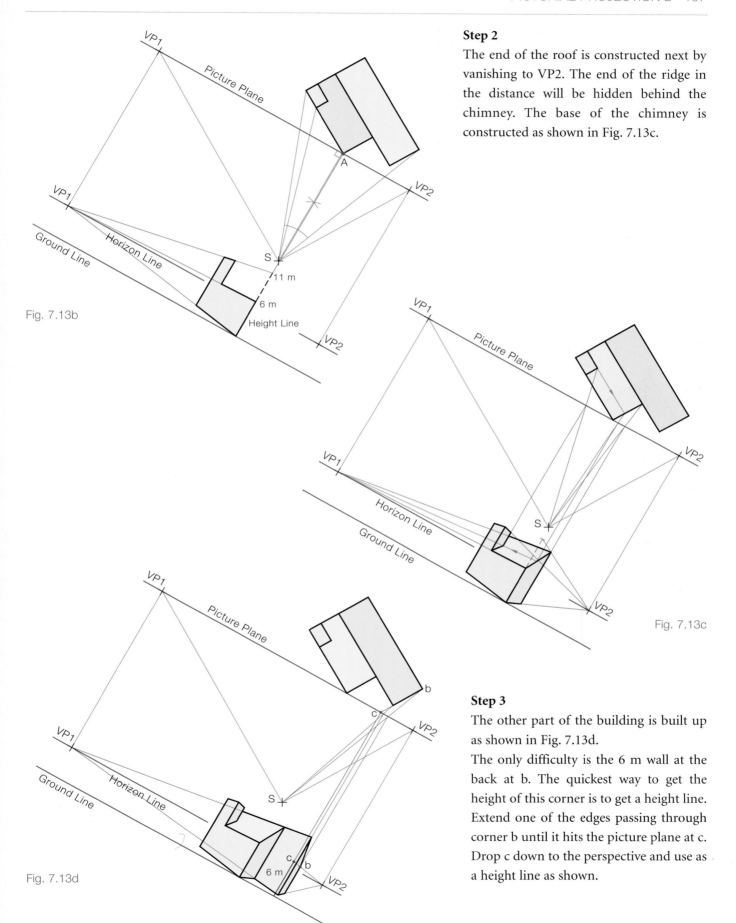

Fig. 7.13b

Fig. 7.13c

Fig. 7.13d

Step 2

The end of the roof is constructed next by vanishing to VP2. The end of the ridge in the distance will be hidden behind the chimney. The base of the chimney is constructed as shown in Fig. 7.13c.

Step 3

The other part of the building is built up as shown in Fig. 7.13d.

The only difficulty is the 6 m wall at the back at b. The quickest way to get the height of this corner is to get a height line. Extend one of the edges passing through corner b until it hits the picture plane at c. Drop c down to the perspective and use as a height line as shown.

Given the plan and elevation of a building, Fig. 7.14a. Make a perspective view of the building when the spectator is 10 m from the corner A, the picture plane touches corner A and the horizon line is 8 m above the ground line.

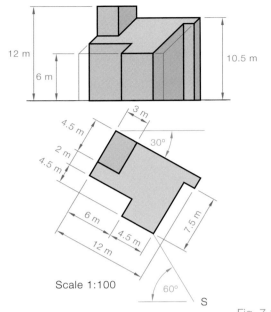

Fig. 7.14a

(1) Join the extreme corners of the plan back to the spectator. Bisect the resulting angle giving the central line of vision. Draw the picture plane parallel to this.

(2) Find VP1 and VP2 on the picture plane and drop to the horizon.

(3) Start the perspective at corner A which is in the picture plane and therefore is a true length. Use this corner as a height line.

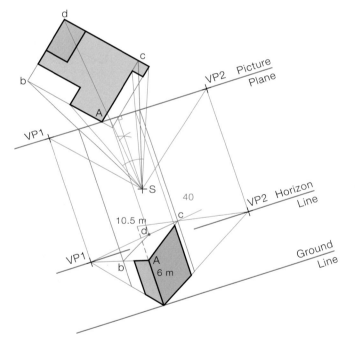

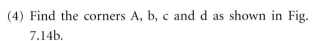

Fig. 7.14b

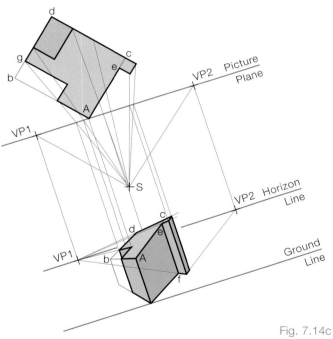

Fig. 7.14c

(4) Find the corners A, b, c and d as shown in Fig. 7.14b.

(5) Lines are projected from VP1 through points c, e and f in the perspective, as shown in Fig. 7.14c. The small protrusion from the building can be completed.

(6) Point g is found on edge bd in the perspective. A line produced from VP1 through g will allow us to complete another section of the perspective.

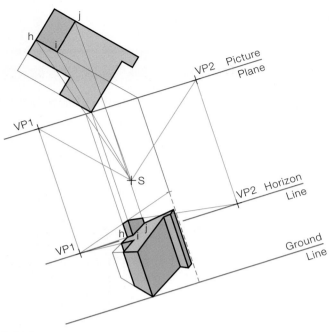

Fig. 7.14d

(7) The three visible edges of the chimney can be found in the perspective, edges h, i and j.

(8) In order to find the height of the chimney we need a 12 m height line. The edge hi is extended to hit the picture plane. Where it hits the picture plane it is dropped to the perspective. 12 m is measured on this line and vanished to VP1. The height line is vanished to VP1 because the edge that was extended, edge hi is parallel to S, VP1. The perspective is finished as shown in Fig. 7.14d.

Circles and Curves in Perspective

We have already established that if a circle is parallel to the picture plane the perspective view of it will be circular. If the circle is inclined to the picture plane we generally get an ellipse.

Fig. 7.15 shows how the circle is divided up into ordinates and from these the circle is built up point by point. The height line is found first by extending the front face of the cylinder to intersect the picture plane. Half the elevation is constructed on this height line in order to find heights for the perspective. The elevation is divided up into divisions using ordinates. The same ordinate spacing is used in the plan and the perspective is built up as shown using these ordinates.

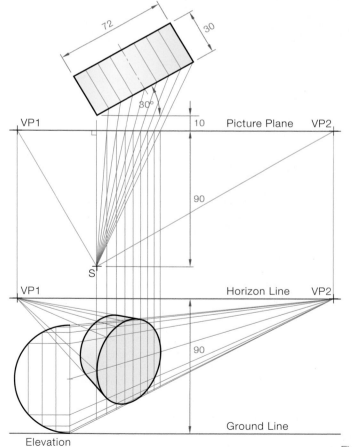

Fig. 7.15

Activities

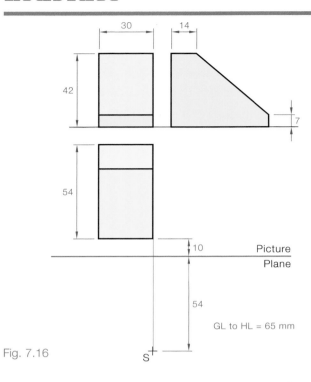

Fig. 7.16

Q1. Fig. 7.16

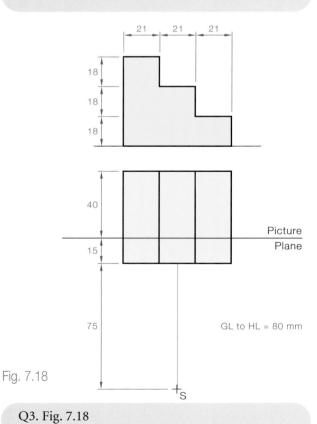

Fig. 7.18

Q3. Fig. 7.18

Draw a one-point perspective of the solids shown in Q1. to Q6.

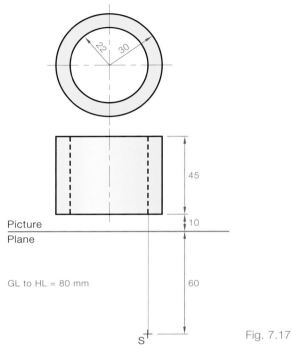

Fig. 7.17

Q2. Fig. 7.17

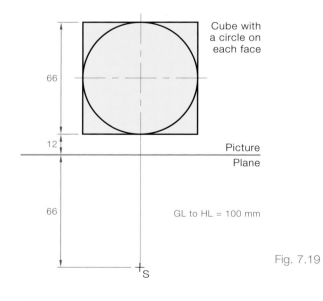

Cube with a circle on each face

Fig. 7.19

Q4. Fig. 7.19

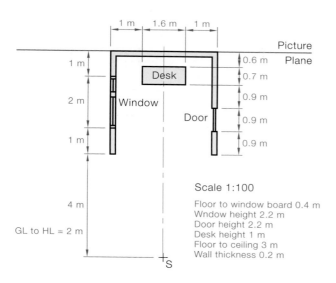

1 m   1.6 m   1 m

Picture Plane

1 m
0.6 m
Desk

2 m   Window   0.7 m

0.9 m

Door   0.9 m

1 m   0.9 m

Scale 1:100

4 m   Floor to window board 0.4 m
Wndow height 2.2 m
Door height 2.2 m
Desk height 1 m
Floor to ceiling 3 m
Wall thickness 0.2 m

GL to HL = 2 m

+S

Fig. 7.20

Q5. Fig. 7.20

Q7. TO Q12.

Make a two-point perspective of the various objects using the information given. The picture plane is to pass through corner A.

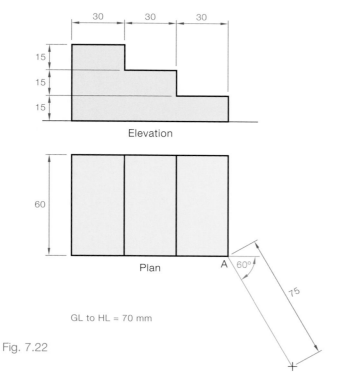

30   30   30

15

15

15

Elevation

60

Plan   A   60°

75

GL to HL = 70 mm

Fig. 7.22

Q7. Fig. 7.22

1.5 m

3 m

0.5 m

Elevation

Picture Plane

5 m

0.2 m

1.5 m

0.2 m

Plan

4.5 m   Scale 1:100

GL to HL = 2 m

+S

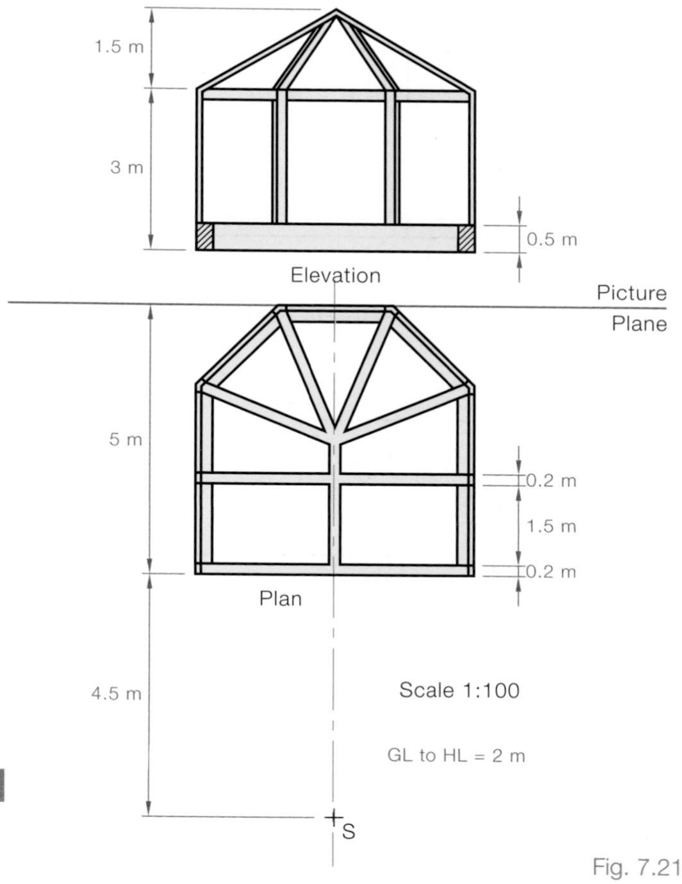

Fig. 7.21

Q6. Base wall is 0.3 m thick. The plan is based on an octagon. Conservatory frame is 0.1 m thick, Fig. 7.21.

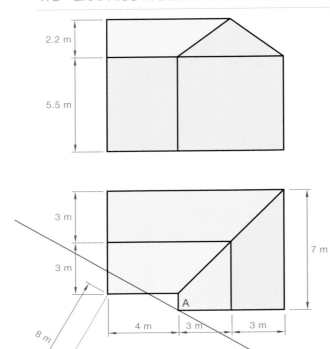

2.2 m

5.5 m

3 m

3 m

7 m

8 m

60°

S

4 m   3 m   3 m

A

Picture
Plane

GL to HL = 4.5 m

Fig. 7.23

Q8. Fig. 7.23

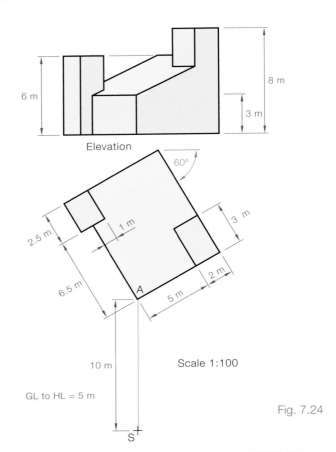

Elevation

6 m

8 m

3 m

60°

2.5 m

1 m

3 m

6.5 m

A

5 m

2 m

10 m

Scale 1:100

GL to HL = 5 m

S

Fig. 7.24

Q9. Fig. 7.24

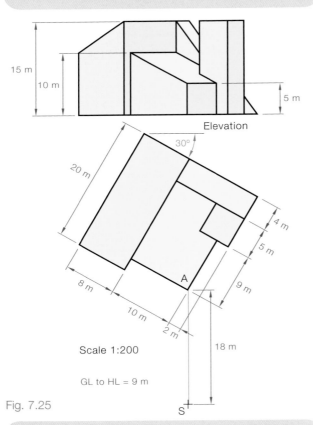

Elevation

15 m

10 m

5 m

30°

20 m

4 m

5 m

8 m

A

9 m

10 m

2 m

18 m

Scale 1:200

GL to HL = 9 m

S

Fig. 7.25

Q10. Fig. 7.25

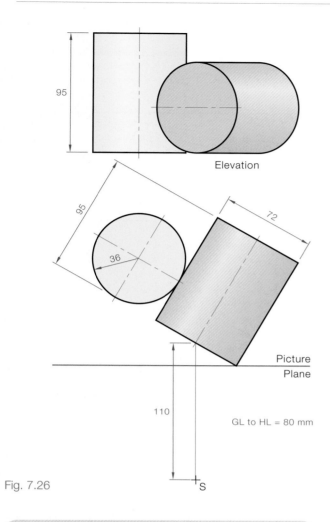

Elevation

95

95

72

36

Picture
Plane

110

GL to HL = 80 mm

S

Fig. 7.26

Q11. Fig. 7.26

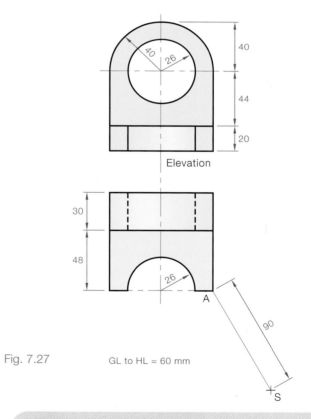

40

26

40

44

20

Elevation

30

48

26

A

90

S

Fig. 7.27   GL to HL = 60 mm

Q12. Fig. 7.27

Vanishing Points of Inclined Lines

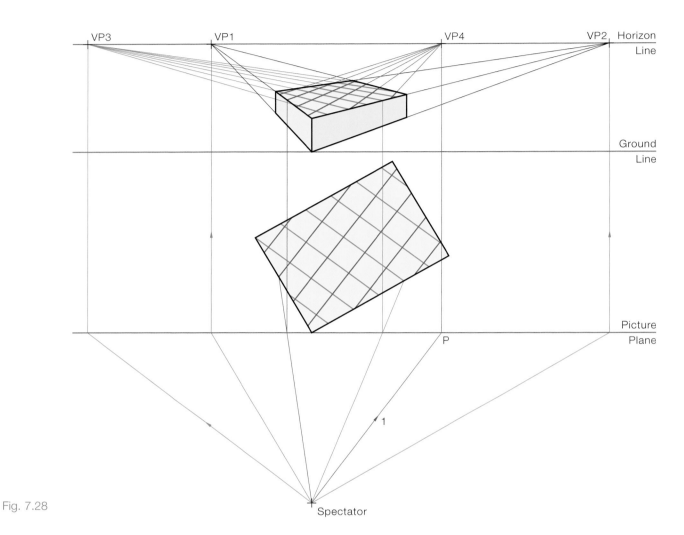

Fig. 7.28

For all the perspectives we have dealt with so far we have used vanishing points of horizontal lines. The vanishing points have been found on the horizon line. **Vanishing points for horizontal lines will always be found on the horizon line**. Furthermore, parallel lines vanish to the same vanishing point, see Fig. 7.28.

The parallel blue lines on the prism's top surface are horizontal and therefore will vanish to a vanishing point (VP) on the horizon, VP4. This vanishing point is found, as for all lines, by finding the piercing point in the picture plane of a line drawn from the spectator, parallel to the given line. A line is drawn from S parallel to the blue set of lines and is continued to the picture plane at p. Point p is projected to the horizon line giving VP4. A similar approach can be used for the green set of lines.

Sets of parallel inclined lines vanish to vanishing points either above or below the horizon line and these vanishing points, are called **auxiliary vanishing points**.

Lines which are sloping upwards as they go away from the spectator will have an auxiliary vanishing point above the horizon.

Lines which are sloping downwards as they go away from the spectator will have an auxiliary vanishing point below the horizon.

Finding Auxiliary Vanishing Points

(1) Identify the set of sloped lines for which we will need the auxiliary vanishing point. If they are sloping upwards as they go away from the spectator then the vanishing point will be above the horizon. If the lines are sloping downwards as they go away from the spectator then the vanishing point will be below the horizon.

(2) Draw a line from S parallel to this set of lines as they appear in plan. Extend this line until it hits the picture plane.

Note: In this example it will be the same line as that used to find VP2. The auxiliary vanishing point will be in line with VP2.

(3) In this step we find how high the auxiliary VP is above the horizon. Step the length of one of the sloped lines (as it appears in plan) out from the spectator, length ab. Step the difference in height between the start and finish of this sloped line, height bc, out perpendicular to the 'length' at b.

(4) This triangle abc is now continued on and enlarged giving the height, at the picture plane, that the auxiliary VP is above the horizon, see Fig. 7.29.

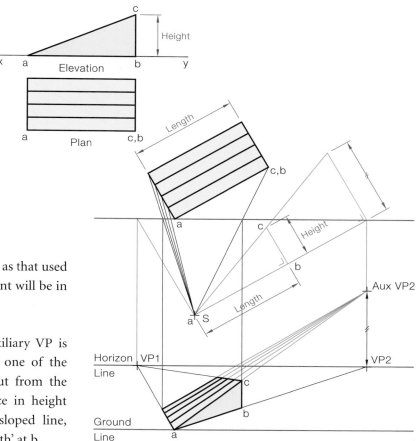

Fig. 7.29

Finding Auxiliary Vanishing Points (Alternative Method)

This method of finding auxiliary vanishing points is almost identical to the first method but uses true angles instead of distances.

Given the solid shown in Fig. 7.30 draw a two-point perspective of this solid using auxiliary vanishing points where appropriate.

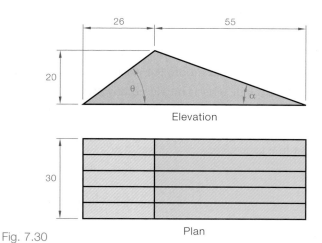

Fig. 7.30

HIGHER LEVEL

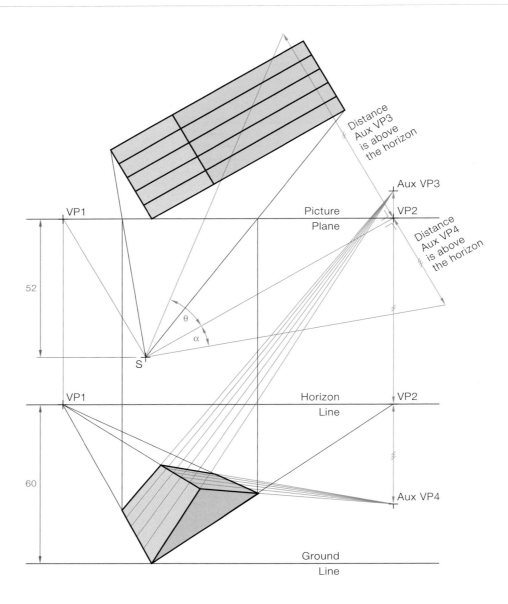

Fig. 7.31

(1) It is worth noting that all perspectives can be drawn by using height lines and avoiding the use of auxiliary vanishing points but the perspective can be completed quicker and more accurately if they are used.

Draw a line from the spectator parallel to the set of lines for which we are finding the auxiliary VP and continue it to hit the picture plane. In this example both sets of inclined parallel lines are running parallel to S, VP2.

(2) From this line create an angle at S equal to the true slope of the lines in elevation. For clarity, since we have two sets of lines, one angle (angle θ) was measured upwards and the other (angle α) was measured downwards, Fig. 7.31

(3) A perpendicular to S, VP2 at the picture plane is produced to intersect each angle. This gives, for angle θ, the distance the auxiliary VP is above the horizon and for angle α, the distance the auxiliary VP is below the horizon.

(4) The perspective is completed in the normal way. No height line is needed.

Worked Example

It should be noted that extra care should be taken when using angles so that it is the **true angle** that is used, not the apparent angle. The following example will attempt to demonstrate the difference.

HIGHER LEVEL

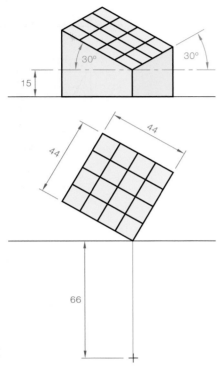

Fig. 7.32

> Given the solid shown in Fig. 7.32. Draw a two-point perspective of this solid when the position of the spectator is as shown and the horizon line is 24 mm above the ground line. Use auxiliary vanishing points where appropriate.

(1) In elevation, edge ab and all lines parallel to it appear to make an angle of 30° to the horizontal plane but their true angle is much less, as shown in Fig. 7.33.
Line ab has a true angle of θ to the horizontal plane and line ac has a true angle of α to the horizontal plane.
(2) The perspective is completed using these angles as shown in Fig. 7.34.

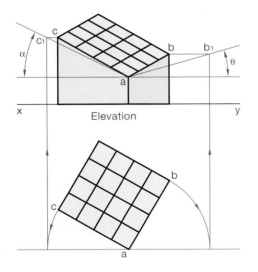

Fig. 7.33

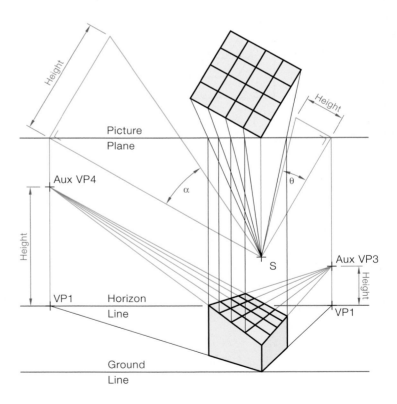

Fig. 7.34

Given the structure shown in Fig. 7.35 which has a plan based on semi-hexagonal prisms. Draw a perspective view of the structure. The picture plane passes through corner A. The spectator is 10 m from corner A and the horizon line is 10 m above the ground line. Use auxiliary vanishing points where appropriate.

On examining this question it can be seen that edges AE and CE and all edges parallel to them have a true angle of 30° to the horizontal plane. It should be noted however that neither edge AB nor edge CD have a true angle of 30° to the HP even though they appear to be inclined at 30° in the elevation.

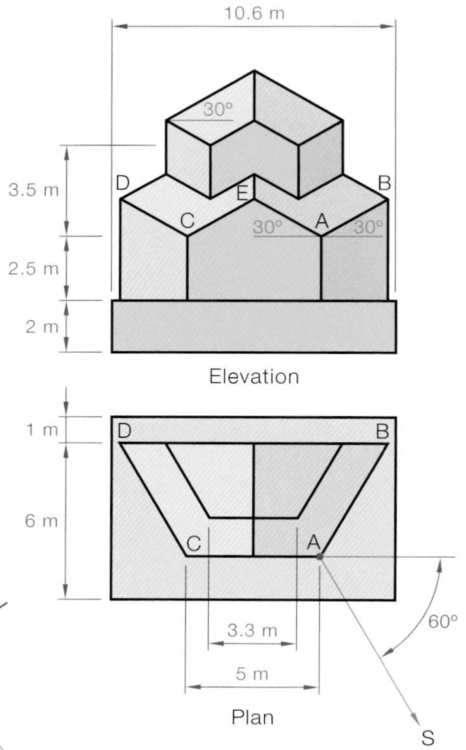

Elevation

Plan

Fig. 7.35

HIGHER LEVEL

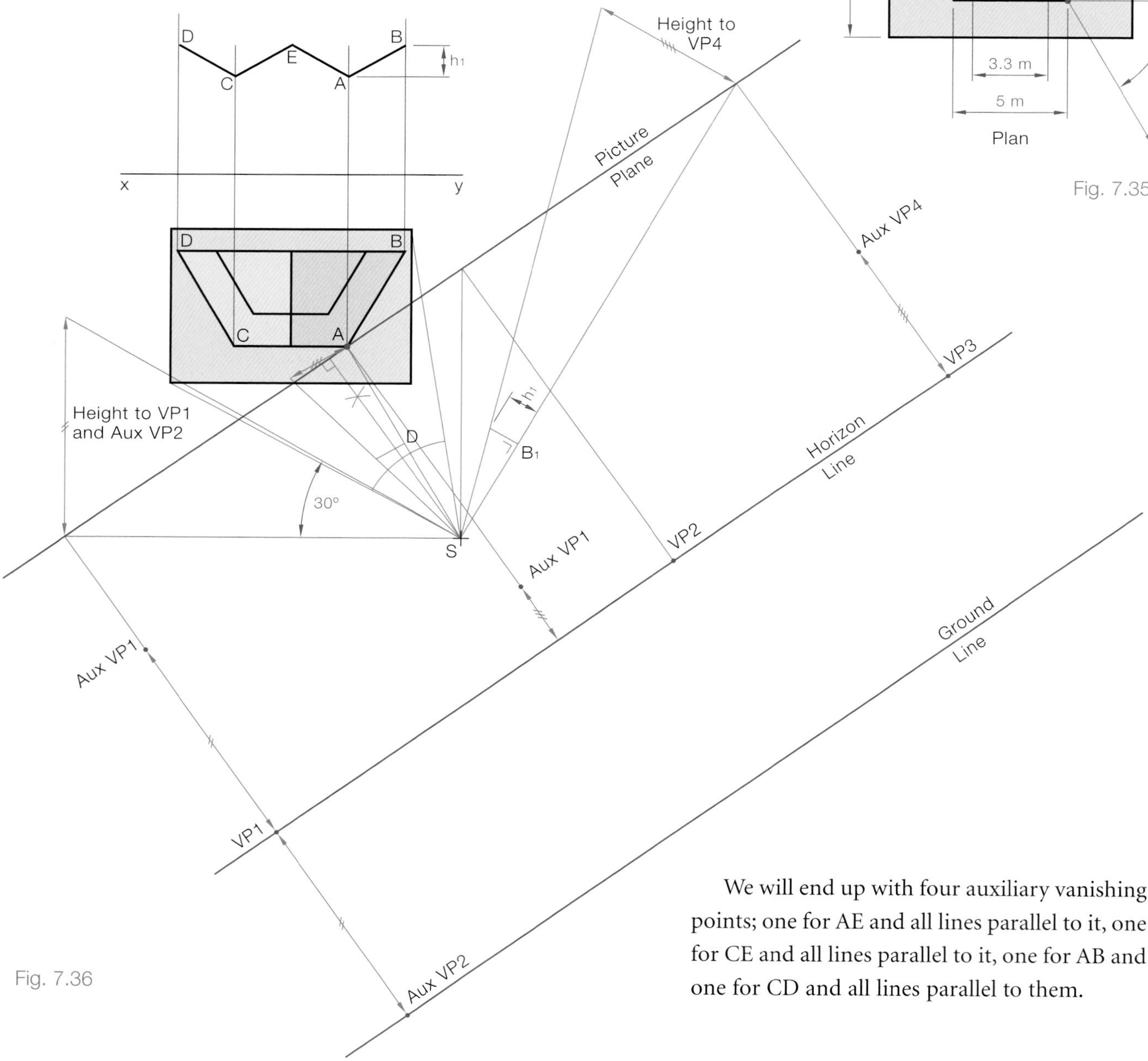

Fig. 7.36

We will end up with four auxiliary vanishing points; one for AE and all lines parallel to it, one for CE and all lines parallel to it, one for AB and one for CD and all lines parallel to them.

(1) The first step is to locate the picture plane. Join the outer corners of the plan back to the spectator. Bisect the angle formed to give the centre of vision. The picture plane is drawn perpendicular to this.

(2) Draw the ground line and horizon line and locate VP1 and VP2, the vanishing points for the horizontal base lines. These vanishing points will be on the horizon.

(3) Vanishing points for edges AE and CE will be on the VP1 line. The auxiliary vanishing point for AE will be above the horizon and the auxiliary vanishing point for CE will be below the horizon. The construction is as shown in Fig. 7.36. We can use the 30° as it is a true angle.

(4) Auxiliary vanishing point for edge AB is found as shown. A line is drawn from S parallel to AB in plan, to hit the picture plane. The length of AB in plan is stepped away from S on this line giving B_1. A perpendicular to SB_1 is drawn at B_1. The difference in height between A and B is found in elevation (h_1) and stepped out on this perpendicular. Complete the triangle and enlarge to the picture plane. We thus find the height of Aux VP4 above the horizon.

(5) Aux VP3 is found in a similar way.

(6) The perspective is completed in Fig. 7.37.

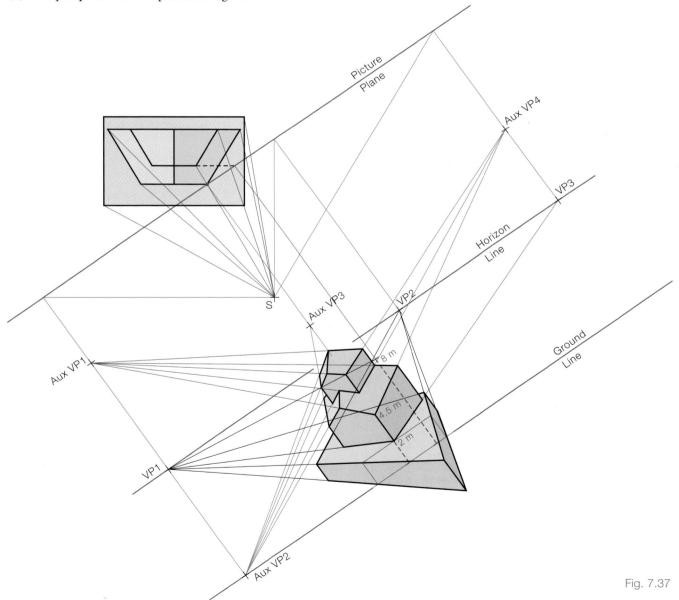

Fig. 7.37

HIGHER LEVEL

Draw a perspective view of the structure shown in Fig. 7.38. The picture plane passes through corner A. The spectator is 10 m from corner A and the horizon line is 10 m above the ground line. Use auxiliary vanishing points where appropriate.

As before we will start by locating the picture plane, ground line and horizon line. We will also find all necessary vanishing points. It should be noted that the elevation is not needed, we only draw a small portion of it as in the previous example.

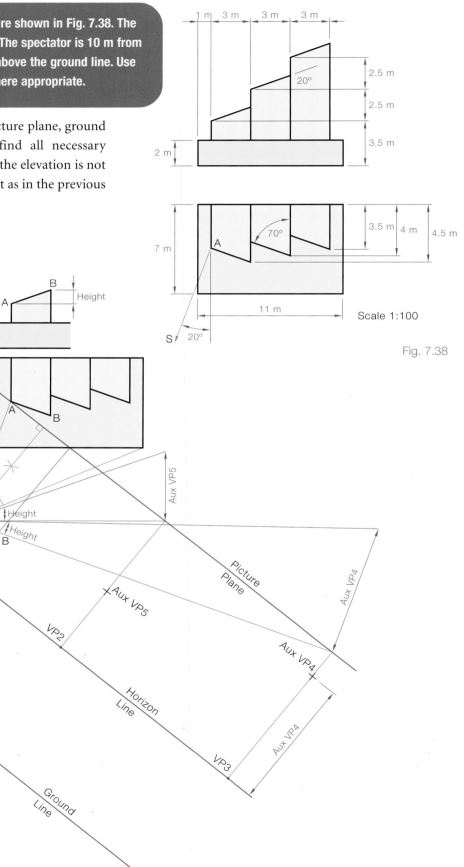

Scale 1:100

Fig. 7.38

Fig. 7.39

(1) Rays are projected from the two outer corners back to S. The angle formed is bisected, giving the centre of vision. The picture plane is drawn perpendicular to this, Fig. 7.39.

(2) Horizon line and ground line are 10 m apart and parallel to the picture plane.

(3) VP1 and VP2 are vanishing points for the rectangular base. These vanishing points will be on the horizon line because they are vanishing points for horizontal lines.

(4) The line AB in plan actually represents two lines. One of these is running along the top surface of the base, is horizontal, and therefore has a vanishing point on the horizon, VP3. The other is sloping upwards as it goes away from the spectator and will therefore have an auxiliary vanishing point above the horizon.

(5) Draw a line from S parallel to AB in plan. Extend to hit the picture plane. Step the distance AB, from the plan, out from the spectator along this line, giving point B.

(6) Step the difference in height between A and B (obtained from the elevation) out perpendicularly. Create a triangle and enlarge to the picture plane. This gives the height Aux VP4 will be above the horizon. Auxiliary VP5 is found in a similar way.

(7) The perspective is finished as before. See Fig. 7.40.

Note: Height lines always vanish to vanishing points on the horizon line.

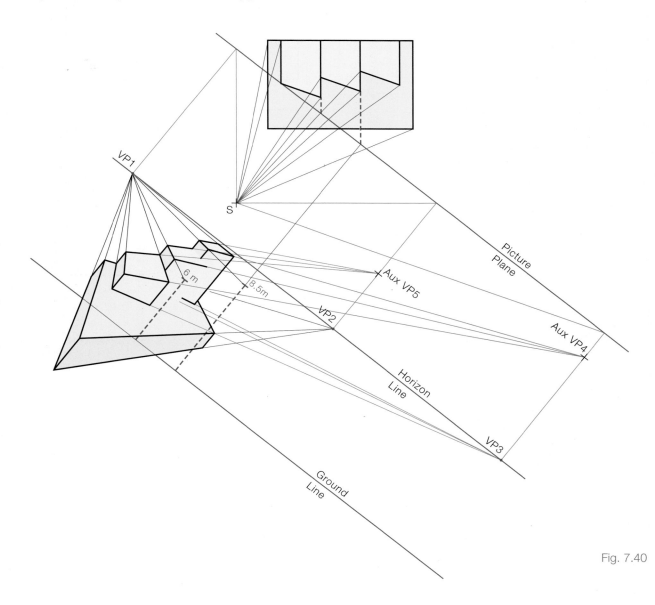

Fig. 7.40

Activities

H I G H E R   L E V E L

For each of these questions draw a perspective view using auxiliary vanishing points where appropriate. Picture plane to pass through point A.

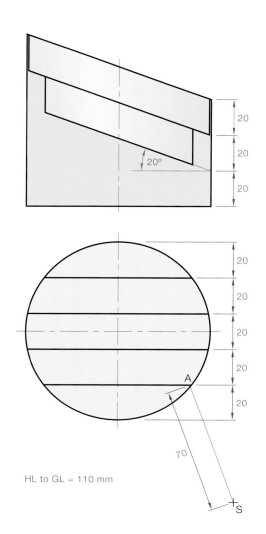

Fig. 7.41

HL to GL = 110 mm

Q1. Fig. 7.41

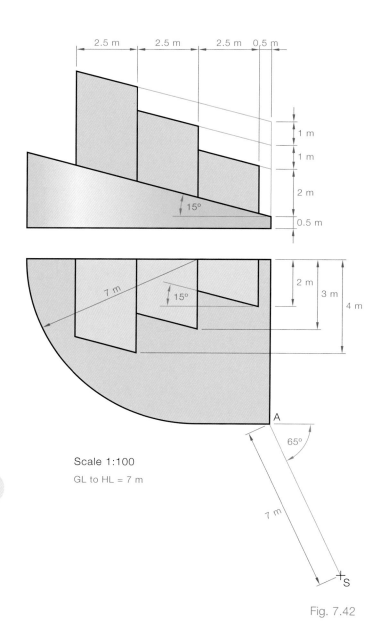

Scale 1:100

GL to HL = 7 m

Fig. 7.42

Q2. Fig. 7.42

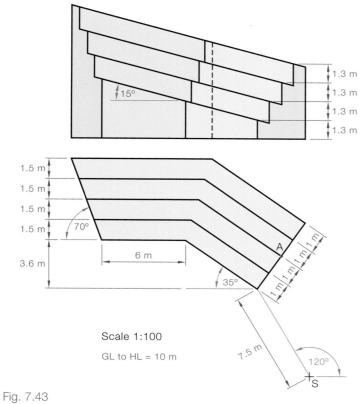

1.3 m
1.3 m
1.3 m
1.3 m

15°

1.5 m
1.5 m
1.5 m
1.5 m

3.6 m

70°

6 m

A

1 m 1 m 1 m 1 m

35°

Scale 1:100

GL to HL = 10 m

7.5 m

120°

S

Fig. 7.43

Q3. Fig. 7.43

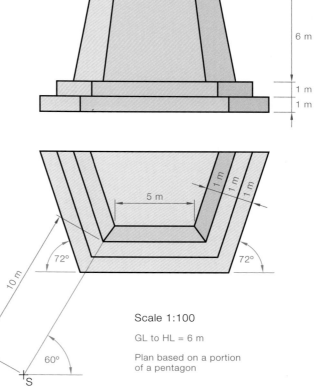

6 m

1 m
1 m

5 m

1 m
1 m
1 m

72°

72°

10 m

60°

S

Scale 1:100

GL to HL = 6 m

Plan based on a portion
of a pentagon

Fig. 7.44

Q4. Fig. 7.44

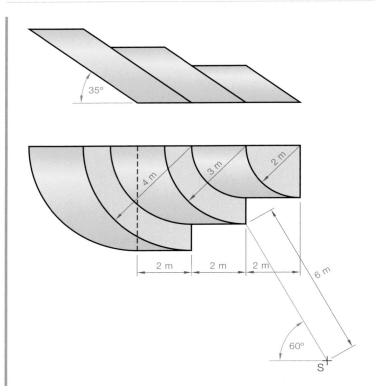

Fig. 7.45a

Q5. Fig. 7.45a and Fig. 7.45b

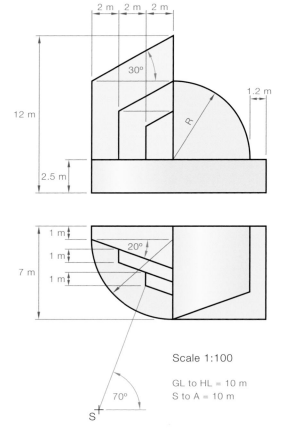

Scale 1:100

GL to HL = 10 m
S to A = 10 m

Fig. 7.45b

3 AREA
CONIC SECTIONS

8 Conic Sections

SYLLABUS OUTLINE

Areas to be studied:

• Terminology for conics. • The ellipse, parabola and hyperbola as sections of a right cone.
• Understanding of focal points, focal sphere, directrix and eccentricity in the context of conic sections.
• *Derivation of focal points, directrix and eccentricity using the focal sphere and solid cone.*
• Construction of conic curves as geometric loci. • Geometric properties common to the conic curves.
• Tangents to conics.
• *Construction of hyperbolae from focal points and transverse axis.*

Learning outcomes

Students should be able to:

Higher and Ordinary levels

- Understand the terms used in the study of conics, e.g. chord, focal chord directrix, vertex, ordinate, tangent, normal, major and minor axes/auxiliary circles, eccentricity, transverse axis.
- Construct ellipse, parabola, hyperbola as true sections of solid cone.
- Construct the conic sections, the ellipse, parabola and hyperbola, as plane loci from given data relating to eccentricity, foci, vertices, directrices and given points on the curve.
- Construct ellipse, parabola and hyperbola in a rectangle given principal vertice(s).
- Construct tangents to the conic sections from points on the curve.

Higher level only

- *Understand the terms used in the study of conics, double ordinate, latus rectum, focal sphere etc.*
- *Construct ellipse, parabola, hyperbola as true sections of solid cone and derive directrices, foci, vertices and eccentricity of these curves.*
- *Construct tangents to the conic sections from points outside the curve.*
- *Construct a double hyperbola given the foci and a point on the curve, or given the length of the transverse axis and the foci.*
- *Determine the centre of curvature and evolute for conic sections.*

Parabola as a Section of a Cone

A parabola is produced by slicing a cone with a plane that is parallel to a side of the cone in elevation.

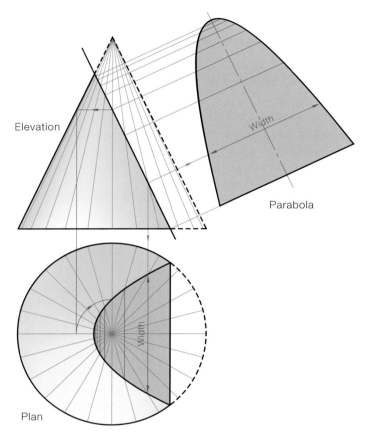

Elevation

Width

Parabola

Width

Plan

Fig. 8.1

HIGHER   LEVEL

CONSTRUCTION

(1) Draw the plan and elevation of a cone.

(2) Divide the plan into a number of generators which are projected onto the elevation.

(3) Draw in the cutting plane parallel to the side of the cone.

(4) As the generators are cut in elevation they are projected down to the corresponding elements in plan, producing a curve as shown in Fig. 8.1.

(5) The parabola is produced by finding the true shape of this section. Projection lines are produced perpendicular to the section plane and widths are taken from the plan.

Focal Sphere for a Parabola

If a sphere is inserted into the tip of the cone so that it touches the side of the cone and also the cutting plane we have the **focal sphere**. This sphere touches the cutting plane at one point only, the focus, hence the name. The sphere also touches the cone all the way round to form a circle. If this circle is extended to form a plane, where the two planes intersect will give the directrix, Fig. 8.3.

The focal sphere can be constructed for the other two conics in a similar fashion as we will see later in this chapter.

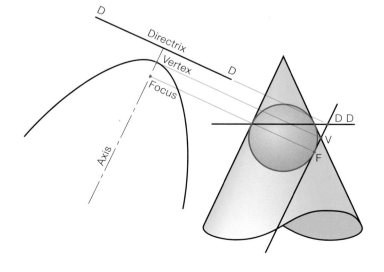

D

Directrix

Vertex

D

Focus

Axis

D D

V

F

Fig. 8.2

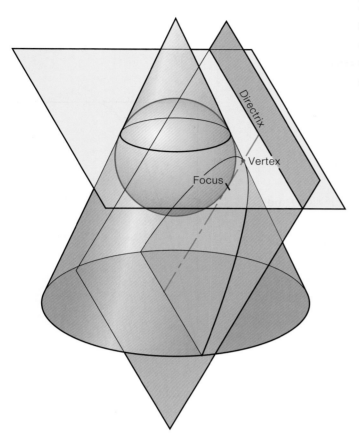

Note: As well as being seen as a conic section, a parabola can also be seen as a locus or path of a point, such that, it is at all stages equidistant from a given line (directrix) and a given point (focus).

Fig. 8.3

Terminology

Chord – A straight line touching the curve in two places.

Focal Chord – As above, but also passing through the focus.

Latus Rectum – Special focal chord perpendicular to the axis.

Ordinate – A line perpendicular to the axis, starting on the axis and ending on the curve.

Directrix – Line of intersection between the section plane and the plane formed by the intersecting points of the focal sphere and the cone.

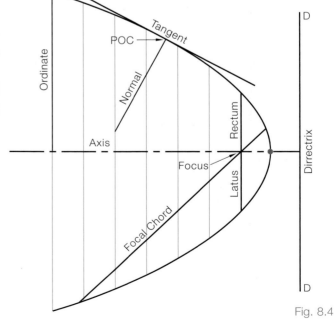

Fig. 8.4

HIGHER LEVEL

Three Methods of Constructing a Parabola

Rectangle Method

(1) Divide one of the sides in half to find the vertex, e.g. side AD.

(2) Draw the axis through V and perpendicular to the side AD. The rectangle is now halved.

(3) Divide edge AB into any number of **equal** divisions and join each up to V as shown.

(4) Point A to the vertex is now divided into the same number of equal divisions.

(5) Lines are drawn from these points parallel to the axis. Where the two sets of lines intersect, plot the parabola as shown in Fig. 8.5.

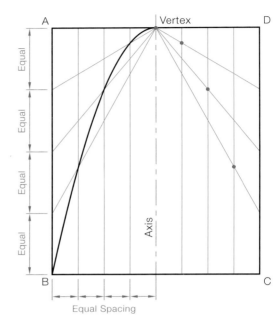

Fig. 8.5

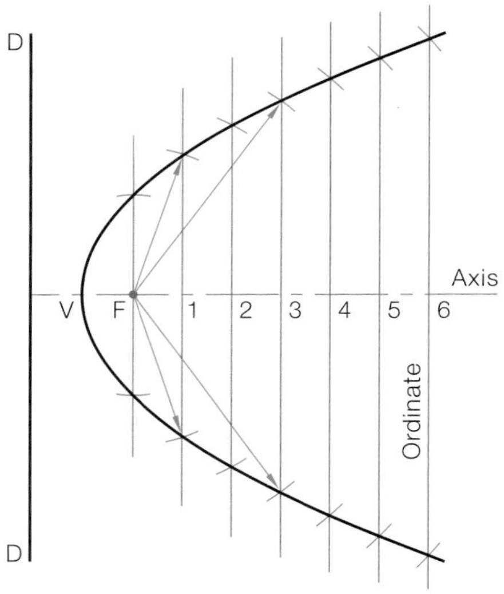

Compass Method

(1) Find the vertex halfway between focus and directrix.

(2) Draw a series of ordinates, F to 6.

(3) Take a radius from the directrix DD to the first ordinate at F.

(4) Move the compass point to the **focus** and scribe arcs above and below the axis on this ordinate at F.

(5) Next take a radius from the directrix to ordinate 1.

(6) Move the compass point to the **focus** and scribe arcs to cut ordinate 1 above and below the axis.

(7) Continue as necessary remembering to always draw the arcs having F as centre.

Fig. 8.6

Eccentricity Method

The eccentricity for a parabola is always **equal to 1 or 1/1**.
Eccentricity is a ratio between the two distances:
(i) from the focus to a point P on the curve,
(ii) from the same point on the curve to the directrix.

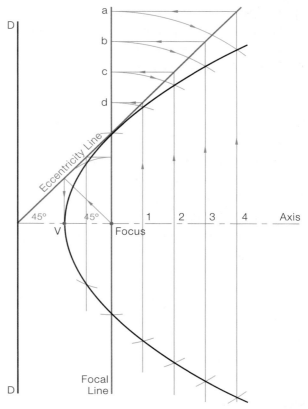

Fig. 8.7

Eccentricity	=	Distance from focus to a point
		Point to directrix
	=	F to P
		P to DD

Since the eccentricity of a parabola is unity, any point on the parabola must be equidistant from the directrix and focus.

    The eccentricity line for a parabola will always be at 45° to the axis.

CONSTRUCTION

Given directrix, axis and focus.

(1) Set up the eccentricity line. This will be a 45° line for a parabola.
(2) The vertex is found by projecting up from the focus at 45° to the axis to hit the eccentricity line and down perpendicular to the axis, giving V.
(3) Draw a perpendicular to the axis through the focus giving the focal line.
(4) Where the eccentricity line and focal line intersect is a point on the curve which can be swung below the axis.

(5) Draw lines **1, 2, 3, 4...** up to the eccentricity line, perpendicular to the axis, and then project across to the focal line, parallel to the axis. This finds points **a, b, c, d...**
(6) With the focus as centre, scribe an arc from a to hit line **1** above and below the axis.
(7) With the focus as centre, scribe an arc from **b** to hit line **2** above and below the axis.
Continue in this manner to plot more points on the curve.

Tangents to a Parabola from a Point on the Curve

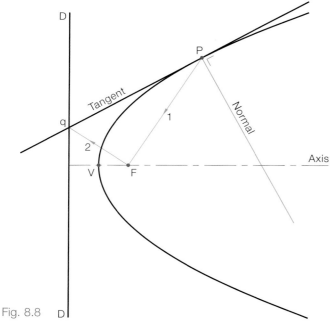

Fig. 8.8

Method 1

Fig. 8.8

(1) Join point P on the curve to the focus F.

(2) At F create a 90° angle and extend to hit the directrix DD at q.

(3) Point q is a point on the tangent.

(4) Join P to q to give the tangent.

A perpendicular to the tangent at P, the point of contact, will give the normal at P.

Method 2

Fig. 8.9

(1) Draw a perpendicular line to the axis from point P to give point r.

(2) With the vertex as centre rotate point r to give q.

(3) Join P to q to form the tangent.

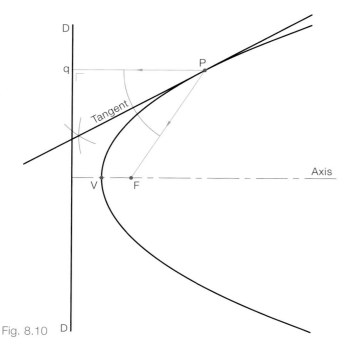

Fig. 8.10

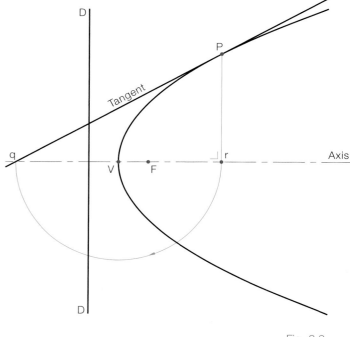

Fig. 8.9

Method 3

Fig. 8.10

(1) Join P on the curve to the focus F.

(2) Draw a line from P parallel to the axis to hit the directrix at q.

Note: This line Pq can be considered to be a line joining to a focal point at infinity and hence will tie in with one of the methods of constructing tangents for the hyperbola and ellipse.

(3) The bisector of the angle formed, qPF will give the tangent.

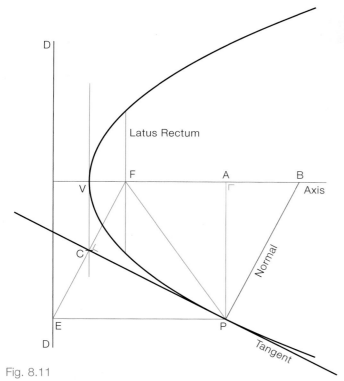

Fig. 8.11

Points of interest about the parabola. Fig. 8.11

The latus rectum equals 4FV.
Length from A to B equals half the latus rectum.
Length CV equals half of PA.
Length FB equals EP.
Length FC equals CE.

Given a parabola to locate the focus and the directrix. Fig. 8.12

(1) Draw any ordinate and extend so that AB equals twice AV.

(2) Join B to the vertex V locating point C on the curve.

(3) C will always be a point on the end of the latus rectum.
    Drop C perpendicular to the axis to locate F the focus.

(4) For a parabola the eccentricity is always one, so VF equals V,DD.
    Draw the directrix.

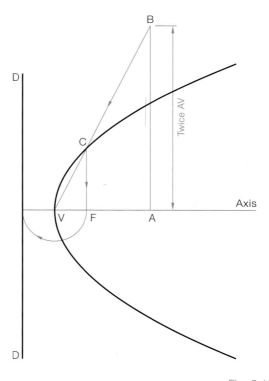

Fig. 8.12

Tangents to a Parabola from a Point P outside the Curve

To draw a tangent from a point P outside the directrix.

Method 1

Fig. 8.13

With P as centre swing an arc from the focus F onto the directrix giving points r and q.

Project these points parallel to the axis to give the points of contact.

Draw the tangents.

Note: The lines from r and q drawn parallel to the axis can be considered to be lines drawn from a focal point at infinity and hence this method will tie in with similar methods for the ellipse and hyperbola.

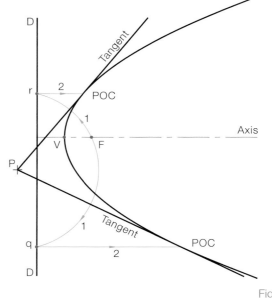

Fig. 8.13

Method 2

Fig. 8.14

Join P to the focus. Bisect this line and draw a circle with PF as diameter. Draw a tangent to the parabola at the vertex V. This tangent will intersect the circle at two places, giving points q and r, which will be points on the required tangents. Draw the tangents.

Note: The tangent drawn at V can be considered to be a circle through V with a radius of infinity. This will tie this construction in with similar methods used for the ellipse and hyperbola.

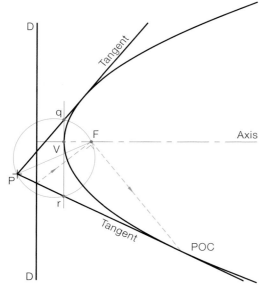

Fig. 8.14

To draw a tangent to a parabola from a point inside the directrix.

Method 1

Fig. 8.15

Similar construction to Fig. 8.14 above.

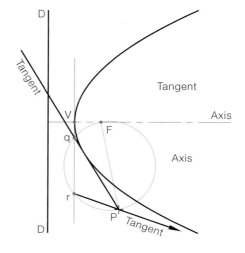

Fig. 8.15

Activities

Q1. Draw the elevation and complete the plan of the cone and find the true shape of the section (parabola), Fig. 8.16.

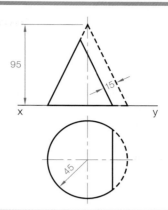

Fig. 8.16

Q2. Construct a parabola in the given rectangle having its vertex in the position shown, Fig. 8.17.

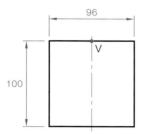

Fig. 8.17

Q3. Construct a parabola in the given rectangle having its vertex in the position shown, Fig. 8.18.

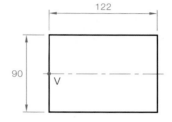

Fig. 8.18

Q4. Given the directrix and the focus construct the parabola using the compass method, Fig. 8.19.

Fig. 8.19

Q5. Given the directrix and the vertex construct the parabola using the eccentricity method, Fig. 8.20.

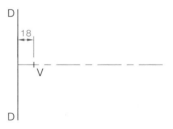

Fig. 8.20

Q6. Construct the given parabola. Draw a tangent to the curve at the given point P, Fig. 8.21.

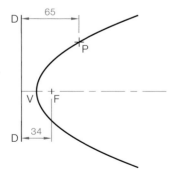

Fig. 8.21

Q7. Given the directrix, axis and a tangent to a parabola. Point P is the point of contact. Draw the parabola, Fig. 8.22.

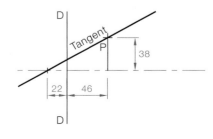

Fig. 8.22

Q8. Given the directrix, axis, tangent and point of contact P of a parabola. Find the focus and draw the parabola, Fig. 8.23.

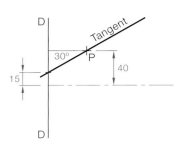

Fig. 8.23

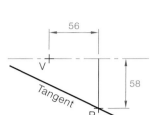

Fig. 8.24

Q9. Given the axis, vertex and point of contact for a tangent. Construct the tangent, find the focus and directrix and draw a portion of the parabola, Fig. 8.24.
Hint: See points of interest about the parabola, Fig. 8.11.

Q10. Given the axis, a normal and its point of contact to a parabola. Find the vertex, the focus and the directrix. Draw a portion of the curve, Fig. 8.25.
Hint: See points of interest about the parabola, Fig. 8.11.

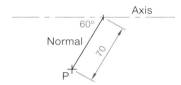

Fig. 8.25

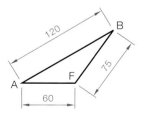

Fig. 8.26

Q11. Given the axis, the vertex and a point P on the curve of a parabola. Draw a portion of the curve, Fig. 8.26.
Hint: See Figures 8.9 and 8.11.

Q12. Given a tangent to a parabola, the point of contact and the axis. Find the vertex, focus, and the directrix. Draw a portion of the curve, Fig. 8.27.
Hint: See Figures 8.9 and 8.115.

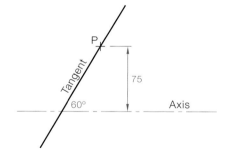

Fig. 8.27

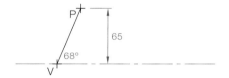

Fig. 8.28

Q13. Draw the triangle AFB shown. Points A and B are points on the curve of a parabola and F is its vertex. Draw a portion of the curve. Construct a tangent at point A, Fig. 8.28.

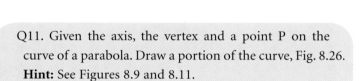

Q14. Given the axis, focus and a point P on the curve of a parabola. Draw a portion of each of the two curves that will satisfy these conditions, Fig. 8.29.

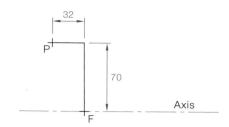

Fig. 8.29

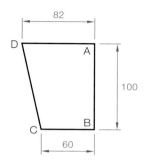

Fig. 8.30

Q15. Draw the given quadrilateral ABCD. Side AB is the directrix of a parabola and points C and D are points on the curve. Draw either one of the two curves that will satisfy these conditions, Fig. 8.30.

Q16. Given the cone in Fig. 8.31 which is sectioned as shown. Construct the focal sphere and hence find the focus, vertex and directrix of the parabola. Draw a portion of the curve.

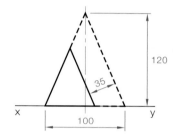

Fig. 8.31

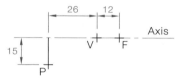

Fig. 8.32

Q17. Given the vertex, focus and a point P outside the directrix. Draw a portion of the curve and draw tangents to the parabola from point P, Fig. 8.32.

Q18. Given two tangents to a parabola, the axis and the vertex. Construct a portion of the curve, and locate the points of contact, Fig. 8.33.
Hint: See construction, Fig. 8.14.

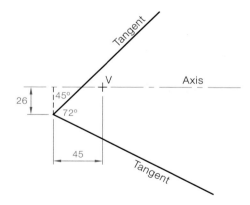

Fig. 8.33

Q19. AB and AC are two tangents to a parabola. They meet at an angle of 70°. The focus of the parabola is 45 mm from AB and 35 mm from AC. Draw a portion of the curve.

Q20. Draw a triangle ABF. AB = 140 mm, AF = 95 mm and BF = 70 mm. If AB is a tangent to a parabola having A on the directrix, and F is the focus, determine the axis, directrix and draw the curve.

HIGHER LEVEL

Ellipse as a Section of a Cone

An ellipse is produced by a cutting plane which passes through both sides of a cone or will cut both sides of the cone when extended.

CONSTRUCTION

(1) Draw the plane and elevation of a cone.
(2) Divide the plan into sections using generators and project these onto the elevation.
(3) In elevation, draw in the cutting plane so that it cuts both sides of the cone or will cut both sides of the cone if the plane and cone are extended.
(4) The points where the generators are cut in elevation are projected down to the plan producing a curve as shown.
(5) The true shape of this curve is an ellipse and is produced by projecting perpendicularly from the cutting plane.
The widths are taken from the plan.

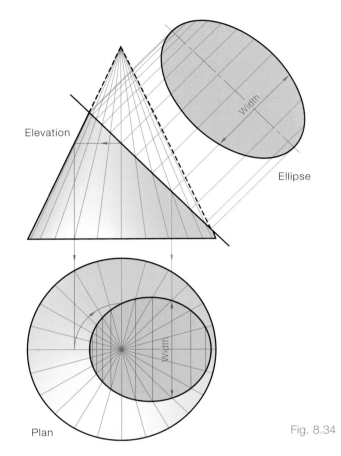

Fig. 8.34

Focal Spheres for an Ellipse

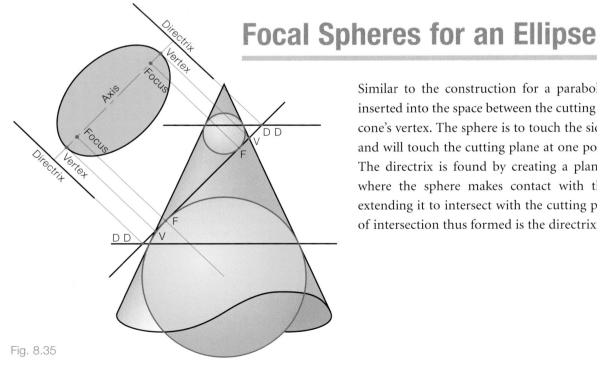

Fig. 8.35

Similar to the construction for a parabola a sphere is inserted into the space between the cutting plane and the cone's vertex. The sphere is to touch the side of the cone and will touch the cutting plane at one point, the focus. The directrix is found by creating a plane at the level where the sphere makes contact with the cone, and extending it to intersect with the cutting plane. The line of intersection thus formed is the directrix, Fig. 8.35.

HIGHER LEVEL

A second focal sphere is found underneath the cutting plane giving the second focus and the second directrix, Fig. 8.36.

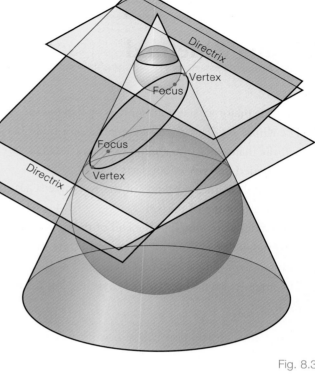

Fig. 8.36

Terminology

Major Axis – The longest axis going through the centre of the ellipse.

Minor Axis – The shortest line going through the centre of the ellipse. The major and minor axes cross at 90° and bisect each other.

Major Auxiliary Circle – The circle passing through both vertices and having its centre on the axis at C.

Minor Auxiliary Circle – The circle passing through both ends of the minor axis and having its centre on the axis at C.

Focal Points – The focal points are two points on the major axis. They are symmetrical about C. They are located a distance of ½ major axis from the ends of the minor axis. Ellipses with focal points near the centre C will be very circular. Ellipses having focal points near the ends of the major axis will be flat ellipses.

Point P – For any point P on the curve the distances F_1P and F_2P added together will equal the length of the major axis. $F_1P + F_2P = V_1V_2$ (Major Axis).

A vertical from the focus to hit the major auxiliary circle and then brought across parallel to the major axis will give the top of the minor axis.

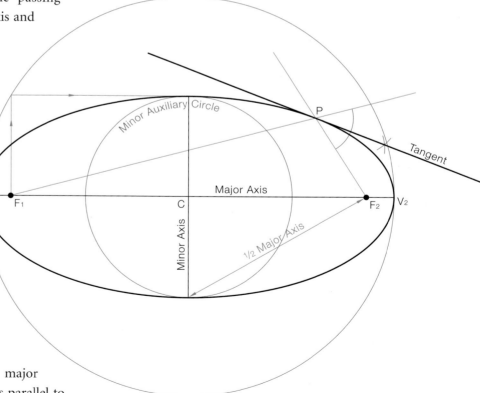

Fig. 8.37

Five Methods of Constructing an Ellipse

Rectangle Method

(1) Find the major axis and minor axis by halving the sides.

(2) The ellipse is constructed one quarter at a time. Divide half the major axis into a number of equal divisions, e.g. OD divided into five equal parts.

(3) Divide half of the short side of the rectangle (CD) into the same number of parts.

(4) These points are joined to the end of the minor axis.

(5) Now radiate lines from the other end of the minor axis through the points found on OD.

(6) The intersection of these two sets of lines plots the ellipse as shown.

Note: This construction will also work to construct an ellipse in a parallelogram.

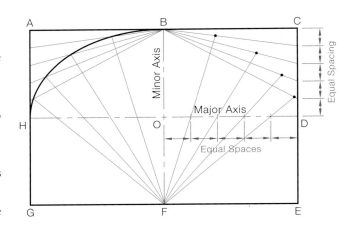

Fig. 8.38

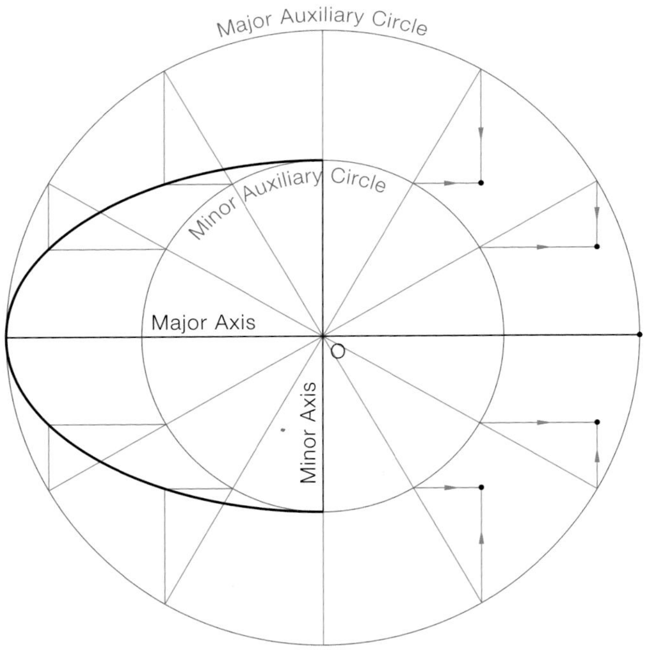

Circle Method

(1) Given the major and minor axes, construct the two circles having O as centre and radii equal to half of the major axis and the minor axis.

(2) Divide the circles up from the centre, usually with the 30°/60° set-square.

(3) Where each radial line hits the major circle, draw lines toward the major axis and parallel to the minor axis.

(4) Where each radial line crosses the minor circle, draw lines away from the minor axis and parallel to the major axis.

(5) Where these lines intersect plots points on the curve.

Fig. 8.39

Eccentricity Method

The eccentricity for an ellipse is always **less than 1**, e.g. 3/4, 2/3, 0.7, 0.61 etc. but is a constant for that particular ellipse.

As in the parabola, it is an expression of the relationship between the two distances:

(i) From the focal point to a point P on the curve.

(ii) From the same point on the curve to the directrix.

Eccentricity	=	Distance from focus to a point
		Point to directrix
	=	$\dfrac{\text{F to P}}{\text{P to DD}}$

The eccentricity line for an ellipse will always be at an angle of less than 45° to the axis.

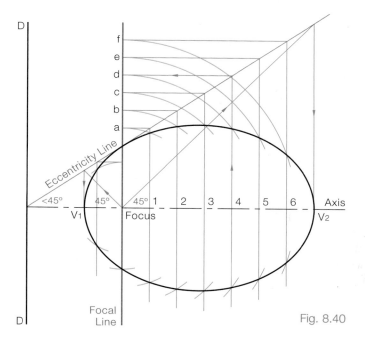

Fig. 8.40

CONSTRUCTION

Given the directrix, axis, focal point and eccentricity of 2/3.

(1) Set up the eccentricity line by measuring out on the axis a set distance from the directrix, e.g. 30 mm. Construct a perpendicular to the axis at this point. Measure up from the axis on this line a distance equal to 2/3 of the previous distance. 20 mm in this example.

(2) This gives a point on the eccentricity line which now can be drawn.

(3) Now follow the normal procedure as explained for the parabola in Fig. 8.7.

(4) The ellipse has two vertices and these are found by constructing 45° lines to the axis from the focus to hit the eccentricity line. These points are projected to give V_1 and V_2.

(5) Points on the curve are found by drawing ordinates. Where these intersect the eccentricity line projects across, parallel to the axis, to the focal line.

(6) With the focus as centre, rotate the points found on the focal line back to each ordinate, above and below the axis.

(7) The points found in this way can be joined giving an ellipse.

Trammel Method

This is a very useful method of constructing an ellipse as it is both quick and accurate.

(1) Cut a piece of paper to use as a trammel. It should be slightly longer than half the major axis.

(2) Mark the length of half the minor axis on the trammel AB.

(3) Using A as an end point, now mark half the major axis on the paper, AC.

(4) The trammel can now be placed on the major and minor axis so that point B rests on the major axis and point C on the minor axis.

(5) Plot the location of point A which is a point on the curve.

(6) Rotate the trammel, keeping the points B and C on their appropriate axes. Continue to plot points at A.

(7) Join these plotted points to form an ellipse.

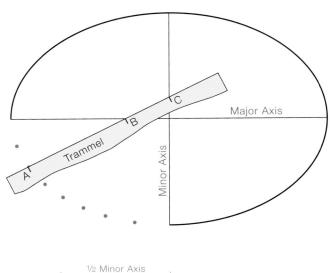

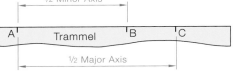

Fig. 8.41

Pin and String Method

This is a good method for drawing large scale ellipses. The method of construction is based on the fact that the distance from F_1P added to F_2P will remain constant and equals the length of the major axis.

$$F_1P + F_2P = \text{Major Axis}$$

(1) The pins are fixed at the focal points.

(2) String is tied to the pins so that the amount of string left between the pins equals the length of the major axis of the required ellipse.

(3) By keeping the string stretched with a pencil and moving it around, an ellipse will be plotted.

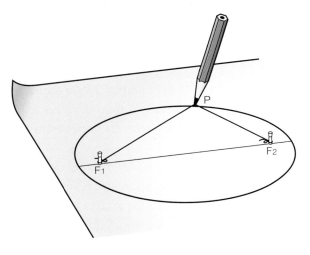

Fig. 8.42

Tangent to an Ellipse from a Point on the Curve

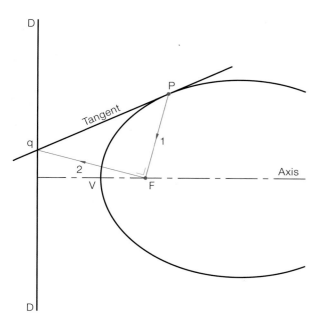

Fig. 8.43

Method 1

Fig. 8.43

This method works for all conics and has already been shown in Fig. 8.8 for the parabola.

(1) Draw a line joining point P back to the focus.

(2) At the focus, draw a new line perpendicular to PF and extend to hit the directrix DD at q.

(3) Point q is a second point on the tangent.

(4) Join P to q, forming the tangent.

Method 2

Fig. 8.44

(1) Join F_1 to P and extent to q.

(2) Join F_2 to P and extent to r.

(3) The line that bisects the angle F_2Pq will be the required tangent.

(4) Alternatively F_1Pr could be bisected.

(5) The normal could be found by bisecting the angle F_1PF_2. See the similarity to that used for the parabola in Method 3, Fig. 8.10.

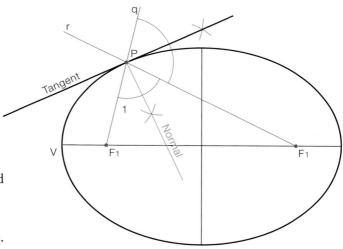

Fig. 8.44

Tangent to an Ellipse from a Point P outside the Curve

To draw a tangent to an ellipse from a point P outside the directrix. Fig 8.45

HIGHER LEVEL

Method 1

Fig. 8.45

With P as centre and PF_1 as radius, swing an arc to hit the directrix at R and q. Join from R and q back to F_2 giving the points of contact. Draw the tangents.

Note the similarity with construction for parabola, Fig. 8.13.

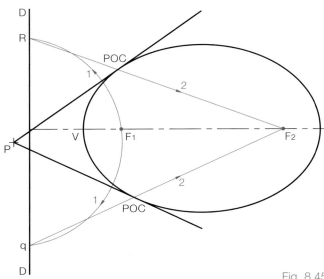

Fig. 8.45

Method 2

Fig. 8.46

Join P to F_1 and place a circle on this line having PF_1 as its diameter. Draw the major auxiliary circle for the ellipse, i.e. the circle which has V_1V_2 as a diameter. These two circles intersect at points r and q, which will be points on the tangents. Draw the tangents.

Note the similarity to construction for a parabola, Fig. 8.14.

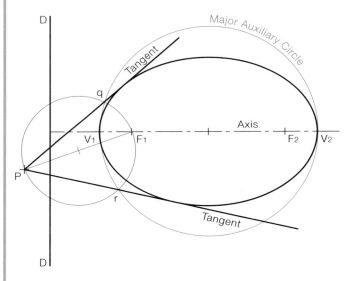

Fig. 8.46

Method 3

Fig. 8.47

With point P as centre and PF_1 as radius, draw an arc. Now take the length of the major axis as radius V_1V_2. Using F_2 as the centre point swing an arc to cut your first arc in two places, q and r. Points q and r are joined back to F_2. Where these lines cross the ellipse give the points of contact for the tangents. Draw the tangents.

Note the similarity between the construction for an ellipse and for a hyperbola.

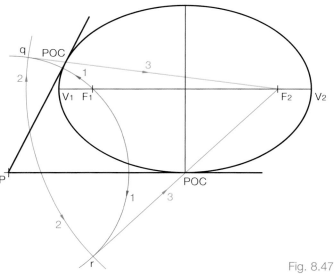

Fig. 8.47

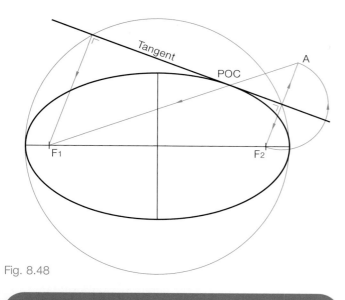

Fig. 8.48

Given a tangent to an ellipse to find the point of contact (POC). Fig 8.48

Fig. 8.48

(1) Draw the major auxiliary circle.

(2) Where the tangent and auxiliary circle intersect draw perpendiculars to the tangent. These perpendiculars will pass through the focal points F_1 and F_2.

(3) On either of these perpendiculars you double its length as shown, finding point A.

(4) Join A back to the focus to find the POC.

Given an ellipse to find its axes.

Fig. 8.49

(1) Draw any two parallel chords.

(2) Bisect these chords giving A and B.

(3) Join A and B.

(4) Bisect the diameter giving C the ellipse centre.

(5) With C as centre draw a circle to cut the ellipse in three places.

(6) Lines joining these points will be parallel to the axes.

(7) Draw the axes through point C.

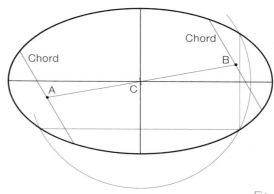

Fig. 8.49

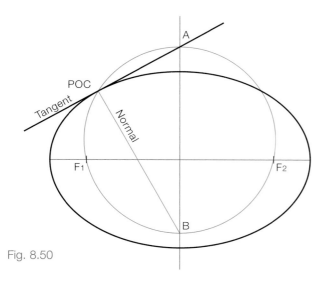

Fig. 8.50

Given a tangent to an ellipse to find its point of contact (POC).

Alternative Method

Fig. 8.50

(1) Extend the minor axis to intersect the tangent at point A.

(2) Construct a circle to contain points A, F_1 and F_2.

(3) This circle locates the point of contact where it crosses the ellipse.

It should be noted that where the circle intersects the minor axis for the second time at B, it locates a point on the normal. (The angle in a semicircle is always a right angle.)

Activities

Q1. Draw the given plan and elevation of the cone and find the true shape of the section (ellipse), Fig. 8.51.

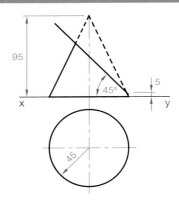

Fig. 8.51

Q2. Construct an ellipse in a rectangle of side 140 mm by 80 mm using the rectangle method.

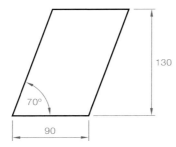

Fig. 8.52

Q3. Construct an ellipse in the given parallelogram such that the sides of the parallelogram form tangents to the ellipse, Fig. 8.52.

Q4. Draw an ellipse having a major axis of 120 mm and a minor axis of 80 mm using the auxiliary circle method. Locate the two focal points.

Q5. Using a trammel like that shown in Fig. 8.53, construct an ellipse and find its foci.

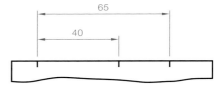

Fig. 8.53

Fig. 8.54

Q6. Given the major axis and the foci, construct the ellipse, Fig. 8.54.

Q7. Given the minor axis and the foci, construct the ellipse, Fig. 8.55.

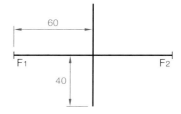

Fig. 8.55

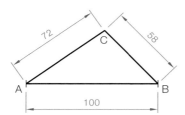

Fig. 8.56

Q8. Given the triangle ABC where A and B are focal points of an ellipse and C is a point on the curve. Draw the ellipse, Fig. 8.56.

Fig. 8.57

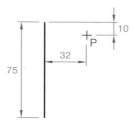

Q9. Given the major axis and a point P on the curve. Draw the ellipse, Fig. 8.57.

Q10. Given the minor axis of an ellipse and a point P on the curve. Construct the ellipse, Fig. 8.58.

Fig. 8.58

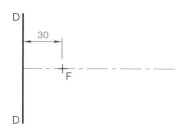

Fig. 8.59

Q11. Given the directrix, axis, focus of an ellipse and an eccentricity of 0.8. Draw a portion of the curve, Fig. 8.59.

Q12. Given the axis, focus, eccentricity of 3/5 and a point P on an ellipse. Draw the curve and construct a tangent at point P, Fig. 8.60.

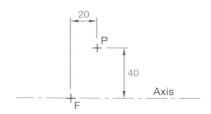

Fig. 8.60

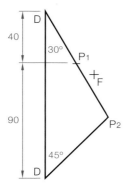

Fig. 8.61

Q13. Construct the triangle shown in Fig. 8.13. DD is the directrix of an ellipse. Points P_1 and P_2 are points on the curve and the eccentricity of the ellipse is 3/4. F shows the approximate position of the focus. Locate the focus and draw the curve, Fig. 8.61.

$$\text{Eccentricity} = \frac{\text{Distance from focus to a point}}{\text{Point to directrix}}$$

$$= \frac{\text{F to P}}{\text{P to DD}}$$

Q14. Given the focus and vertex of an ellipse having an eccentricity of 0.8. Draw a portion of the curve, Fig. 8.62.

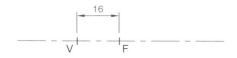

Fig. 8.62

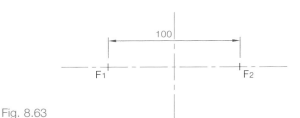

Fig. 8.63

Q15. In an ellipse the distance between the focal points is 100 mm. The length of the major axis and the minor axis are in the ratio 3:2. Draw the ellipse, Fig. 8.63.

Q16. Given the directrix, axis, eccentricity of 0.75 and a point P on the curve. Determine the position of the focus and draw a portion of the curve. Construct a tangent to the curve from point A, Fig. 8.64.

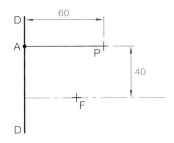

Fig. 8.64

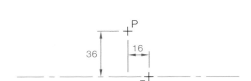

Fig. 8.65

Q17. Given the major axis of 110 mm, focus and a point P on an ellipse. Draw the curve, Fig. 8.65.

Q18. Given the axis, focus, tangent and point of contact P to an ellipse. Construct a portion of the curve, Fig. 8.66.

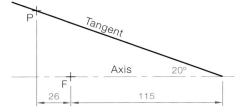

Fig. 8.66

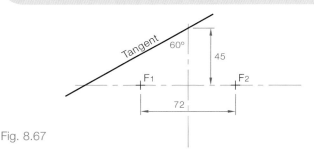

Fig. 8.67

Q19. Given F_1, F_2 and a tangent to an ellipse. Find the point of contact and draw the curve, Fig. 8.67.
Hint: See Figures 8.48 and 8.50.

Q20. Given the latus rectum of an ellipse and the vertex. Construct a portion of the curve, Fig. 8.68.

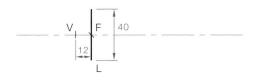

Fig. 8.68

HIGHER LEVEL

Fig. 8.69

Q21. Given the cone in Fig. 8.69 which is sectioned as shown. Construct the focal spheres and hence find the focus, vertex and directrix of the ellipse. Draw the ellipse.

Q22. Given the triangle APF. AP is a tangent to an ellipse with P as the point of contact. F is a focal point and the major axis is 120 mm long, Fig. 8.70. Draw the ellipse.

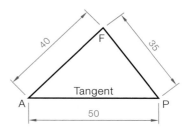

Fig. 8.70

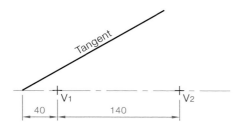

Fig. 8.71

Q23. Given the major axis V₁V₂ of an ellipse and a tangent to it. Draw a portion of the curve to include the point of contact, Fig. 8.71

Q24. Given the line P₁FP₂ as shown in Fig. 8.42. F is the focal point of an ellipse and both P₁ and P₂ are points on the curve. The directrix is 50 mm from point P₁. Draw a portion of the curve. Construct a tangent at P₂, Fig. 8.72.

Fig. 8.72

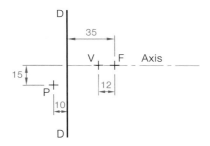

Fig. 8.73

Q25. Given the directrix focus and vertex construct the ellipse. Construct a tangent to the ellipse from point P, Fig. 8.73.

Q26. In Fig. 8.74, AB is a tangent to an ellipse. V is the vertex and F is the focus. Construct the ellipse.

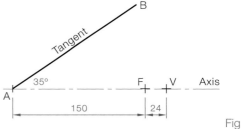

Fig. 8.74

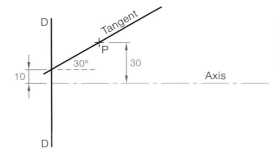

Fig. 8.75

Q27. Given the directrix, axis, tangent and the point of contact P. The focus is closer to the point P than the directrix. Draw the curve, Fig. 8.75.

Q28. Given the focus, axis, directrix and tangent to an ellipse. Construct the ellipse and find the point of contact, Fig. 8.76.

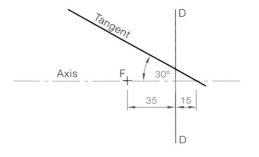

Fig. 8.76

HIGHER LEVEL

Hyperbola as a Section of a Cone

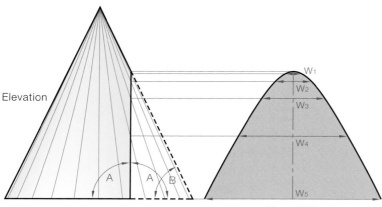

Elevation

Hyperbola

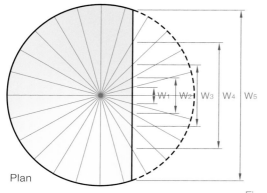

Plan

Fig. 8.77

If a cone is cut by a cutting plane such that either angle at the base (angle A) is equal to 90°, or is between 90° and the angle of the side of the cone (angle B), then a hyperbola is produced. The cutting plane only cuts one side of the cone no matter how far the cone and plane are extended.

CONSTRUCTION

Fig. 8.77

The construction is the same as that for the parabola and ellipse.

(1) Draw the plan, elevation, elements and cutting plane.
(2) The auxiliary view is projected perpendicularly from the cutting plane in elevation.
(3) Points where the cutting plane crosses elements are projected out.
(4) Widths are taken from the plan as shown.

Focal Sphere

The hyperbola has one focal sphere. The position and size of the sphere is such that it is tangential to both the sides of the cone and the cutting plane, i.e. it fits neatly into the top of the cone and also touches the cutting plane at one spot, the focus. The directrix is found by finding the intersection between the plane through the sphere containing all the points of contact between the sphere and the cone and the cutting plane.

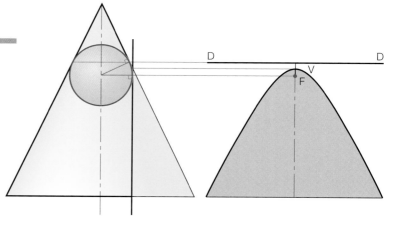

Fig. 8.78

HIGHER LEVEL

Terminology

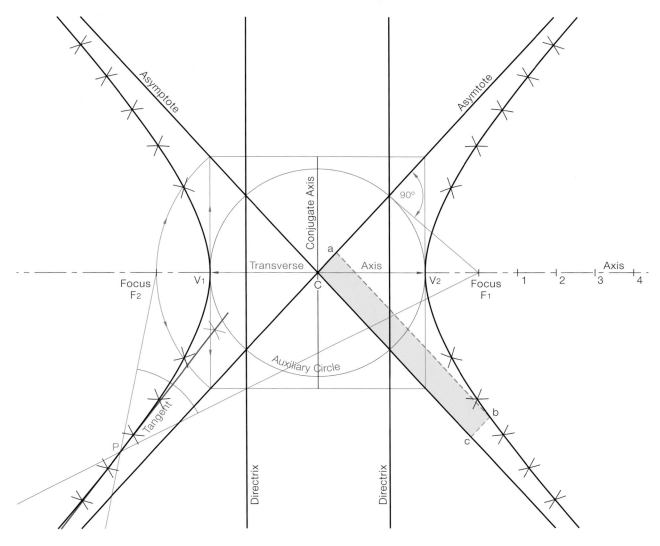

Fig. 8.79

Distance from Focus$_2$ to P − Distance from Focus$_1$ to P = Transverse Axis

$F_2P − F_1P$ = Transverse Axis

$F_2P − F_1P = V_1V_2$

Transverse Axis – The part of the axis between the vertices V_1 to V_2 = Transverse Axis.

Auxiliary Circle – The circle passing through both vertices and having its centre on the axis at C is called the auxiliary circle.

Asymptotes – These are the outer limits of the cones. They are straight lines which cross at C. The hyperbola curve will get closer and closer to the asymptote but will never touch it.

Conjugate Axis – A perpendicular to the axis through the centre C is called the conjugate axis.

Rectangle abcC – Select any point b on the curve. From b draw ba and bc parallel to the asymptotes. The resulting parallelogram has an area which is constant no matter where on the curve point b is selected.

Three Methods of Constructing a Hyperbola

Method 1: Rectangle Method

Fig. 8.80

(1) The two rectangles must be of equal size and share an axis as shown.

(2) V_1 and V_2, the vertices of the hyperbolas, are located.

(3) The edge CB is divided into a number of equal parts, five in this example.

(4) These points are joined to V_2.

(5) The edge AB is now divided into the same number of parts as edge CB.

(6) These points are joined to V_1.

(7) Where the two sets of construction lines cross, plot points on the curve as shown.

(8) The rest of the curve is found in a similar way.

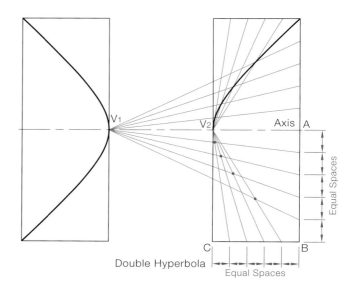

Fig. 8.80

Method 2: Compass Method

Fig. 8.81

(1) Draw an axis and mark the two vertices V_1 and V_2.

(2) Locate the focal points F_1 and F_2. The distance from F_1 to V_1 must be the same as from F_2 to V_2.

(3) Choose points a, b, c, d etc. on the axis beyond F_2.

(4) With radius V_1a and centre F_1 draw an arc.

(5) With F_2 as centre draw another arc.

(6) With radius V_2a and centre F_2 draw arcs above and below the axis to cut the previous arc giving two points on one branch of the curve.

(7) Using the same radius repeat this process using F_1 as centre giving two points on the second branch of the curve.

(8) Repeat this process using points b, c, d etc. plotting the path of the curve.

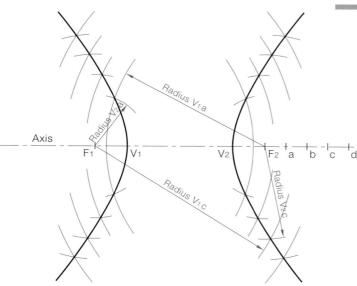

Fig. 8.81

Method 3: Eccentricity Method

Fig. 8.82

The eccentricity for a hyperbola is always **greater than one**, e.g. 7/4, 12/5, 1.6 etc.

The eccentricity line for a hyperbola will always make an angle of greater than 45° with the axis.

Eccentricity is a ratio between two distances

$$= \frac{\text{Distance from focus to a point on the curve}}{\text{Distance from the same point to directrix}}$$

$$= \frac{\text{F to P}}{\text{P to DD}}$$

The ratio is a constant for a particular curve, no matter where on the curve the point P is chosen.

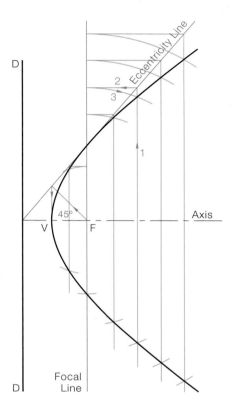

Fig. 8.82

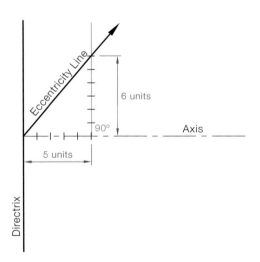

Fig. 8.83

CONSTRUCTION

Given directrix focus and eccentricity of 1.2.

The advantage of the eccentricity method is that once the eccentricity line is set up correctly the process of construction is the same for all three conics.

(1) Draw the directrix, axis and focus.
(2) Eccentricity of 1.2 can be written as a fraction 6/5.
(3) Measure out from the directrix five units, e.g. 5 × (5 mm units) = 25 mm, and mark a point on the axis.
(4) Draw a perpendicular to the axis at this point and measure up from the axis six units, e.g. 6 × (5 mm units) = 30 mm.
(5) The eccentricity line can now be drawn.

Note: The bottom portion of the eccentricity fraction is measured out along the axis and the top is measured up on a perpendicular.

(6) A line drawn up from the focus, at 45° to the axis, to hit the eccentricity line and dropped to the axis finds the vertex.
(7) Construction for the curve is the same as for the ellipse and parabola.

Tangent to a Hyperbola from a Point on the Curve

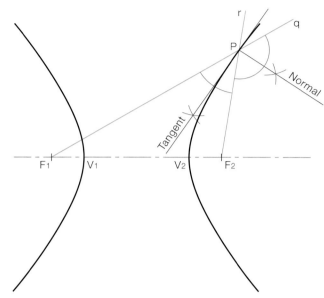

Fig. 8.84

Method 1

Fig. 8.84

(1) Join F_1 to P and extend to q.

(2) Join F_2 to P and extend to r.

(3) The line that bisects angle F_1PF_2 or angle qPr will be the tangent.

(4) The normal is perpendicular to the tangent and can be found by bisecting the angle F_2Pq.

Note: The similarity to the method used for the parabola, Fig. 8.10, and the ellipse, Fig. 8.44.

Method 2

Fig. 8.85

This method works for all three conics and has already been shown in Fig. 8.8 for the parabola and Fig. 8.43 for the ellipse.

(1) Join P back to the focus.

(2) At the focus draw a perpendicular to PF to hit the directrix at q.

(3) Point q is a point on the tangent. Join P to q, forming the tangent.

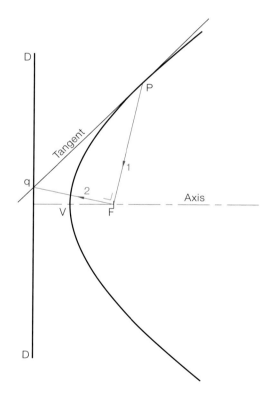

Fig. 8.85

Tangent to a Hyperbola from a Point P outside the Curve

Method 1

Fig. 8.86

(1) Join P to F_2 and place a circle on this line having PF_2 as its diameter.

(2) Draw the auxiliary circle for the double hyperbola, i.e. the circle which has V_1V_2 as its diameter.

(3) The circles cross at q and r which will be points on the tangents.

(4) Draw the tangent p to q extended.

Note: The similarity to construction for a parabola, Fig. 8.14, and construction for an ellipse, Fig. 8.46.

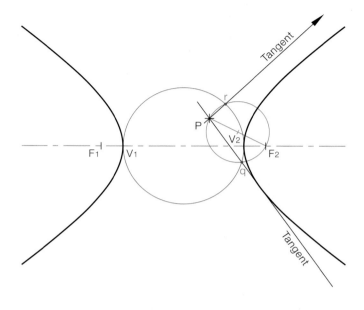

Fig. 8.86

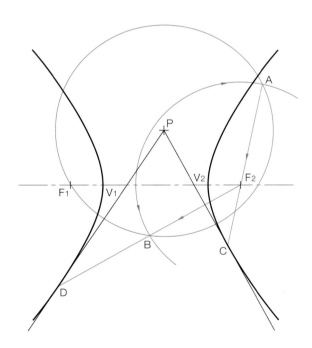

Method 2

Fig. 8.87

(1) Draw a circle with P as centre and PF_1 as radius.

(2) With radius V_1V_2 (transverse axis) and F_2 as centre, scribe an arc to cut this circle at A and B.

(3) Join A to F_2 and extend to C, join B to F_2 and extend to D.

(4) Draw the tangents PC and PD.

Note: Similar to the construction for an ellipse, Fig. 8.47.

Fig. 8.87

HIGHER LEVEL

Activities

Q1. Given the plan and elevation of a cone which has been sectioned as shown. Draw the views and determine the true shape of the section. Hyperbola, Fig. 8.88.

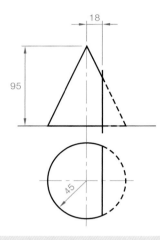

Fig. 8.88

Q2. Given the directrix, axis, focus and eccentricity of 6/5. Draw a portion of the hyperbola, Fig. 8.89.

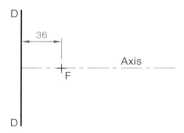

Fig. 8.89

Q3. Given the axis, focus, point P on the curve and eccentricity of 1.25. Draw a portion of the hyperbola Fig. 8.90.

Fig. 8.90

Q4. Given the axis, vertex and directrix. Construct a hyperbola having an eccentricity of 7/5. Construct a tangent to this hyperbola from a point P which is 40 mm from the directrix, Fig. 8.91.

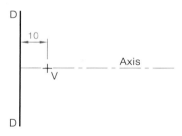

Fig. 8.91

Q5. Construct the triangle P_1P_2F where P_1 and P_2 are points on the curve of a hyperbola and F is its focus. The eccentricity is 10/7, Fig. 8.92.

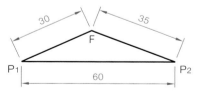

Fig. 8.92

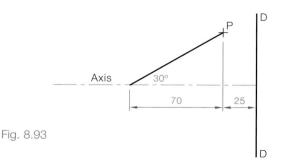

Fig. 8.93

Q6. Given the normal, axis, point of contact and directrix. Find the focus and construct a portion of the curve, Fig. 8.93.

Q7. Given the focus and vertex of a hyperbola having an eccentricity of 1.1. Draw a portion of the curve, Fig. 8.94.

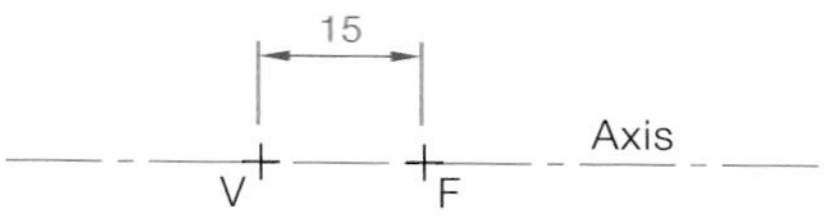

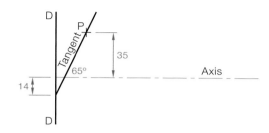

Fig. 8.94

Q8. Given the axis, directrix, tangent and point of contact P. Draw a portion of the hyperbola, Fig. 8.95.

Fig. 8.95

Q9. Given the cone in Fig. 8.96 which is sectioned as shown. Construct the focal sphere and hence find the focus, vertex and directrix of the hyperbola. Draw the hyperbola.

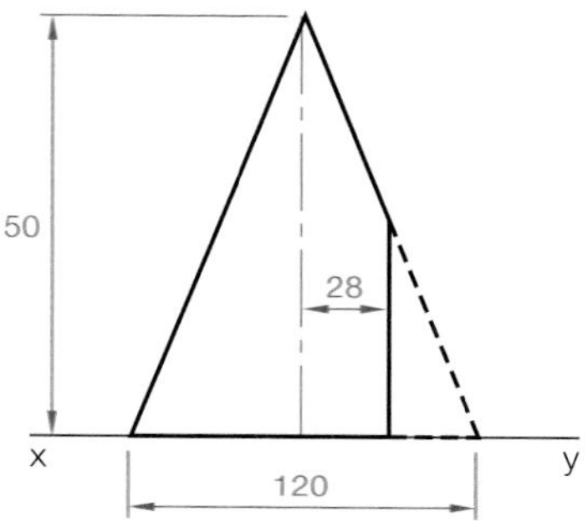

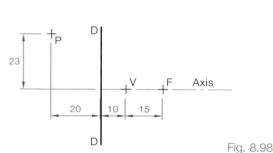

Fig. 8.96

Q10. Construct a double hyperbola in the rectangles shown, Fig. 8.97.

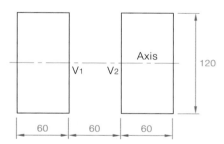

Fig. 8.97

Q11. Given the directrix, vertex, axis and focus. Draw the hyperbola. Construct a tangent to the curve from the given point P, Fig. 8.98.

Fig. 8.98

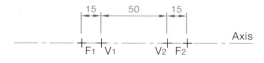

Fig. 8.99

Q12. Given the foci and vertices of a double hyperbola. Construct a portion of each curve. Construct a tangent to the curve from a point 50 mm from F_1, Fig. 8.99.

Q13. Given the transverse axis of 80 mm and the distance between F and V of 20 mm. Construct a double hyperbola, directrices, asymptotes, auxiliary circle and conjugate diameter.

HIGHER LEVEL

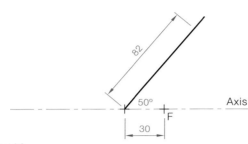

Fig. 8.100

Q14. Given a tangent, point of contact and focus of a double hyperbola. Draw the double curve, Fig. 8.100.

Q15. Given the line P$_1$FP$_2$ as shown in Fig. 8.101. P$_1$ and P$_2$ are points on the curve of a hyperbola, F is the focus and the eccentricity is 7/5. Draw the curve.

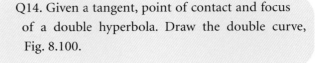

Fig. 8.101

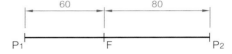

Fig. 8.102

Q16. Given the line FPA as shown in Fig. 8.102. If F is the focus, P is a point on the curve and A is a point on the directrix. Construct the hyperbola if the eccentricity is 6/5.

Q17. Given the triangle FP$_1$P$_2$. F is one of the focal points on a double hyperbola, P$_1$ is a point on one branch of the curve and P$_2$ is a point on the other branch. The transverse axis is 60 mm long. Find the other focal point and draw both curves, Fig. 8.103.

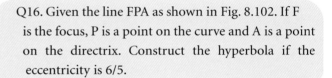

Fig. 8.103

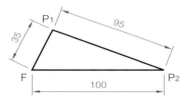

Fig. 8.104

Q18. Given a tangent, the point of contact P and the focal point of a double hyperbola. The transverse axis is 50 mm. Draw a portion of the double hyperbola, Fig. 8.104.

Q19. Given the two focal points of a double hyperbola and a point P on one branch of the curve. Draw the double curve, Fig. 8.105.

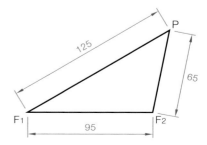

Fig. 8.105

Q20. Given the line P_1FP_2. P_1 and P_2 are points on one branch of a hyperbola and F is its focus. If the transverse axis is 30 mm long construct the double curve, Fig. 8.106.

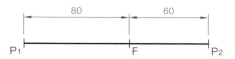

Fig. 8.106

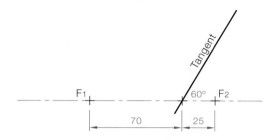

Q21. Given the two focal points and a tangent as shown. Construct the double curve, Fig. 8.107.

Fig. 8.107

Q22. Given two asymptotes and a point P on the curve of a hyperbola. Draw the curve, Fig. 8.108.

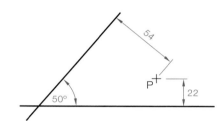

Fig. 8.108

Constructions Common to all Conics

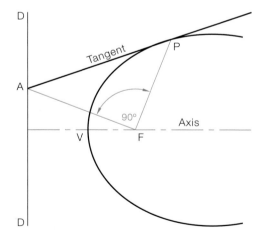

Fig. 8.109

Fig. 8.109

For all conic sections this construction can be used to draw the tangent at a given point P on the curve.

(1) Join P to the focus.

(2) At the focus draw a line FA at 90° to FP. Extend this line to intersect the directrix at A.

(3) Point A is a point on the tangent. Draw the tangent.

Fig. 8.110

Tangents drawn at both ends of a focal chord will always meet on the directrix.

This construction is a follow-on from Fig. 8.109.

P_1FA forms a 90° angle as does P_2FA. These two angles added together make 180°, a straight line, a focal chord.

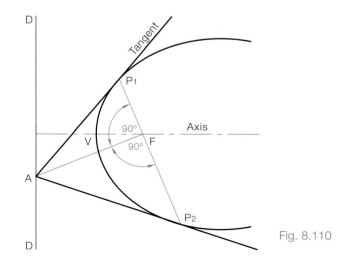

Fig. 8.110

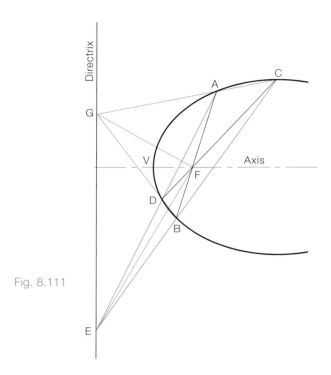

Fig. 8.111

Fig. 8.111

For any two focal chords, when the ends are joined and extended, the lines meet on the directrix.

AC extended and BD extended meet at G on the directrix.

AD extended and CB extended meet at E on the directrix.

Furthermore, the angle GFE will always be 90°.

Fig. 8.112

For any point A outside the curve. Tangents drawn from point A to the curve will give points of contact P_1 and P_2. Angles P_1FA and P_2FA will always be equal.

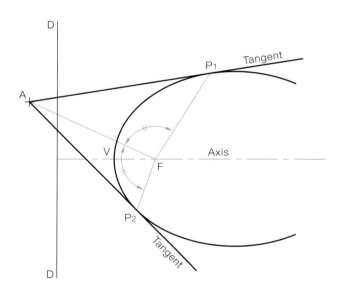

Fig. 8.112

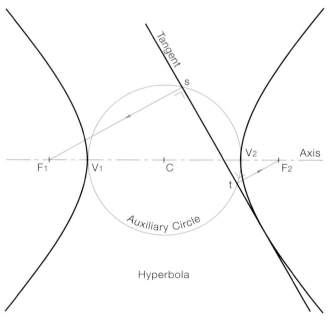

Fig. 8.113

Fig. 8.113

A tangent is drawn to a double hyperbola and will cut through the auxiliary circle in two places, s and t. Perpendicular lines are drawn to the tangent to form these two points. These perpendiculars will always pass through F_1 and F_2, the focal points of the curves. Fig. 8.114

A tangent drawn to an ellipse will cross the major auxiliary circle in two places, s and t. Perpendiculars drawn to the tangent from these two points will always pass through the focal points F_1 and F_2.
Fig. 8.115

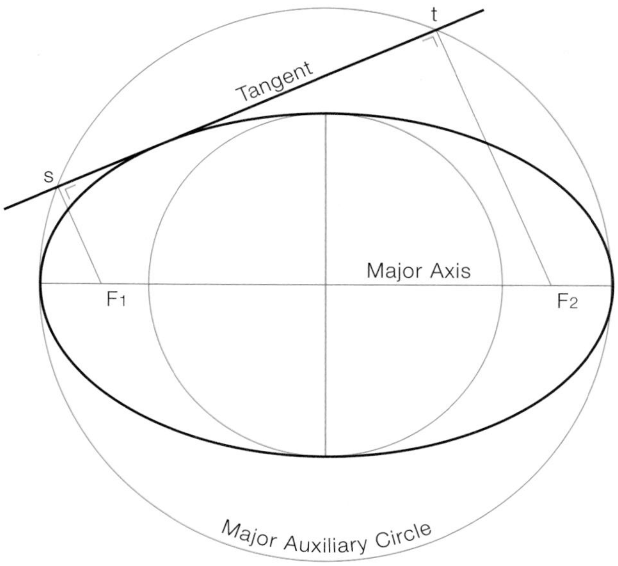

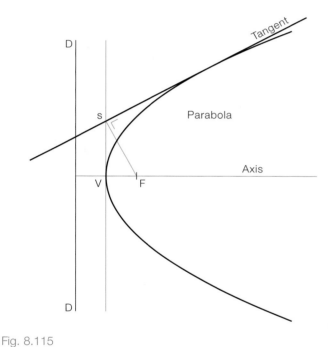

Fig. 8.114

Fig. 8.115

A tangent drawn to the parabola will cross the tangent at the vertex at one point, point s. If a perpendicular is drawn to the tangent at s it will pass through the focus. For a parabola, the tangent at the vertex should be considered as a circle of radius infinity, a small section of which will look like a straight line.

Centre of Curvature and Evolute

The centre of curvature is a specific point inside the curve relating to a specific point P on the curve. If the point of the compass is placed on the centre of curvature C and a radius taken of CP, the curvature of the resulting arc would match the curvature of the conic at point P. Each point on the conic will have its own centre of curvature. If all the centres of curvature are plotted and joined, the resulting path is the evolute of that conic. An evolute is the locus of the centres of curvature.

HIGHER LEVEL

H I G H E R   L E V E L

To draw the centre of curvature for a point P on a parabola. Fig. 8.116

(1) Construct a tangent at point P.
(2) Draw the normal to the tangent.
(3) Join P to the focus and extend.
(4) Where the normal crosses the axis at point A construct a perpendicular to intersect the PF line extended. These lines intersect at B.
(5) At B draw a perpendicular to PB to intersect the normal at C. Point C is the centre of curvature for point P.

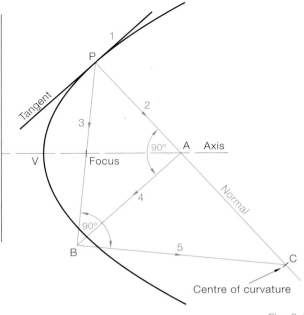

Fig. 8.116

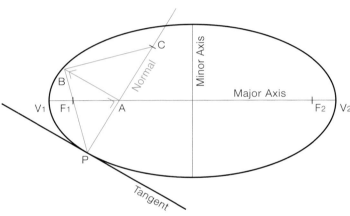

Fig. 8.117

Note: The construction for the centre of curvature for a point P on a hyperbola is the same as above.

To draw the centre of curvature for a point P on an ellipse. Fig. 8.117

(1) The construction for an ellipse is the same as that for a parabola. Construct a tangent at P.
(2) Draw the normal to the tangent.
(3) Join P to F_1 and extend.
(4) Where the normal crosses the major axis at A construct a perpendicular to intersect PF_1 at B. At B construct a perpendicular to intersect the normal at C. C is the centre of curvature for P.

To find the centre of curvature at the vertex of a parabola. Fig. 8.118

The method discussed previously will not work at the vertex. A separate construction must be used.

For a parabola, the distance from V to F will equal the distance from F to C, the centre of curvature.

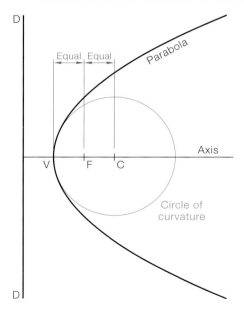

Fig. 8.118

HIGHER LEVEL

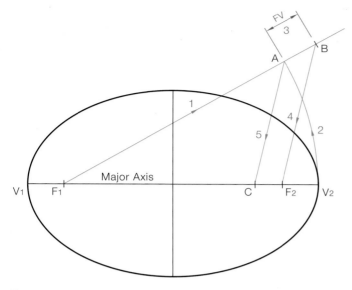

Fig. 8.119

To find the centre of curvature at the vertex of an ellipse. Fig. 8.119

(1) Draw any sloping line from F_1.
(2) With F_1 as centre and radius F_1V_2, draw an arc to hit this line at point A.
(3) Add the distance between the focus and vertex, FV, beyond point A. This locates point B.
(4) Join B to F_2.
(5) Draw a line parallel to BF_2 starting at point A. This locates point C on the axis, the centre of curvature at the vertex.

To find the centre of curvature at the vertex of a hyperbola. Fig. 8.120

(1) Draw any sloping line from F_1.
(2) With F_1 as centre and radius F_1V_2, draw an arc to hit this line at point A.
(3) Step the distance FV past point A to find B.
(4) Join A back to F_2.
(5) From B draw a line parallel to AF_2 finding C the centre of curvature at the vertex.

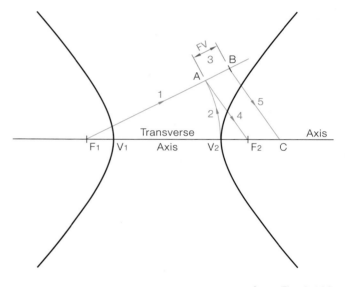

Fig. 8.120

H I G H E R   L E V E L

Parabola

Evolute

Axis

F   V

Evolute

Fig. 8.121

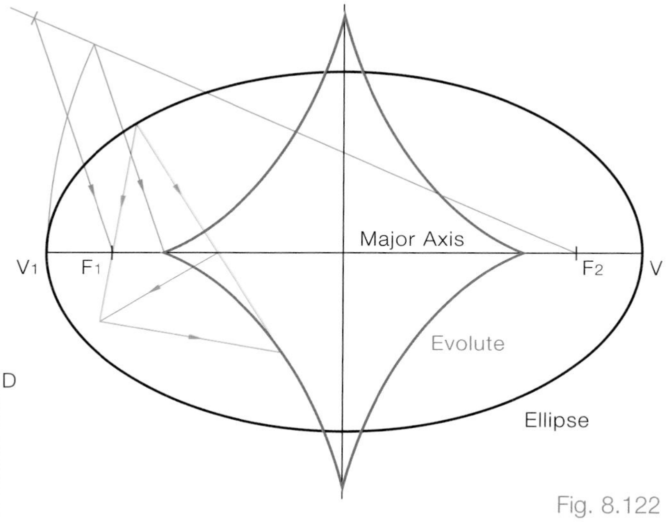

Evolute

Axis

C   F   V

Evolute

FV   V DD

Hyperbola

Fig. 8.123

Locate a number of centres of curvature to plot the locus of the evolute.

The evolute will always be symmetrical about the axis.

Note: To locate the centre of curvature at the vertex of a hyperbola when the second focus is unavailable you can use the construction shown. The ratio CF:FV will be equal to the eccentricity of the curve.

Eccentricity = Focus to point:Point to directrix, or FV:VDD.

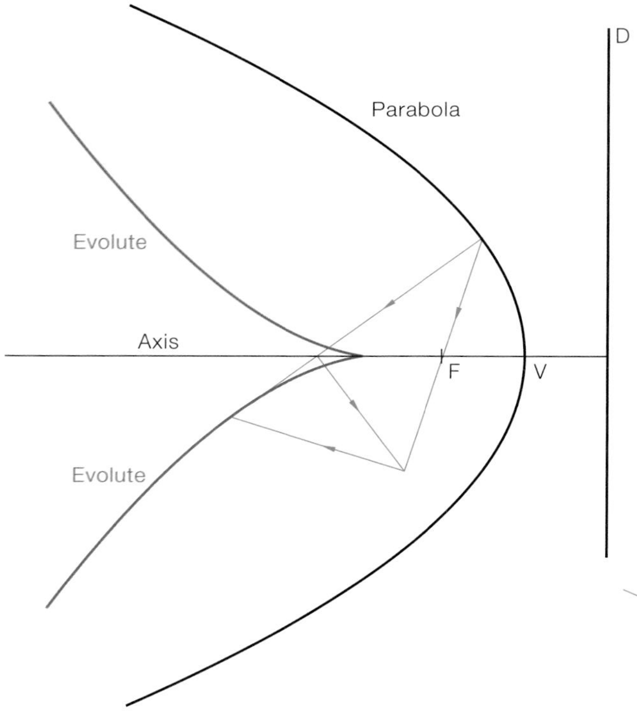

V_1 F_1 Major Axis F_2 V

Evolute

Ellipse

Fig. 8.122

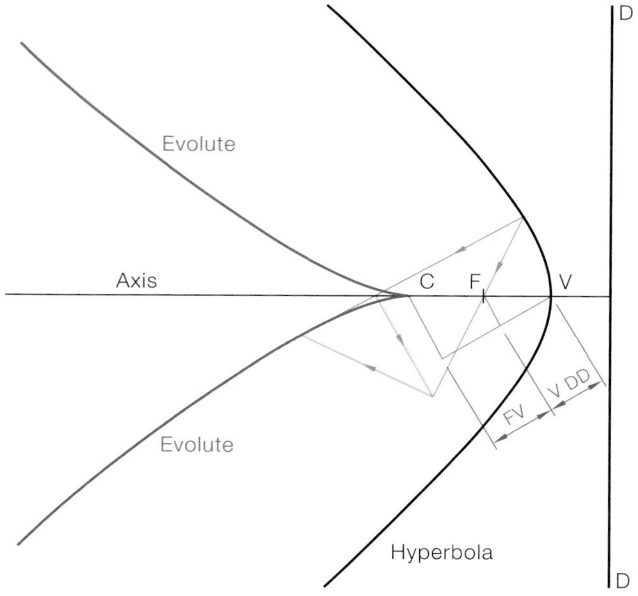

Activities

Q1. Given the vertex, axis and directrix construct the parabola.
Construct a tangent from point P.
Find the centre of curvature for the point of contact, Fig. 8.124.

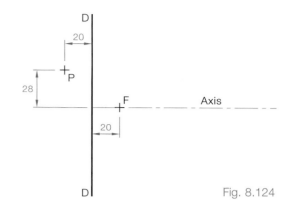

Fig. 8.124

Q2. Draw a parabola having its focus and vertex 18 mm apart. Construct the evolute to this curve.

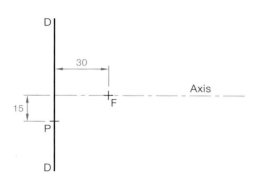

Fig. 8.125

Q3. Given the directrix and focus of an ellipse having an eccentricity of 0.75. Construct a portion of the curve. Draw a tangent to the ellipse from the point P on the directrix. Find the centre of curvature for the point of contact, Fig. 8.125.

Q4. Construct an ellipse having a major axis of 160 mm and a minor axis of 80 mm. Draw the evolute to this curve.

Q5. Given the vertex and focus of a hyperbola having an eccentricity of 6/5. Draw the curve. Draw a tangent to the curve from a point P which is 40 mm from the focus. Find the centre of curvature for point P, Fig. 8.126.

Fig. 8.126

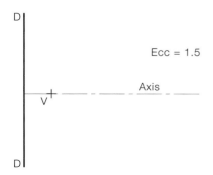

Fig. 8.127

Q6. Given the axis, vertex, directrix and eccentricity of 1.5. Construct a portion of the curve and draw an evolute to it, Fig. 8.127.

AREA 4

DESCRIPTIVE GEOMETRY OF LINES AND PLANES

9 The Oblique Plane

SYLLABUS OUTLINE

Areas to be studied:

• Definition of planes, simply inclined and oblique. • Determination of oblique and *tangent* planes.
• True shape and inclinations of planes to principal planes of reference. • Intersection of oblique planes, lines and *dihedral angle.*
• Sectioning of right solids by oblique planes. • *Treatment of planes as laminar surfaces given rectangular coordinates.*
• *Properties and projections of skew lines.* • *Spatial relationships between lines and planes.*

Learning outcomes

Students should be able to:

Higher and Ordinary levels

- Distinguish between simply inclined and obliquely inclined plane surfaces.
- Determine the angle of inclination between given planes and the principal planes of reference.
- Determine the true length and inclination of given lines.
- Establish the true shape of an obliquely inclined plane.
- Determine the line of intersection between two planes.
- Determine the projections and true shape of sections of solids resulting from simply inclined and oblique cutting planes.

Higher level only

- *Construct obliquely inclined planes given the angles of inclination to the principal planes of reference and to include a given line or point.*
- *Establish the dihedral angle between two intersecting planes.*
- *Display knowledge of the relationships between planes and lines.*
- *Understand the concept of a laminar surface defined by spatial coordinates.*
- *Solve a variety of problems involving the intersection, inclination and positioning of laminar plane surfaces.*
- *Define the concept of skew lines and their use in solving practical problems.*
- *Establish various spatial relationships between skew lines and other lines and planes, including distance, inclination and direction.*

A plane is usually represented by its lines of intersection with the principle planes of reference. These lines are called the **traces** of the plane. The line of intersection between the plane and the vertical plane is called the **vertical trace** and the line of intersection between the plane and horizontal plane is called the **horizontal trace**.

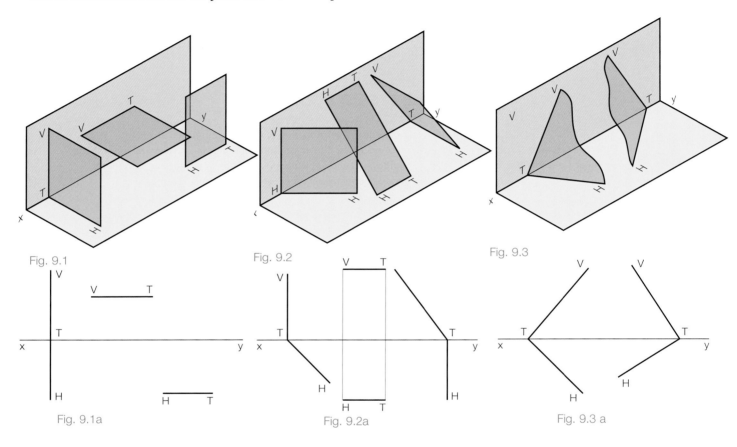

Fig. 9.1

Fig. 9.2

Fig. 9.3

Fig. 9.1a

Fig. 9.2a

Fig. 9.3 a

Given the plan of a point P on an oblique plane VTH. Find the elevation of this point. Fig. 9.4

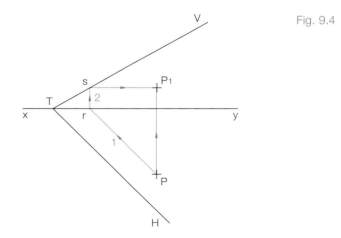

Fig. 9.4

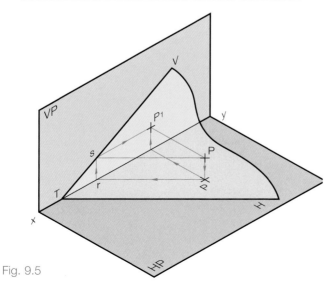

Fig. 9.5

(1) Draw a line parallel to the horizontal trace from point P to hit the xy line at r.

(2) Erect a perpendicular at r to hit the vertical trace at s.

(3) From s, project horizontally (parallel to the xy line).

(4) Project vertically from P in plan to intersect this horizontal thus locating P_1 in elevation, Fig. 9.5.

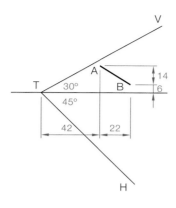

Fig. 9.6

Given the elevation of a line AB on an oblique plane
VTH. Find its plan. Fig. 9.6

(1) From A, project parallel to the VT line to meet the xy
line at r.
(2) Project vertically down from r to s on the HT line.
(3) Project s parallel to the xy line.
(4) Drop a perpendicular from A in elevation to find A_1.
(5) Point B is done in a similar manner, Fig. 9.7.

Lines drawn parallel to the vertical trace in elevation will be
parallel to the xy line in plan.

Lines drawn parallel to the horizontal trace in plan will be
parallel to the xy line in elevation.

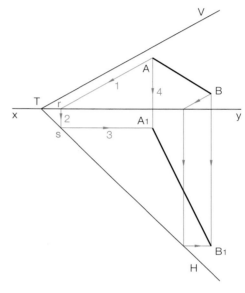

Fig. 9.7

Given the plan of a lamina ABC on an oblique plane
VTH. In plan AB = 32 mm, BC = 55 mm and AC = 44 mm.
Find the elevation. Fig. 9.8

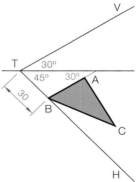

Fig. 9.8

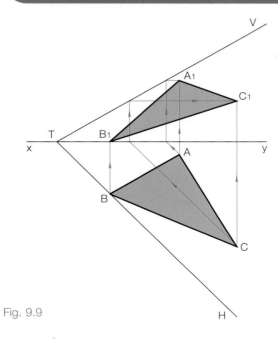

Fig. 9.9

(1) Each point is brought up as in previous examples and
found in elevation.
(2) Index each point and join finding $A_1B_1C_1$ in elevation,
Fig. 9.9.

Point B is on the HT. Since the horizontal trace is the line of
intersection between the oblique plane and the horizontal
trace, every point on the HT will also be on the horizontal
trace.

Given the plan of a figure resting on the oblique plane VTH. Find its elevation. Fig. 9.10

The construction is the same as in previous examples.

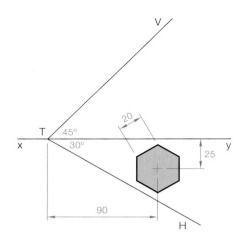

Fig. 9.10

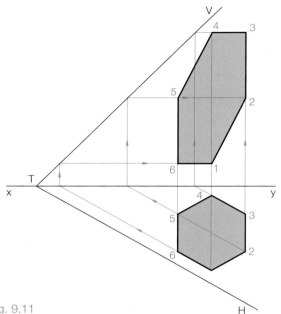

Fig. 9.11

Given the elevation of a figure resting on the oblique plane VTH. Find its plan. Fig. 9.12

Since this figure is not made up of straight lines we must choose points on the curve. In Fig. 9.13 we have chosen eight points. Once the points are found in plan they are joined freehand with a fair curve, Fig. 9.13.

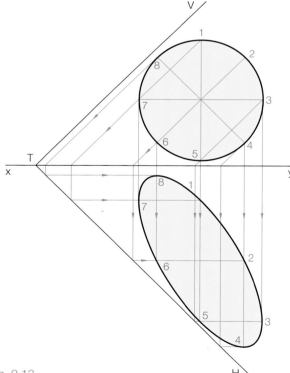

Fig. 9.13

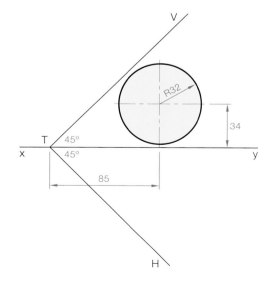

Fig. 9.12

True Inclination of an Oblique Plane to the VP and the HP

To find the true angle, insert a half cone underneath the plane and tangential to it. The base angle of this cone will be the true angle of the plane to the horizontal plane.

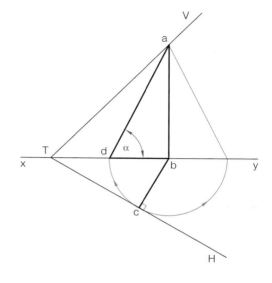

Fig. 9.14

(1) Draw a vertical line ab in elevation.
(2) From b on the xy line, draw a perpendicular to the HT finding c.
(3) Line bc equals the radius of the cone. Draw the half cone in plan.
(4) Draw the elevation of the cone. The base angle of the cone is the true angle of the plane to the horizontal plane, Fig. 9.15.

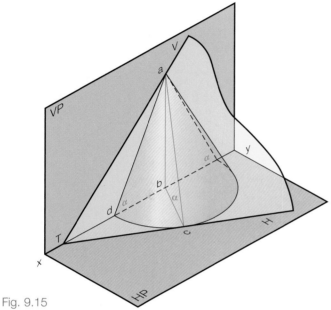

Fig. 9.15

Alternative Method

The true angle an oblique plane makes with the horizontal plane can be found by using an auxiliary elevation. Fig. 9.16

Note: The point P on the oblique plane is usually chosen at position A as it reduces the amount of projection involved.

(1) Choose any point P on the plane in plan and project it to elevation.
(2) Take an auxiliary elevation viewing along the horizontal trace.
(3) x_1y_1 is drawn perpendicular to the line of sight.
(4) The horizontal trace projects as a point view.
(5) Point P is projected to the auxiliary elevation and its height h is taken from the elevation.
(6) The oblique plane is seen as an edge view showing its true angle to the horizontal plane.

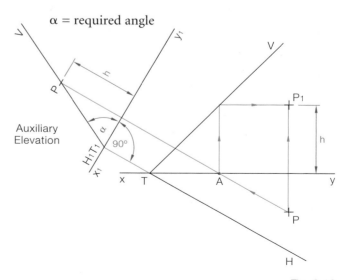

α = required angle

Fig. 9.16

To find the true inclination of an oblique plane to the vertical plane. Fig. 9.17

The construction is similar to Figures 9.14 and 9.15.

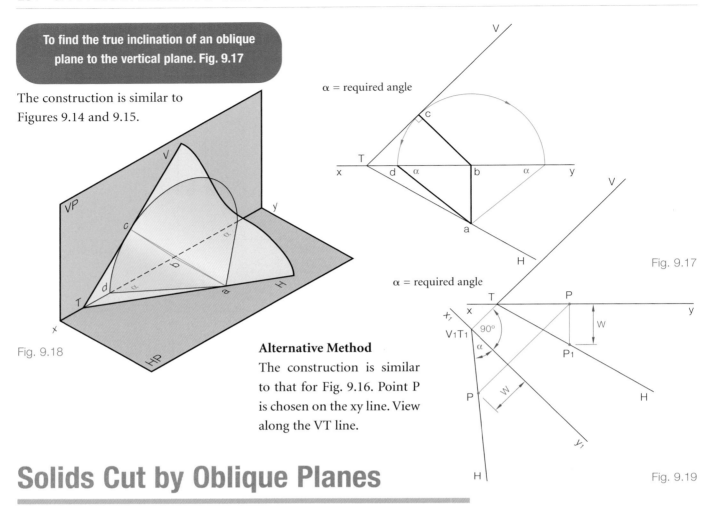

α = required angle

Fig. 9.17

α = required angle

Alternative Method

The construction is similar to that for Fig. 9.16. Point P is chosen on the xy line. View along the VT line.

Fig. 9.18

Fig. 9.19

Solids Cut by Oblique Planes

Given the plan and elevation of a square-based prism and the traces of a plane VTH. Show the projections of the prism when it is cut by the oblique plane VTH. Fig. 9.20

The prism when cut will still look the same in the plan. The cut surface in plan can be projected to elevation as has been explained earlier, Fig. 9.21.

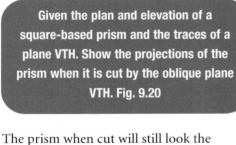

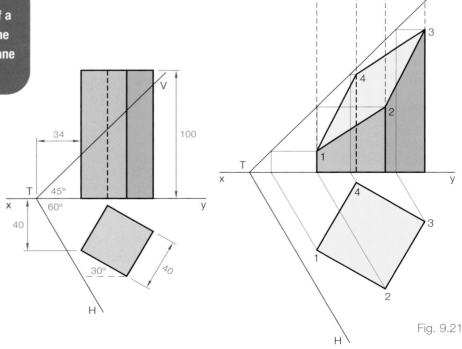

Fig. 9.20

Fig. 9.21

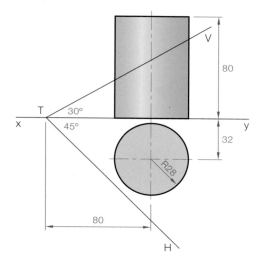

Fig. 9.22

Given the plan and elevation of a cylinder and the traces of a plane VTH. Show the projections of the cylinder when it is cut by the oblique plane VTH. Fig. 9.22

As in the last example, the plan of the solid is unchanged after it has been cut by the plane. Divide the plan up into a number of divisions. Index the points and project each point to elevation as usual, Fig. 9.23.

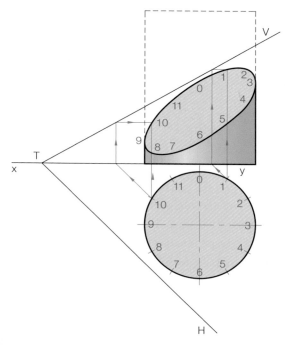

Fig. 9.23

Given the plan and elevation of a square-based pyramid and the traces of a plane VTH. Draw the projections of the solid after it has been cut by the oblique plane. Fig. 9.24

The plan does not show the cut surface in this case. This type of problem is solved by getting an edge view of the oblique plane and hence determining the cut points on the solid.

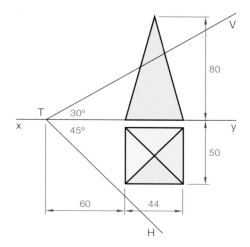

Fig. 9.24

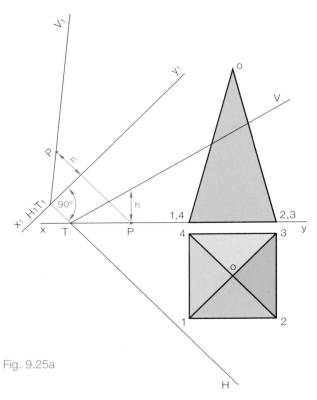

Fig. 9.25a

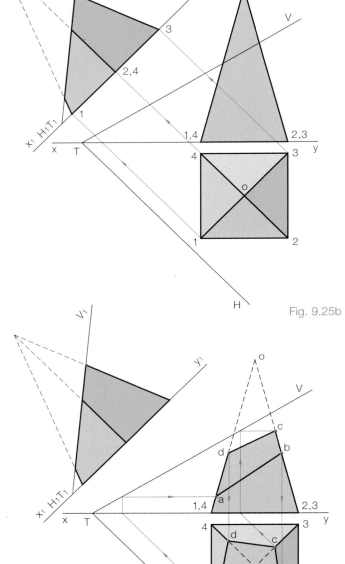

Fig. 9.25b

(1) An edge view of the oblique plane is found by viewing along the horizontal trace. Extend the horizontal trace. Draw the x_1y_1 perpendicular to HT, Fig. 9.25a.

(2) Choose any point P on the xy line and project to the elevation giving height h.

(3) Project P to the auxiliary elevation and use the height h. Draw the edge view of the plane.

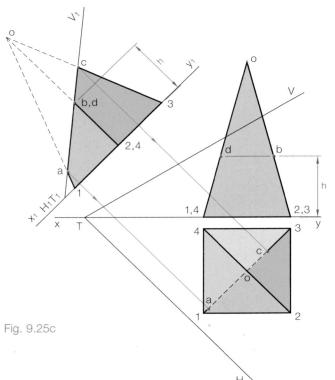

Fig. 9.25c

Fig. 9.25d

(4) Project the auxiliary elevation of the pyramid, Fig. 9.25b.

(5) The auxiliary elevation shows the cut points a, b, c and d. Points a and c are projected to plan, the heights of b and d are used to find them in elevation, Fig. 9.25c.

(6) Complete the plan and elevation by projection, Fig. 9.25d.

Shown in Fig. 26 is a regular hexagonal-based pyramid which is to be cut by the plane VTH. Draw the plan and elevation of the cut solid. Fig. 9.26

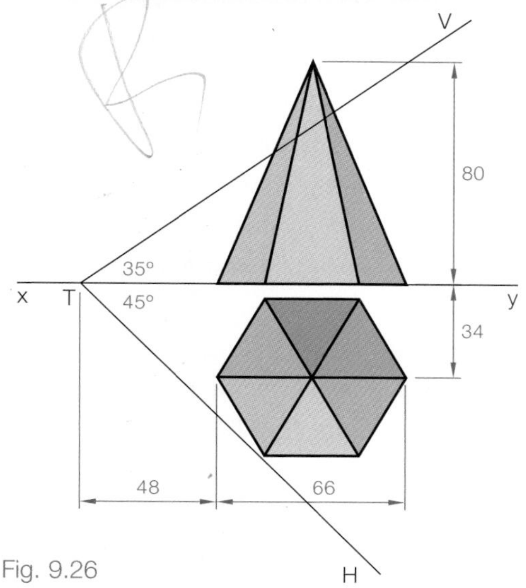

Some points, when projected down from the auxiliary elevation to the plan, do not show a clear intersection, e.g. the point on line 5,0. In cases like this the height of the point can be taken from the auxiliary and used in the elevation to find the point which may then be projected to plan.

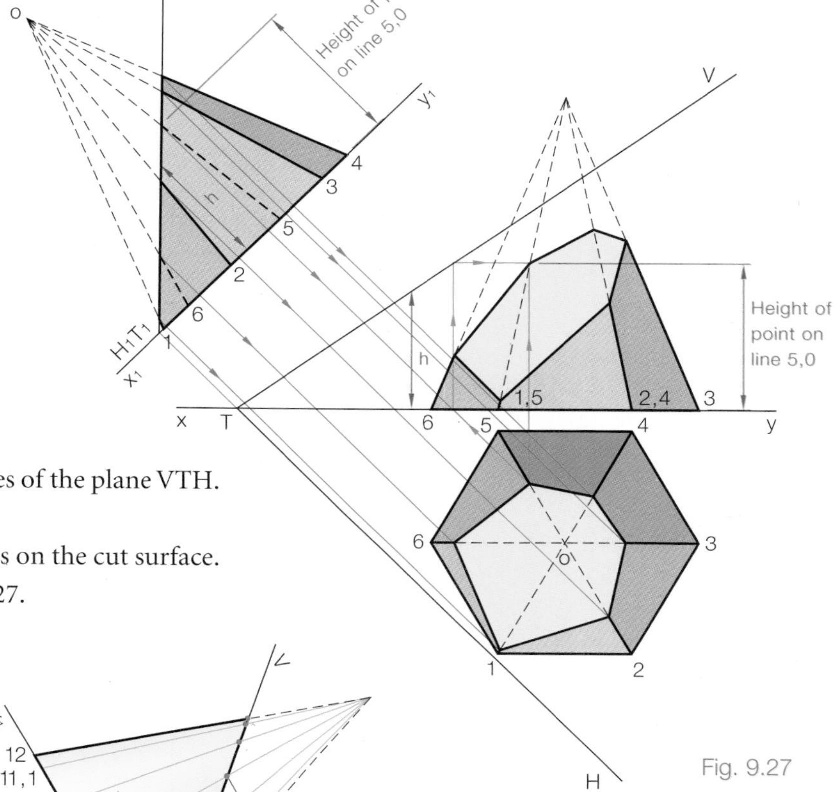

Fig. 9.26

(1) Draw the given plan and elevation and the traces of the plane VTH.
(2) Index the corners.
(3) Project the auxiliary elevation to find the points on the cut surface.
(4) Project to plan and up to the elevation, Fig. 9.27.

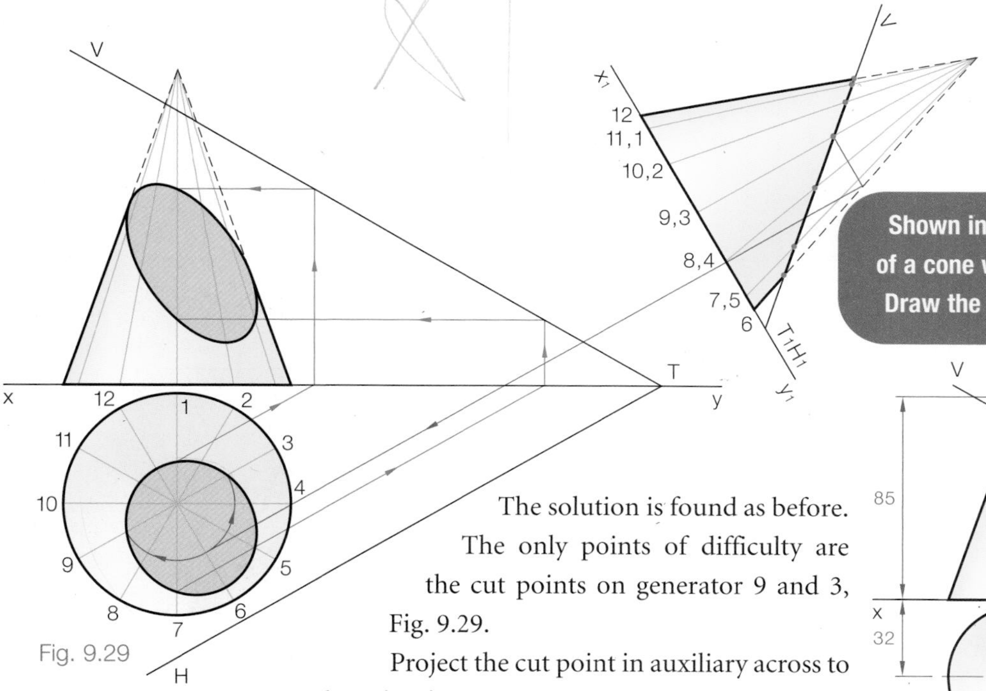

Fig. 9.27

Shown in Fig. 9.28 is the plan and elevation of a cone which is to be cut by the plane VTH. Draw the plan and elevation of the cut solid.

The solution is found as before. The only points of difficulty are the cut points on generator 9 and 3, Fig. 9.29.
Project the cut point in auxiliary across to the side of the cone, generator 6. Project to plan on generator 6 and rotate onto generator 9 and 3. The cut points on generators 1 and 7 in plan must be projected around via the xy line and VT as shown.

Fig. 9.29

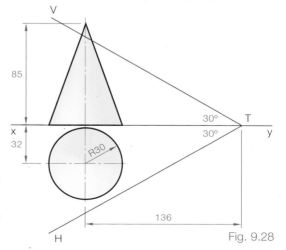

Fig. 9.28

To Find the True Shape of an Object on an Oblique Plane

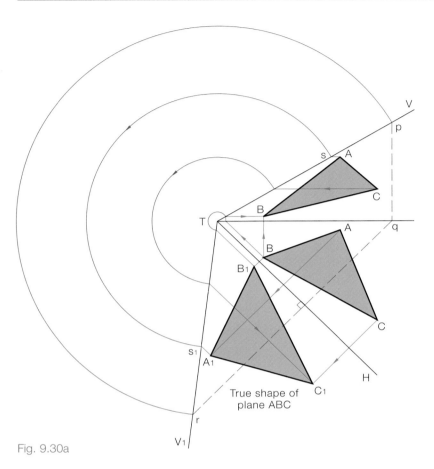

Fig. 9.30a

Method 1: Rebatment of the Plane

Fig. 9.30a

What is happening here is that the plane is rotated onto the horizontal plane and is hinged about the horizontal trace HT.

(1) From any point p on the vertical trace drop a vertical to the xy line giving q.

(2) Draw a perpendicular to the horizontal trace from q and extend.

(3) With centre T and radius Tp rotate to cut this perpendicular giving r.

(4) Join r to T giving V_1HT, the rebatted plane.

To find the triangle on the rebatted plane:

(1) From point A in elevation project horizontally to the VT giving s.

(2) With T as centre rotate point s to V_1T giving s_1.

(3) Project s_1 parallel to the HT.

(4) From A in plan project across perpendicular to the HT to locate A_1.

(5) Repeat for the other points.

Method 2: Rebatment of the Plane

Fig. 9.30b

This is very similar to Method 1.

(1) Rebat the plane as before.

(2) Project A in plan parallel to the HT to give point s on the xy line.

(3) Project s perpendicular to the HT to give s_1 on the V_1T line.

(4) Project s_1 parallel to the HT.

(5) Project from A in the plan, perpendicular to the HT to locate A_1.

(6) Repeat for other points.

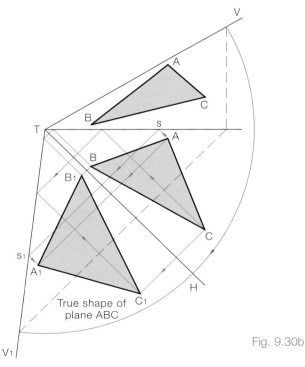

Fig. 9.30b

Method 3: Auxiliary Elevation and Rebatment

Fig. 9.31

An edge view of the oblique plane is found and the plane can
  then be easily rebatted onto the horizontal plane.

(1) View along the HT to see the plane as an edge view.
  Extend the horizontal trace.

(2) Draw x_1y_1 perpendicular to the HT line extended.

(3) Choose any point p on the xy line and project to the
  auxiliary.

(4) Find the height of point p from the elevation, height h,
  and measure on the auxiliary.

(5) Draw the plane in the auxiliary V_1TH.

(6) Project the triangular surface ABC to the auxiliary.

(7) Rotate the points A_1B_1C in the auxiliary, about point T,
  onto the x_1y_1 line.

(8) Project back to plan.

(9) Project from the plan perpendicular to the HT to locate
  the points A_2B_2 and C_2.

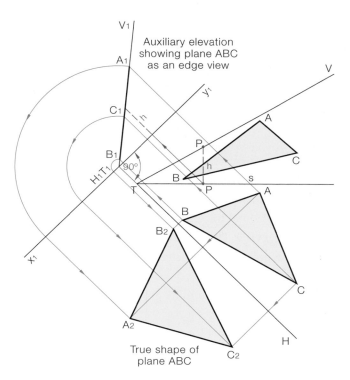

Fig. 9.31

Method 4: Second Auxiliary Plan

Fig. 9.32

(1) Set up the auxiliary view as before.

(2) Draw x_1y_1 parallel to $V_1T_1H_1$.

(3) Project points $A_1B_1C_1$ perpendicular to x_2y_2.

(4) The distance from x_1y_1 to A is taken and used to locate A_2.

(5) Similar for B_2 and C_2.

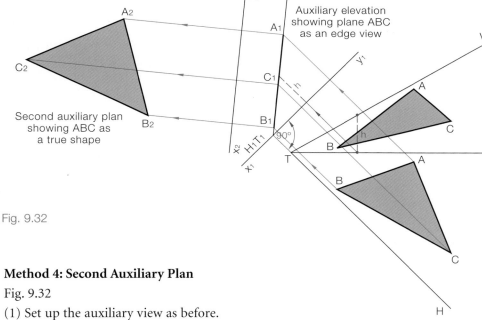

Fig. 9.32

Worked Examples

Fig. 9.33 shows the elevation and plan of a regular hexagonal prism. The solid is cut by the oblique plane VTH.
(i) Draw the plan and elevation of the solid when it is cut by the oblique plane VTH.
(ii) Draw the true shape of the cut surface of the prism.

(1) Draw the given views.
(2) Project an auxiliary elevation viewing in the direction of the horizontal trace. This will show the oblique plane as an edge view. The cut points 1, 2, 3 and 4 are found.
(3) These points are projected to plan, giving two point 1's and two point 2's.
(4) The elevation is found by projection.

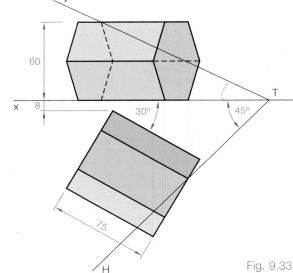

Fig. 9.33

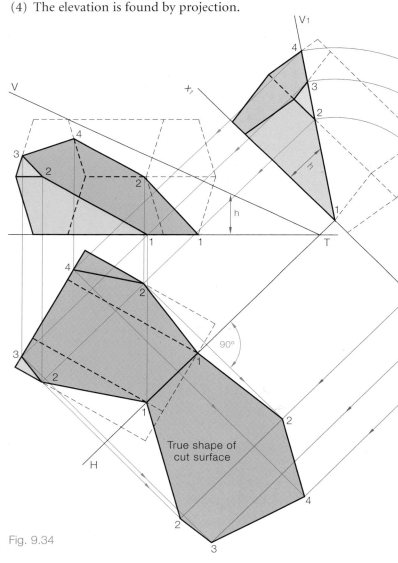

Fig. 9.34

True shape of cut surface

(5) The true shape is found by rebatting the plane onto the x_1y_1 in the auxiliary view.
(6) Project the points down from the auxiliary parallel to the HT.
(7) Project the points across from the plan perpendicular to the HT.
(8) Plot the points on the true shape, Fig. 9.34.

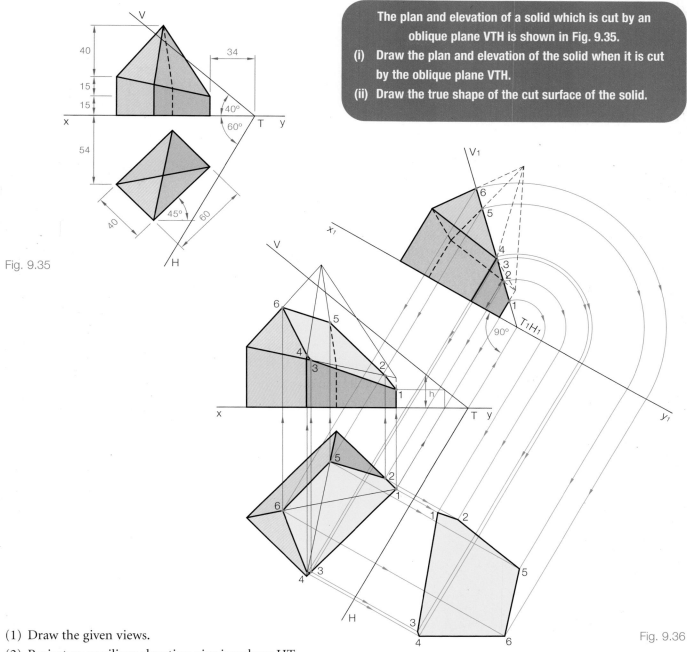

The plan and elevation of a solid which is cut by an oblique plane VTH is shown in Fig. 9.35.
(i) Draw the plan and elevation of the solid when it is cut by the oblique plane VTH.
(ii) Draw the true shape of the cut surface of the solid.

Fig. 9.35

Fig. 9.36

(1) Draw the given views.
(2) Project an auxiliary elevation viewing along HT.
(3) Draw the solid in the auxiliary thus determining six points on the cut surface.
(4) Project the points down from the auxiliary. Point 1 is on a vertical and will be in the corner in plan.
(5) Project all points to elevation. Point 1 being on a vertical, may not be projected directly, but must be brought parallel to the HT to the xy line, vertically to the VT and then horizontally.
(6) The true shape is found by rebatting the oblique plane in the auxiliary, Fig. 9.36.

FINDING THE TRACES OF A PLANE

> **Given the plan and elevation of a lamina ABC. Find the traces of the plane that contains this lamina. Fig 9.37**

(1) Draw the plan and elevation as given.

(2) In elevation extend an edge, e.g. CA, until it hits the xy line and the horizontal plane at point p.

(3) Extend line CA in plan also.

(4) Drop point p to hit CA in plan, at point q. Point q is on the horizontal trace.

(5) Repeat this process for another edge, e.g. CB. This will find point s which is also on the horizontal trace.

(6) Join s and q and extend to the xy line. This is the horizontal trace.

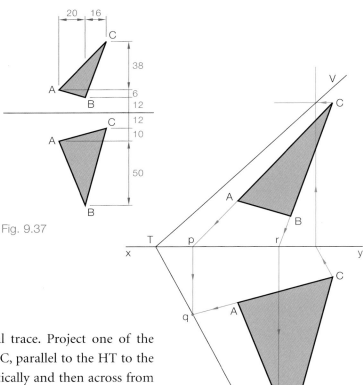

Fig. 9.37

Fig. 9.38

(7) To find the vertical trace. Project one of the points in plan, e.g. C, parallel to the HT to the xy line. Project vertically and then across from the elevation. The intersection point of these two lines is a point on the vertical trace. Draw the trace, Fig. 9.38.

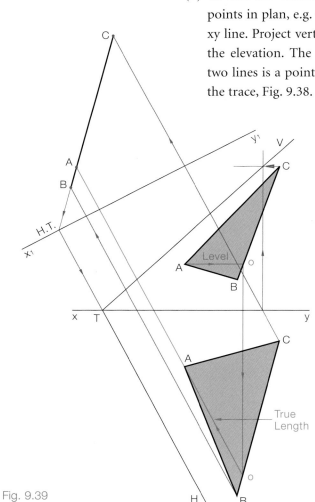

Fig. 9.39

Alternative Method

Fig. 9.39

(1) Draw the plan and elevation.

(2) In elevation draw a level line across the surface. Line AO for example.

(3) Find this line in plan. Point O is projected to plan and is found on edge CB. Join point O to corner A.

(4) View in the direction of OA and project an auxiliary elevation. The lamina projects as an edge view because we are viewing along a true length on its surface.

(5) Extend the edge view in auxiliary to the x_1y_1 line thus giving a point view of the HT. Project the horizontal trace back to plan.

(6) Find the vertical trace as above.

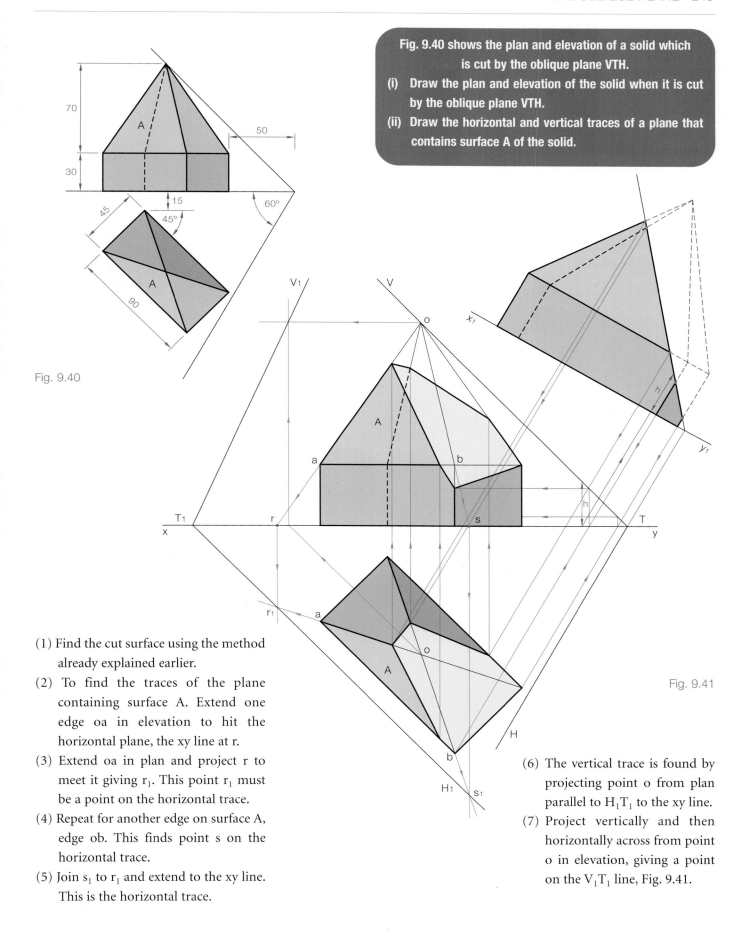

Fig. 9.40

Fig. 9.41 shows the plan and elevation of a solid which is cut by the oblique plane VTH.

(i) Draw the plan and elevation of the solid when it is cut by the oblique plane VTH.
(ii) Draw the horizontal and vertical traces of a plane that contains surface A of the solid.

Fig. 9.41

(1) Find the cut surface using the method already explained earlier.

(2) To find the traces of the plane containing surface A. Extend one edge oa in elevation to hit the horizontal plane, the xy line at r.

(3) Extend oa in plan and project r to meet it giving r_1. This point r_1 must be a point on the horizontal trace.

(4) Repeat for another edge on surface A, edge ob. This finds point s on the horizontal trace.

(5) Join s_1 to r_1 and extend to the xy line. This is the horizontal trace.

(6) The vertical trace is found by projecting point o from plan parallel to H_1T_1 to the xy line.

(7) Project vertically and then horizontally across from point o in elevation, giving a point on the V_1T_1 line, Fig. 9.41.

INTERSECTING OBLIQUE PLANES

The diagram, Fig. 9.42, shows a pictorial view of the planes of reference and two intersecting oblique planes.

When two planes intersect the line of intersection will always be a straight line.

It should be noted from the diagram that the intersection of the two horizontal traces HT and H_1T_1 at p gives one end of the line of intersection. Similarly the intersection of the two vertical traces at q gives the other end of the line of intersection.

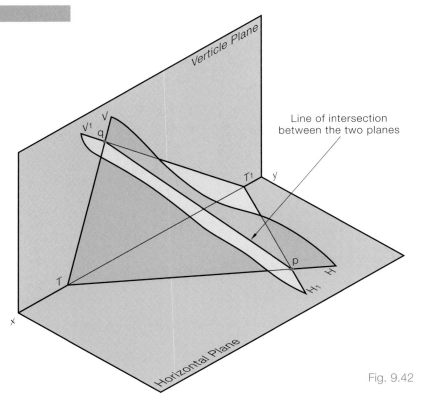

Fig. 9.42

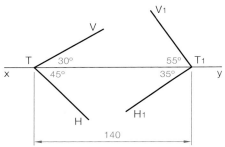

Fig. 9.43a

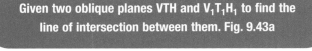

Given two oblique planes VTH and $V_1T_1H_1$ to find the line of intersection between them. Fig. 9.43a

(1) Extend the vertical traces until they intersect at q.
(2) Extend the horizontal traces until they intersect at p. Point q is the elevation of one end of the line of intersection and point p is the plan of the other end.
(3) Project p to elevation (xy line) and join to q.
(4) Project q to plan (xy line) and join to p, Fig. 9.43b.

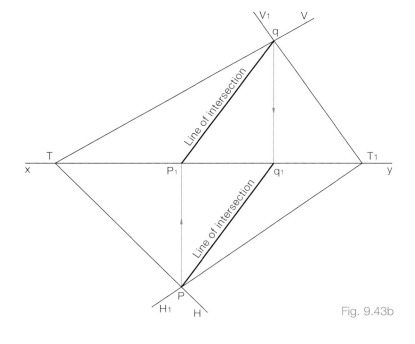

Fig. 9.43b

To find the true length of the line of intersection between two oblique planes.

(1) Find the line of intersection as above.
(2) Consider pq as the hypotenuse of a right-angled triangle that stands vertically underneath the line of intersection. Rotate this triangle until it lies horizontally, thus showing the true length of the line pq, Fig. 9.44.

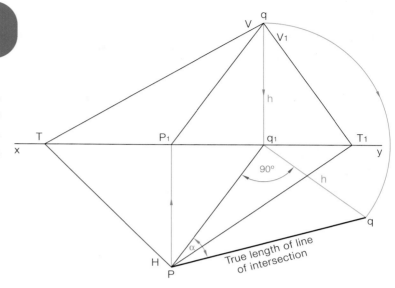

Fig. 9.44

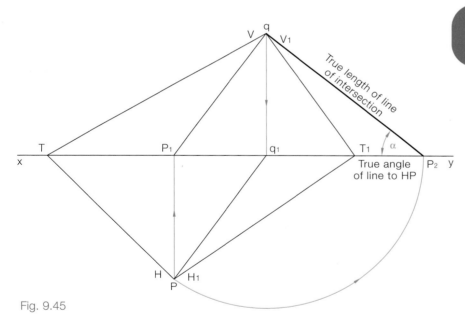

Fig. 9.45

Alternative method of finding the true length of the line of intersection. Fig. 9.45

(1) With the compass on q_1 rotate point p to p_2 on the xy line.
(2) Join p_2 to q giving the true length of the line of intersection.

Note: In both methods the true angle, α, that the line makes with the horizontal plane is also found.

Activities

Q1. Given the traces of an oblique plane VTH and the plan of a regular pentagon, which rests on the plane. Draw the given plan and project the elevation, Fig. 9.46.

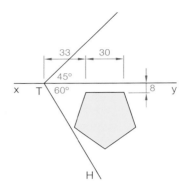

Fig. 9.46

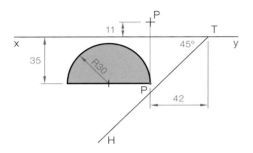

Fig. 9.47

Q2. Given the plan of a figure resting on an oblique plane of which you are given the horizontal trace. Also given is the elevation of the corner P. Find the vertical trace and complete the views, Fig. 9.47.

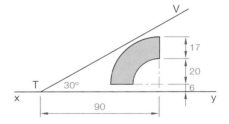

Fig. 9.48

Q3. Given the elevation of an object resting on an oblique plane VTH. Also, given the VT and the true angle the plane makes with the vertical as 60°. Find the HT and complete the plan, Fig. 9.48

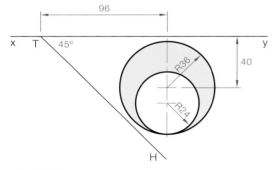

Fig. 9.49

Q4. Given the plan of a figure resting on an oblique plane VTH. Also, given the HT and the true angle the plane makes with the horizontal plane as 50°. Find the VT and project the elevation, Fig. 9.49.

Q5. Given the plan of a tetrahedron resting on the horizontal plane and the traces of a plane VTH. Draw the projections of the solid when it is cut by the plane, Fig. 9.50.

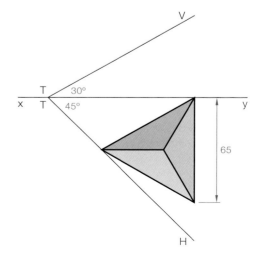

Fig. 9.50

Q6. Given a square-based pyramid which is to be cut by the oblique plane VTH. Draw the plan and elevation of the cut solid, Fig. 9.5[1].

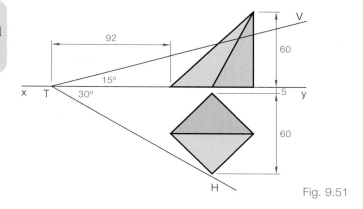

Fig. 9.51

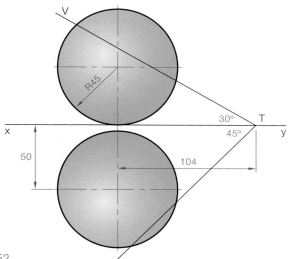

Fig. 9.52

Q7. Given the plan and elevation of a sphere to draw its projections when it is cut by the oblique plane VTH, Fig. 9.52.

Q8. Given the plan and elevation of a cone having its base resting on the VP. Draw the plan and elevation of this cone when it is cut by the oblique plane VTH, Fig. 9.53.

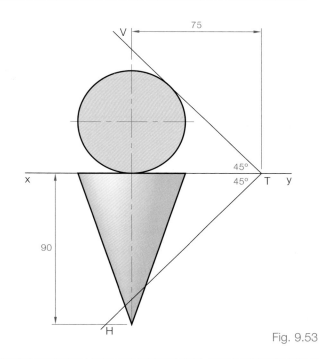

Fig. 9.53

SECTIONS AND TRUE SHAPES

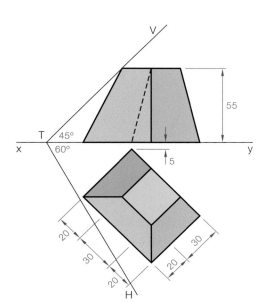

Fig. 9.54

Q9. The elevation and plan of a solid which is to be cut by the oblique plane VTH is shown in Fig. 9.54.
(i) Draw the elevation and plan of the solid when it is cut by the oblique plane VTH.
(ii) Draw the true shape of the cut surface.

Q10. Fig. 9.55 shows the elevation and plan of a solid that is cut by the oblique plane VTH.

(i) Draw the plan and elevation of the solid when it is cut by the oblique plane VTH.

(ii) Draw the true shape of the cut surface.

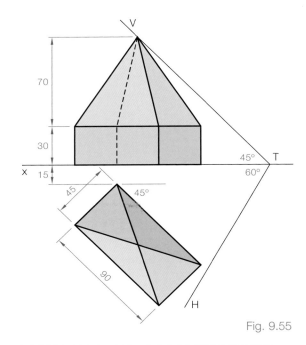

Fig. 9.55

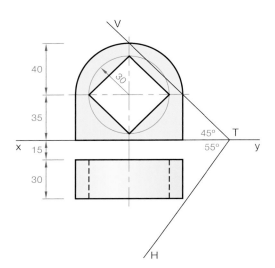

Fig. 9.56

Q11. Fig. 9.56 shows the elevation and plan of a solid which is to be cut by the plane VTH.

(i) Draw the plan and elevation of the solid when it is cut by the oblique plane VTH.

(ii) Draw the true shape of the cut surface of the solid.

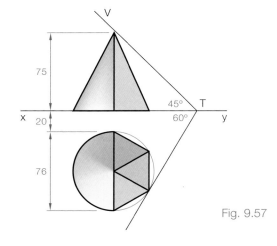

Fig. 9.57

Q12. The plan and elevation of a solid which is to be cut by the oblique plane VTH.

(i) Draw the plan and elevation of the cut solid.

(ii) Draw the true shape of the cut surface, Fig. 9.57.

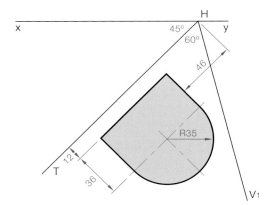

Fig. 9.58

Q13. Fig. 9.58 shows the rebatment of an oblique plane which contains a plane figure. Find the VT and the plan and elevation of the figure.

Q14. The object shown in Fig. 9.59 is to be cut by the oblique plane VTH.
(i) Draw the plan and elevation of the cut solid.
(ii) Draw the true shape of the cut solid.

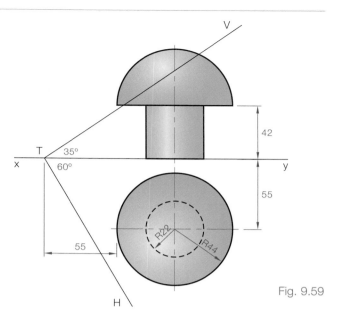

Fig. 9.59

Given two planes VTH and $V_1T_1H_1$. Find the line of intersection between the planes. Determine the dihedral angle between the two planes. Fig. 9.60

(1) Find the line of intersection in plan and elevation.
(2) Find the true length of the line of intersection.
(3) At any point c on the true length draw a perpendicular to the length giving cab. The line cab represents the edge view of the triangle which fits between the planes and measure the dihedral angle.
(4) Rebat the triangle onto the horizontal plane by rotating vertex c as shown. Edge ab is perpendicular to the plan of the line of intersection.

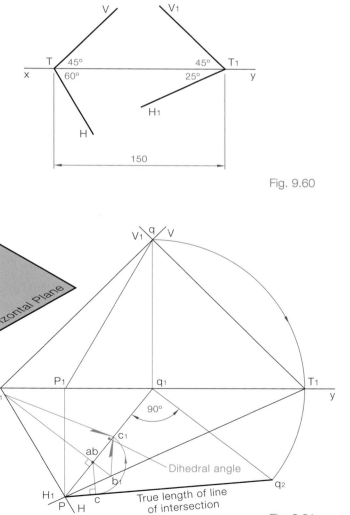

Fig. 9.60

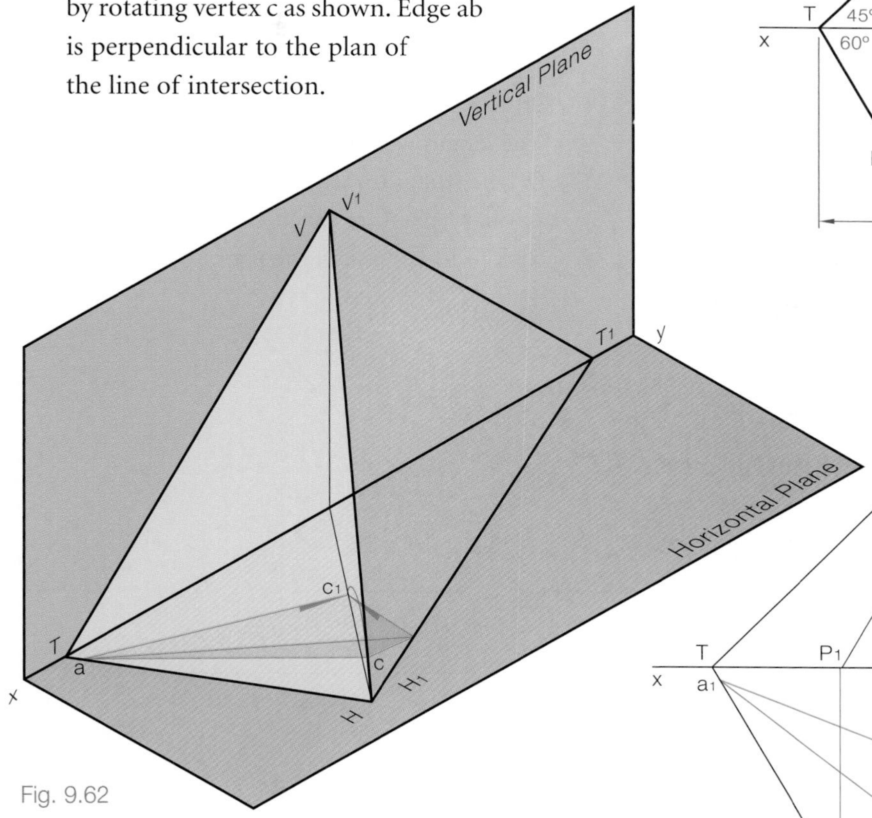

Fig. 9.62

(5) Angle acb is the required dihedral angle, Figures 9.61 and 9.62.

Fig. 9.61

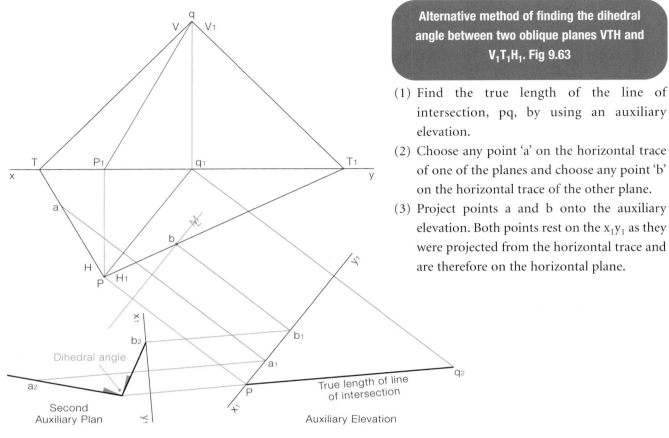

Fig. 9.63

Alternative method of finding the dihedral angle between two oblique planes VTH and V₁T₁H₁. Fig 9.63

(1) Find the true length of the line of intersection, pq, by using an auxiliary elevation.
(2) Choose any point 'a' on the horizontal trace of one of the planes and choose any point 'b' on the horizontal trace of the other plane.
(3) Project points a and b onto the auxiliary elevation. Both points rest on the x_1y_1 as they were projected from the horizontal trace and are therefore on the horizontal plane.

(4) Project a second auxiliary plan viewing along the true length which will show pq as a point view.
(5) In the diagram the distances for the second auxiliary plan are taken from the measuring line back to the points in the plan.

To draw the traces of a plane VTH given the inclination to the horizontal plane as 60° and the inclination to the vertical plane as 45°. Fig. 9.64

(1) Draw a circle having its centre on the xy line.
(2) Draw a cone in elevation of base angle 60°, tangential to this sphere. Draw the cone in plan.
(3) Draw a cone in plan of base angle 45° tangential to the sphere.
(4) The traces of the required plane will pass through the vertex of each cone and be tangential to the base of each cone.

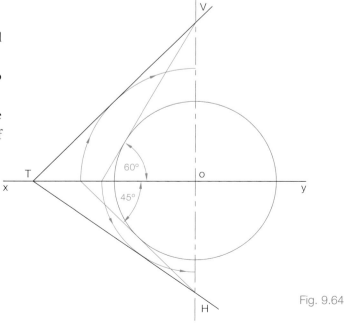

Fig. 9.64

(1) Using P as the apex of the cone in elevation draw a cone with base angle of 60°.

(2) Draw the plan of this cone. The horizontal trace must be tangential to this cone in plan.

(3) Draw the hemisphere that fits under this cone and is tangential to it. Find the plan of the hemisphere.

(4) The angle required to the vertical plane is 45°. Draw a line at 45° to the xy line in plan that is tangential to the plan of the hemisphere. This line intersects the centre line of the cone and hemisphere at point s. Point s is a point on the HT line

(5) Draw the HT from s, tangential to the plan of the cone.

(6) The VT line can be found by projecting the cone apex parallel to the HT to xy. Then vertically and horizontally across in elevation to find a point on the vertical trace.

(7) Alternatively the VT line can be found by drawing it tangentially to the 45° angle rotated about point o, Fig. 9.66.

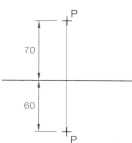

Fig. 9.65

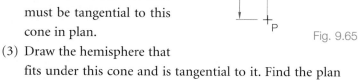

Given the plan and elevation of a point P. Find the traces of a plane that contains point P and is inclined at 60° to the HP and 45° to the VP. Fig. 9.65

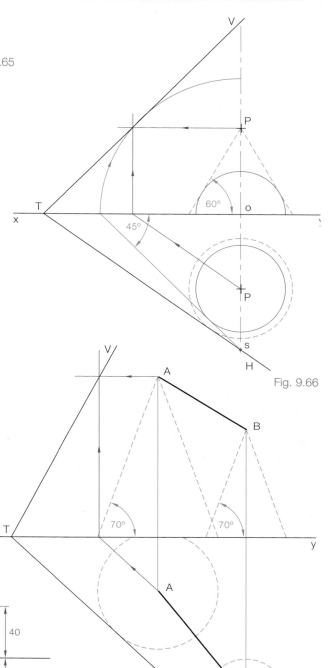

Fig. 9.66

Given the projections of a line AB. Find the traces of the oblique plane that contains line AB and is inclined at 70° to the horizontal plane. Fig. 9.67

(1) Draw the plan and elevation of the line as given.

(2) Draw the plan and elevation of a cone of base angle 70°, resting on the horizontal plane and having its vertex at A.

(3) Draw a similar cone having B as vertex.

(4) The HT line will be tangential to the cones in plan.

(5) The VT line is found by projecting the vertex of either cone parallel to the HT as far as the xy line. Then projecting vertically and across horizontally in elevation to find a point on the VT which can then be drawn in, Fig. 9.68.

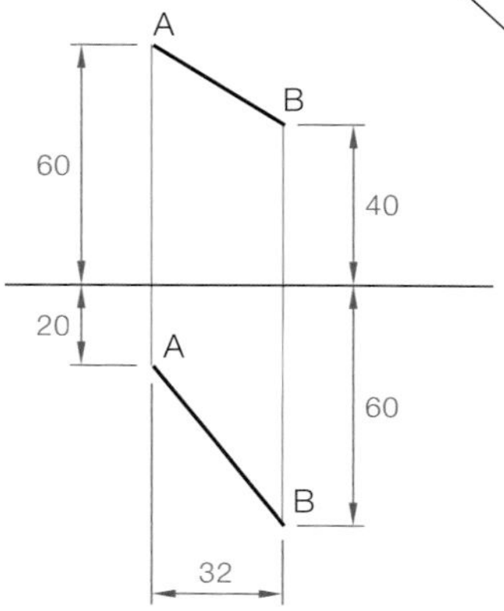

Fig. 9.67

Fig. 9.68

HIGHER LEVEL

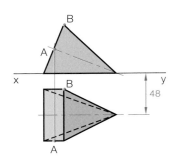

Fig. 9.69

(1) Draw the plan and elevation of the solid resting on its base.
(2) Rotate the solid onto its side.
(3) Locate points A and B in plan and elevation.
(4) Draw cones of base angle 60° having A as apex and B as apex.
(5) The horizontal trace will be tangential to the base circles in plan.
(6) The vertical trace is then found in the usual way, Fig. 9.70.

Fig. 9.69 shows the projections of a right square-based pyramid resting on the horizontal plane as shown. The pyramid is to be cut by an oblique plane which is inclined at 60° to the horizontal plane and passes through points A and B. Draw the projections of the cut pyramid.
Pyramid base = 60 mm, Altitude = 75 mm.

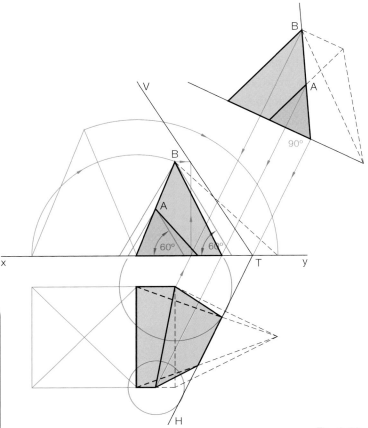

Fig. 9.70

Fig. 9.71 shows the plan of a triangular pyramid abco resting on the horizontal plane. The three sloping surfaces of the pyramid are inclined at 60° to the horizontal plane and the cut surface is inclined at 30° to the horizontal plane.
(i)   Draw the plan and elevation of the cut solid.
(ii) Find the dihedral angle between the cut surface and surface S.

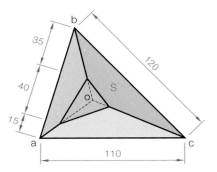

Fig. 9.71

(1) Draw the plan outline. Since the three sloping surfaces of the pyramid have equal inclinations to the HP the lines ao, bo and co will bisect the angles.
(2) The height of the pyramid is found by drawing an auxiliary to show an edge view of one of the surfaces and using the given inclination and the projection of the apex o. Draw the elevation.
(3) Locate points 1 and 2 in plan and elevation, Fig. 9.72.
(4) Place cones, of base angle 30°, underneath points 1 and 2 and having them at their apex.
(5) The horizontal trace of the cut surface will be tangential to the cone base circles. Project an auxiliary viewing along the HT line. This will show the cut point 3 on the line co. Complete the plan and elevation.

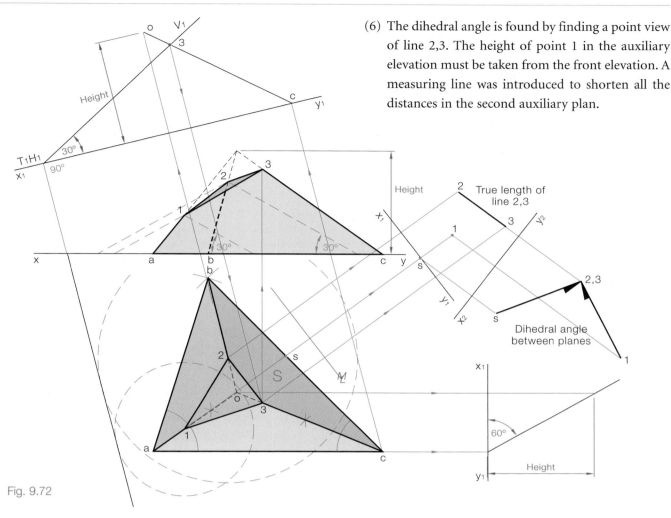

(6) The dihedral angle is found by finding a point view of line 2,3. The height of point 1 in the auxiliary elevation must be taken from the front elevation. A measuring line was introduced to shorten all the distances in the second auxiliary plan.

Fig. 9.72

Spatial Coordinates

All points in space can be defined by their coordinates. When dealing with three dimensions it is necessary to define a point using three coordinates, x, y and z. With reference to Fig. 9.73 we can see how point P can be established relative to a datum line, the horizontal plane and the vertical plane.

The first coordinate, coordinate x, refers to the distance to the right of the datum line. The second coordinate, coordinate y, refers to the distance the point P is above the horizontal plane. The third distance, coordinate z, refers to the distance point P is in front of the vertical plane.

Since we can define points in space using coordinates we can also define lines and planes using the same method.

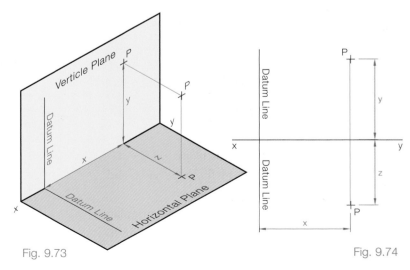

Fig. 9.73

Fig. 9.74

Given the coordinates of a laminar surface. To draw the plan and elevation of that surface Fig. 9.75

A	=	120	48	12
B	=	72	15	30
C	=	84	43	54

(1) Draw the xy line and a vertical reference line.
(2) To find point A measure 120 mm to the right of the reference line and draw a light vertical.
(3) Measure 48 mm above the xy line and mark A in elevation.
(4) Measure 12 mm below the xy line and mark A in plan.

x	y	z
120	48	12
→	↑	↓

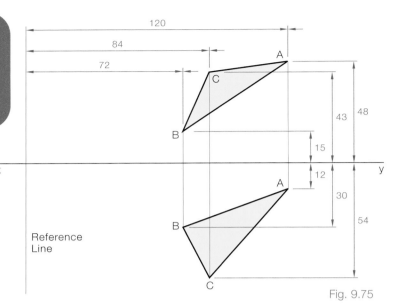

Fig. 9.75

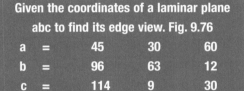

Fig. 9.76

Given the coordinates of a laminar plane abc to find its edge view. Fig. 9.76

a	=	45	30	60
b	=	96	63	12
c	=	114	9	30

(1) Draw the plan and elevation of the triangle.
(2) Draw a level line in elevation and project to plan.
(3) The level line in elevation will project as a true length in plan. View in the direction of the true length and project an auxiliary elevation. The plane will appear as an edge view.

Given the coordinates of a laminar plane abc, to find its true shape. Fig. 9.77

a	=	33	33	6
b	=	66	8	8
c	=	108	45	36

(1) Draw the plan and elevation.
(2) Find an edge view of the plane.
(3) Draw x_2y_2 parallel to the edge view and project the three points.
(4) The distances for the second auxiliary plan are found by measuring from x_1y_1 back to the plan or from a measuring line which is parallel to the x_1y_1 back to the plan.

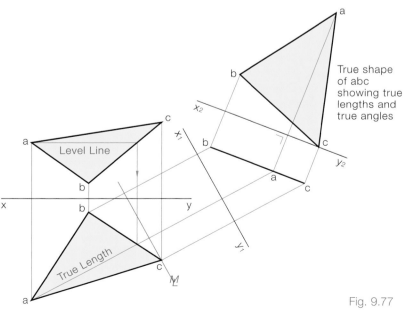

Fig. 9.77

Line of Intersection and Dihedral Angles for Triangular Lamina

When given the coordinates of meshing lamina it is often necessary to find the line of intersection between the planes and hence find the dihedral angle between the planes. There are three possible ways this problem can be presented:

(1) Given the line of intersection.

(2) Given one point on the line of intersection.

(3) Given no point on the line of intersection.

(1) GIVEN THE LINE OF INTERSECTION

> **Given the coordinates for two planes ABC and ABDE. Determine the dihedral angle between the planes, Fig. 9.78.**
>
> A = 35   5   115   B = 90 20 45
> C = 105 45 80   D = 70 75 10
> E = 15 50 90

Here we are given the line of intersection.

(1) Project an auxiliary view from plan showing the true length of the line of intersection between the planes. View perpendicular to AB in plan.

(2) Project from this auxiliary viewing down along the true length. The x_2y_2 will therefore be perpendicular to the true length found. Both planes will be seen as edge views thus showing the dihedral angle. Note that the distances for the second auxiliary are taken from the x_1y_1 back to the plan or from a suitable measuring line.

HIGHER LEVEL

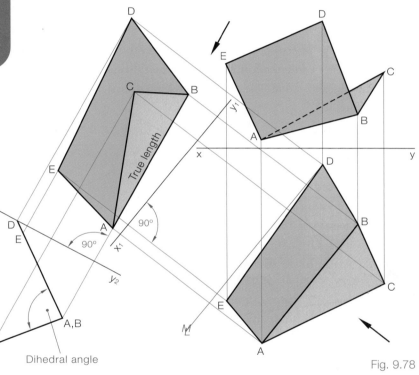

Fig. 9.78

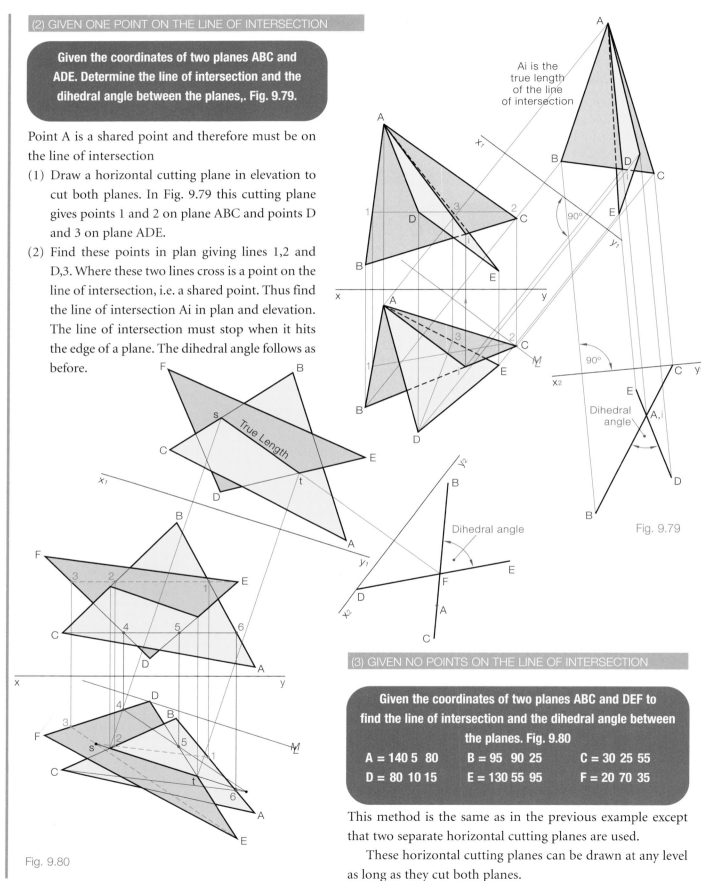

H I G H E R   L E V E L

(2) GIVEN ONE POINT ON THE LINE OF INTERSECTION

Given the coordinates of two planes ABC and ADE. Determine the line of intersection and the dihedral angle between the planes,. Fig. 9.79.

Point A is a shared point and therefore must be on the line of intersection

(1) Draw a horizontal cutting plane in elevation to cut both planes. In Fig. 9.79 this cutting plane gives points 1 and 2 on plane ABC and points D and 3 on plane ADE.

(2) Find these points in plan giving lines 1,2 and D,3. Where these two lines cross is a point on the line of intersection, i.e. a shared point. Thus find the line of intersection Ai in plan and elevation. The line of intersection must stop when it hits the edge of a plane. The dihedral angle follows as before.

Ai is the true length of the line of intersection

Fig. 9.79

Fig. 9.80

(3) GIVEN NO POINTS ON THE LINE OF INTERSECTION

Given the coordinates of two planes ABC and DEF to find the line of intersection and the dihedral angle between the planes. Fig. 9.80

| A = 140 5 80 | B = 95 90 25 | C = 30 25 55 |
| D = 80 10 15 | E = 130 55 95 | F = 20 70 35 |

This method is the same as in the previous example except that two separate horizontal cutting planes are used.

These horizontal cutting planes can be drawn at any level as long as they cut both planes.

Note 1: Line E,3 in plan will be parallel to 4,5. Also line 1,2 will be parallel to C,6 in plan.

Note 2: If the lines do not intersect they are extended until they do intersect.

To draw the shortest horizontal line to a plane from a given point P outside it, Fig. 9.81.

A = 75 75 10   B = 20 50 90
C = 40 5   115   D = 95 20 45
P = 110 45 80

(1) Draw an auxiliary showing the plane as an edge view. Project P onto this view.

(2) In the auxiliary draw the horizontal line from P to hit the plane at i. Project i to plan.

(3) Since the horizontal line from P to i in plan will be seen as a true length, then the line iP in plan must be the shortest distance from P to the line projected from the auxiliary elevation. Draw from P perpendicular to the projection lines to the auxiliary to find i.

(4) iP will be horizontal in elevation.

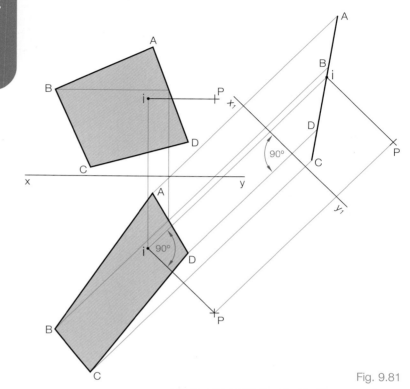

Fig. 9.81

To draw the perpendicular to a plane ABC from a point P outside it. Fig. 9.82

A = 120 88 2   B = 50   50   94
C = 160 20 84   P = 148 76   96

(1) Draw an auxiliary elevation showing the plane as an edge view and project point P onto this view.

(2) In the auxiliary, draw the perpendicular from P to the plane finding point q.

(3) It should be noted that **a perpendicular to a plane will appear perpendicular to the traces of that plane**. We can therefore draw the required line Pq in plan as it will appear perpendicular to the level line on the plane. The level line will be parallel to the HT line.

(4) Line Pq can be found in elevation as shown in Fig. 9.82.

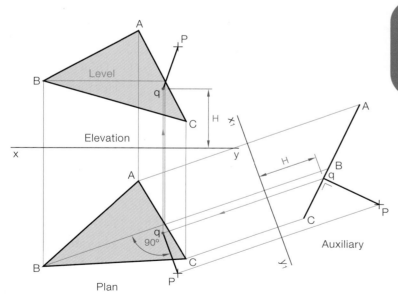

Fig. 9.82

H I G H E R   L E V E L

(1) This problem is solved under the principle that any line generator on the surface of a right cone will have the same inclination to the horizontal plane as the cone base angle. Furthermore all generators on a right cone will have the same length.

Draw an auxiliary showing ABCD as an edge view. Project point E onto this view.

(2) Draw a cone in this view having E as apex, base angle of 45° and side length of 90 mm.

(3) Where the base of the cone is cut by the plane will give the required line when projected back.

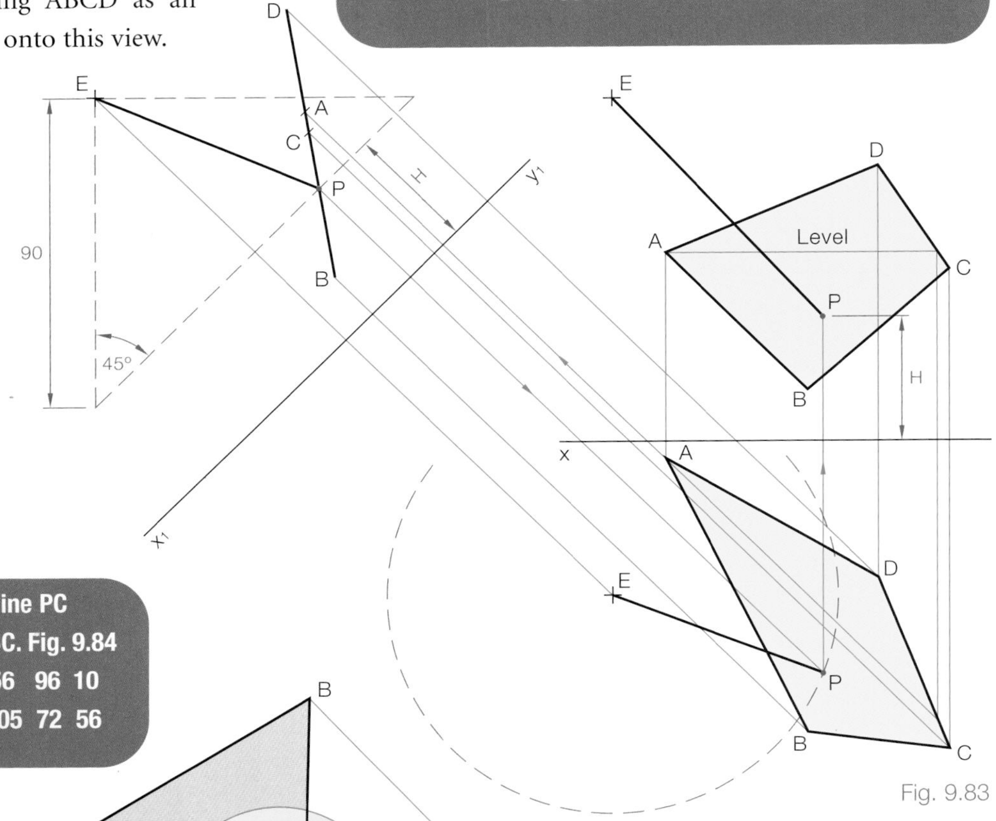

To draw the projections of a line drawn from a point E outside a plane that will touch the plane at a distance of 90 mm from E and that shall be inclined at an angle of 45° to the horizontal plane. Fig. 9.83

A = 125 55 5   B = 165 15 85   C = 205 50 90

D = 185 80 40   E = 110 100 45

Fig. 9.83

(1) Draw an auxiliary elevation showing an edge view of the plane.

(2) Project a true shape of this plane by viewing the edge view at 90°.

(3) Find the line PC on both of these views. If PC is used as a generator of a cone with P as vertex then the base angle of that cone will equal the angle the line PC makes with the plane.

To find the angle that a line PC makes with a given plane ABC. Fig. 9.84

A = 45   14   66   B = 56   96   10

C = 128   40   33   P = 105   72   56

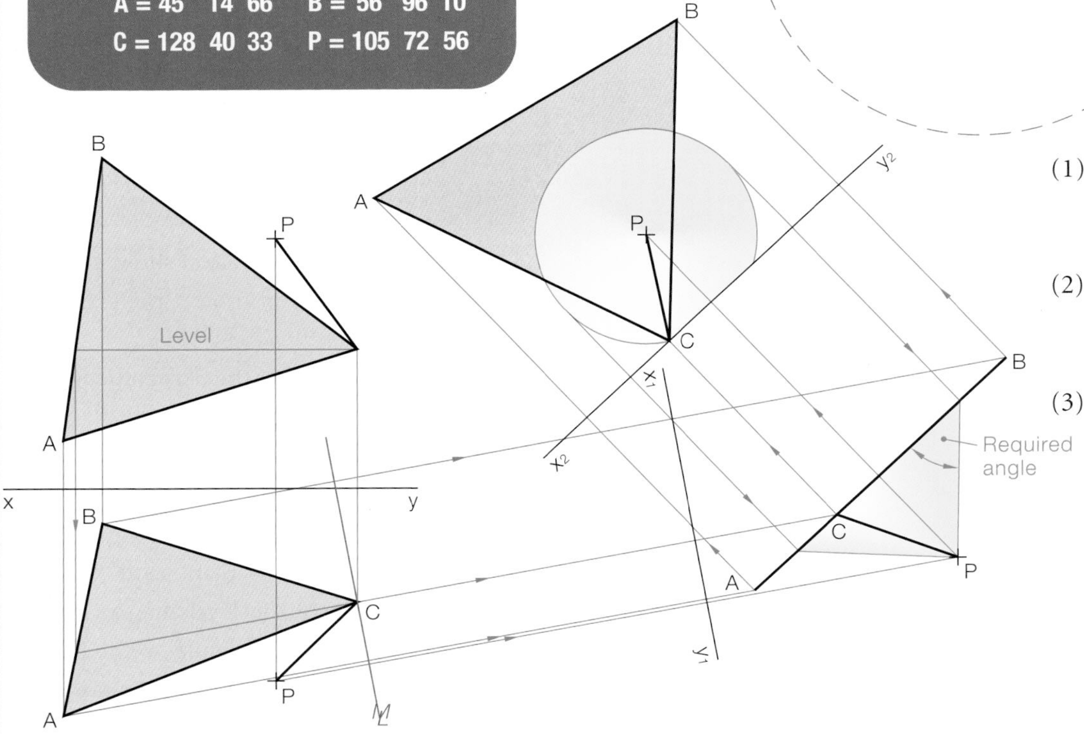

(4) With PC as radius and P as centre draw the plan of this cone in the second auxiliary plan. The edges of this circle produced back to the first auxiliary will give the required angle.

Fig. 9.84

Given a plane ABC and a point E outside it. To draw a line from E that is 40 mm long, is parallel to the plane ABC and the vertical plane. Fig. 9.85
A = 110 15 105   B = 165 85 20   C = 50 70 85   E = 65 100 30

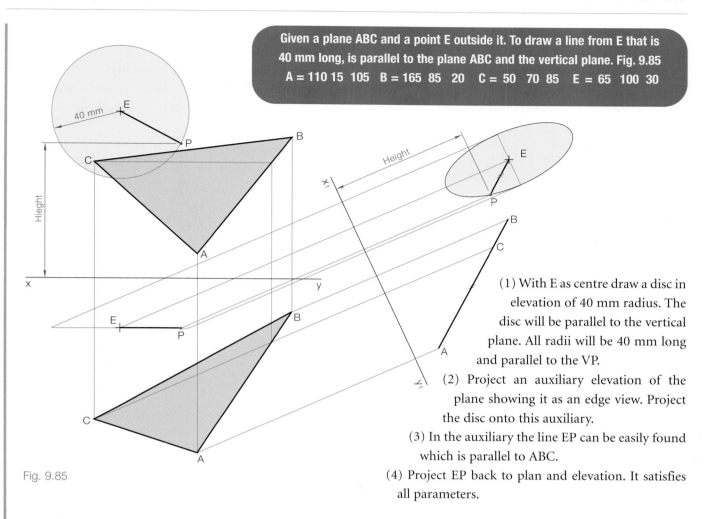

Fig. 9.85

(1) With E as centre draw a disc in elevation of 40 mm radius. The disc will be parallel to the vertical plane. All radii will be 40 mm long and parallel to the VP.

(2) Project an auxiliary elevation of the plane showing it as an edge view. Project the disc onto this auxiliary.

(3) In the auxiliary the line EP can be easily found which is parallel to ABC.

(4) Project EP back to plan and elevation. It satisfies all parameters.

Given the coordinates of a plane ABC. Draw the projections of a line on the plane ABC, that passes through A and makes an angle of 60° with the edge BC. Fig. 9.86
A = 125 85 30   B = 170 10 100   C = 80 75 65

(1) Draw the plan and elevation of the plane.

(2) Get an edge view of the plane in the usual way.

(3) By viewing perpendicular to the edge view we can project a true shape of the lamina.

(4) On the true shape draw the required line. Project point p back through the views to find the line in plan and elevation as shown in Fig. 9.86.

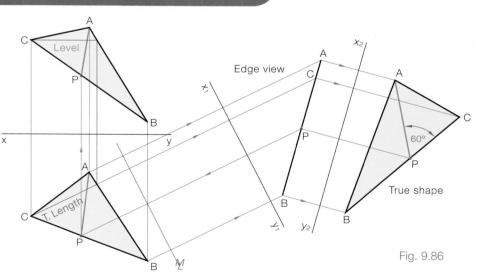

Fig. 9.86

Given the coordinates of a plane ABC. Draw the projections of a line on the plane ABC, 70 mm long, which starts at A and ends on edge BC. Also find the true angle between AB and BC. Fig. 9.87

A = 205   80   25
B = 175   105   55
C = 130   65   20

(1) Draw the plan and elevation of the lamina.

(2) Find the true shape of the plane by first getting the edge view and viewing this perpendicularly.

(3) On the edge view the required angle may be marked.

(4) With centre A and radius 70 mm scribe an arc to cut edge BC. Draw the required line.

(5) Project back through the views, Fig. 9.87.

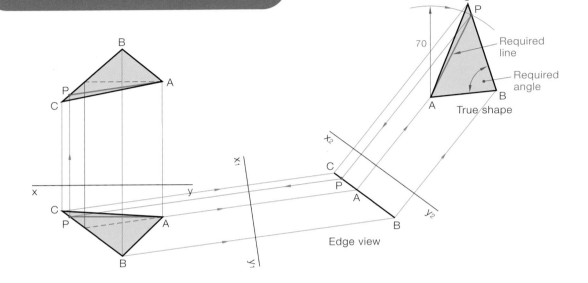

Fig. 9.87

Skew Lines

Definition: Two lines are called skew lines if they are neither parallel nor intersecting.

In many practical areas of engineering, the shortest level distance between skew lines or the shortest perpendicular distances between skew lines, is often required. For example, in pipework, mining, structural frames etc., it is often necessary to connect two skew pipes, with another new pipe; two mining shafts, with another new tunnel; or two skew members of a frame with another new member. In cases like these it is of great advantage to know the shortest horizontal distance, or the shortest perpendicular distance, between the two elements. At a later stage we will apply the principles learned here about skew lines, to solve problems on mining and on the hyperbolic paraboloid.

HIGHER LEVEL

If we produce a plane that contains one of the lines and has an edge that is parallel to the other line, then an edge view of that plane will show both lines as parallel.

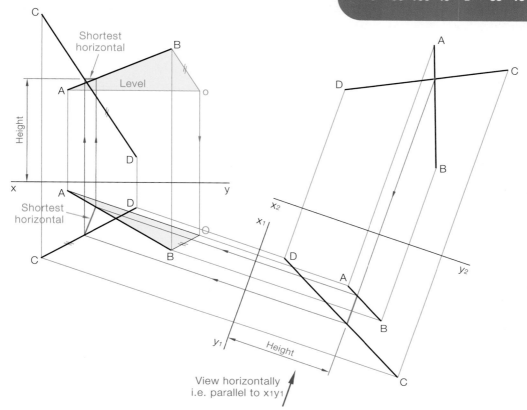

To find the shortest horizontal distance between two skew lines AB and CD. Fig. 9.88

A = 45 55 5   B = 105 80 40

C = 30 100 45   D = 85 15 15

Fig. 9.88

(1) Draw the plane to contain AB and be parallel to CD. Draw a level line from A in elevation. From B draw a line parallel to the other skew line CD. These two lines intersect at O. This completes the plane in elevation.

(2) Drop O to plan.

(3) From B in plan draw a line parallel to CD in plan. This line intersects the line dropped from O in elevation to give point O in plan.

(4) Join O back to A thus completing the plan of the plane.

(5) An auxiliary elevation viewing along AO will show both lines as parallel.

(6) Project a second auxiliary plan by projecting horizontally, i.e. parallel to the x_1y_1. Both lines appear to cross. Where they appear to cross is the location of the shortest horizontal line.

(7) Project the line back through the views as shown.

To find the shortest distance (shortest perpendicular distance) between two skew lines.

Fig. 9.89

A = 170 5   55   B = 250 20 65
C = 175 55 90   D = 230 25 30

(1) The initial part of this problem is solved in the same way as the previous example up to the stage of projecting an auxiliary showing the two lines appearing parallel.

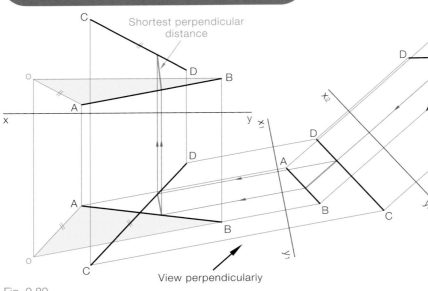

Fig. 9.89

(2) A view is taken of this auxiliary which is perpendicular to the two parallel lines.

(3) The second auxiliary shows the two lines appearing to cross. Where they appear to cross is the location of the required line. The line is projected back to all views.

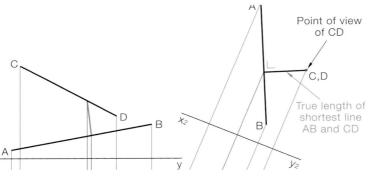

Fig. 9.90

Alternative Method: Line Method

Given the same problem.

(1) Project an auxiliary from plan that will show one of the lines as a true length. Fig. 9.90 shows x_1y_1 drawn parallel to CD thus showing line CD as a true length in the auxiliary elevation.

(2) Project a second auxiliary viewing along the true length line. This new auxiliary shows CD as a point view.

(3) The shortest line between two skew lines will always appear as a true length in a view that shows one of the lines as a true length. When projected back to the first auxiliary the shortest line must therefore be parallel to the x_2y_2 line.

(4) Project back to all views.

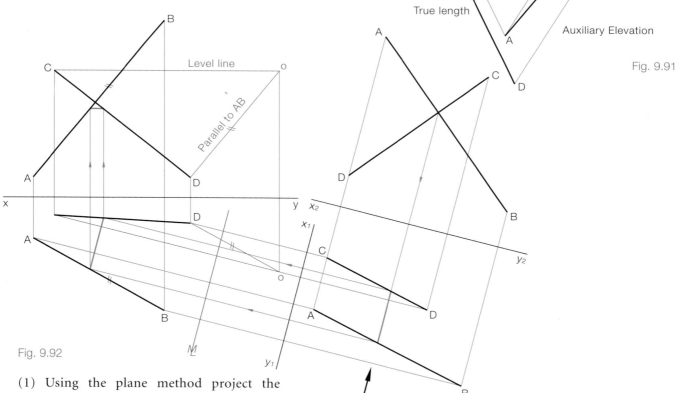

Given the coordinates of the centre lines of two 15 mm diameter pipes. Determine the clearance between them using the line method.
Fig. 9.91
A = 125 55 80   B = 175 10 10
C = 100 25 10   D = 165 75 50

The construction is as in the previous example. The pipes need only be drawn in the secondary auxiliary view.

(1) Draw the plan and elevation of the centre lines.

(2) Find the true length of one of these, e.g. CD, by auxiliary projection.

(3) Project a second auxiliary viewing along the true length CD.

(4) A point view of centre line CD is found. Draw in the pipe details which will show clearly the clearance between the pipes.

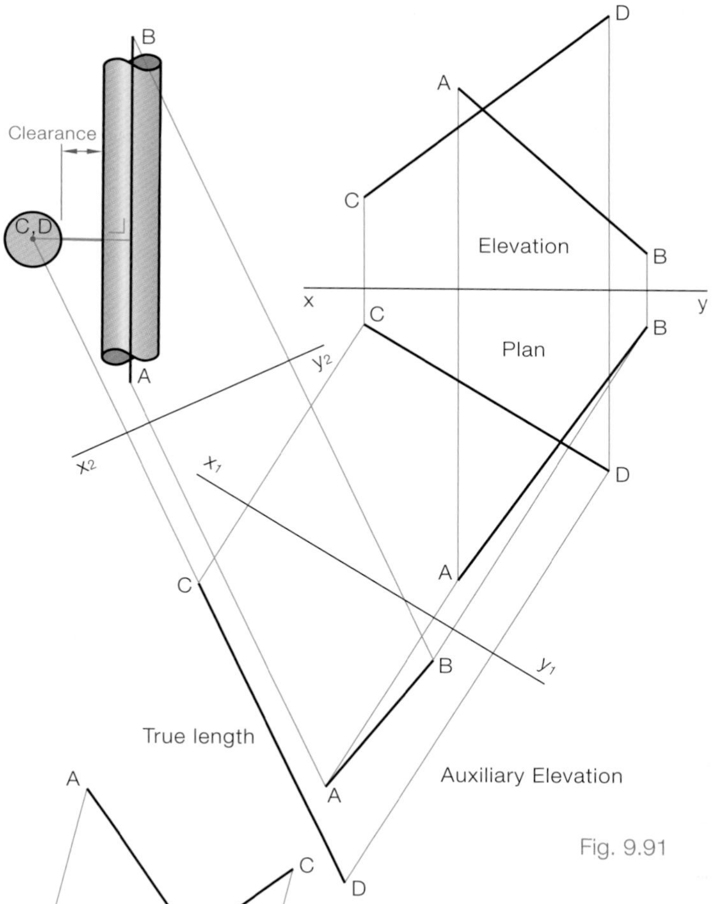

HIGHER LEVEL

Fig. 9.92

(1) Using the plane method project the auxiliary which shows the two lines appearing parallel.

(2) View parallel to x_1y_1 (horizontally) for the second auxiliary. The lines appear to cross which is the location of the required brace.

(3) Project back through the views.

Given the coordinates of two struts. Show the projections of the shortest horizontal brace strut between them. Fig. 9.92
A = 30 8 16   B = 80 70 44
C = 38 50 7   D = 90 8 10

H I G H E R   L E V E L

Given the coordinates of two skew lines. To find the shortest distance between them at 30° to the HP. Fig. 9.93
A = 120 9   33   B = 48 60 69
C = 60 25 16   D = 96 65 65

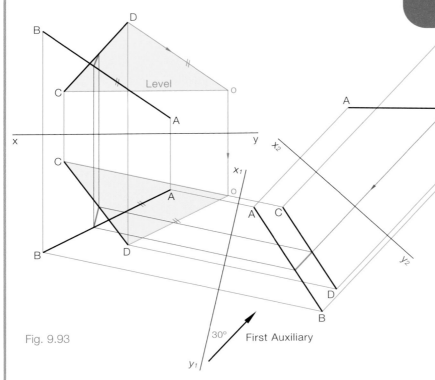

Fig. 9.93

The construction is nearly identical to that described for shortest perpendicular or shortest horizontal distance between two skew lines. The first auxiliary must be viewed at 30° to the x_1y_1. The resulting auxiliary on x_2y_2 shows the lines crossing thus showing where the required line is located.

Activities

DIHEDRAL ANGLE

Q1. Given two planes VTH and $V_1T_1H_1$. Find the line of intersection between the planes. Determine the dihedral angle between the planes using the triangle method, Fig. 9.94.

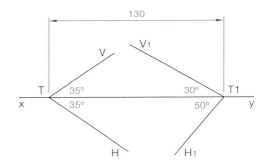

Fig. 9.94

Q2. Given two planes VTH and $V_1T_1H_1$. Find the line of intersection between the planes. Determine the dihedral angle between the planes using the point view method, Fig. 9.95.

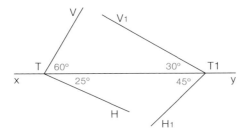

Fig. 9.95

PLANE INCLINATION

HIGHER LEVEL

Q3. Draw the traces of a plane VTH given the inclination to the vertical plane as 40° and the inclination to the horizontal plane as 70°.

Q4. Draw the traces of a plane VTH given the inclination to the vertical plane as 45° and the inclination to the horizontal plane as 55°.

Q5. Given the plan and elevation of a point P as shown in Fig. 9.96. Find the traces of a plane that contains point P and is inclined at 55° and 40° to the HP and VP respectively.

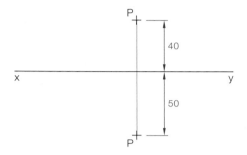

Fig. 9.96

Q6. Point P is to rest on an oblique plane which makes an angle of 60° to the HP and 50° with the VP, Fig. 9.97.

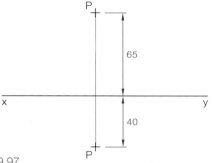

Fig. 9.97

Q7. Given the projection of a line AB. Find the traces of the plane that contains line AB and is inclined at 55° to the HP, Fig. 9.98.

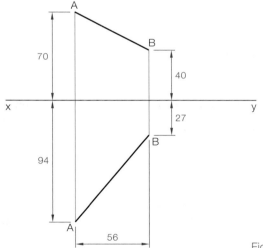

Fig. 9.98

Q8. Fig. 9.99 shows the plan of an oblique rectangular pyramid which has been cut by an oblique plane. Surfaces A, B, C and D are inclined at 50°, 60°, 70° and 35° respectively to the horizontal plane.

(i) Draw the plan and elevation of the cut solid.

(ii) Determine the inclination of the surface D to the vertical plan.

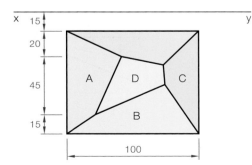

Fig. 9.99

Q9. Fig. 9.100 shows the plan and elevation of a prism with a square base of 60 mm side which has been cut by an oblique plane. The cut surface abcd is inclined at 45° to the horizontal plane and the edge ab is inclined at 20° to the horizontal plane.

(i)   Draw the plan and elevation of the cut solid.
(ii) Find the traces of the oblique plane.
(iii) Determine the plane's inclination to the VP.
(iv) Find the dihedral angle between surface S and the oblique plane.

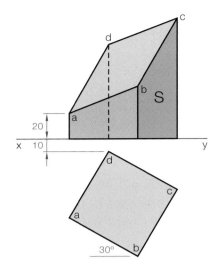

Fig. 9.100

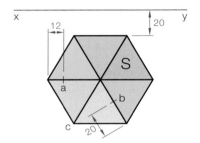

Fig. 9.101

Q10. The plan of a regular hexagonal pyramid of edge 40 mm and height 90 mm resting on the HP is shown. The solid is to be cut by an oblique plane which passes through points b and c, Fig. 9.101.

(i)   Find the traces of the oblique plane.
(ii) Draw the plan and elevation of the cut solid.
(iii) Find the dihedral angle between the cutting plane and surface S.

Q11. A regular pentagonal pyramid of altitude 105 mm is shown in Fig. 9.102. The pyramid is cut by an oblique plane that contains the points a and b. The oblique plane is inclined at 55° to the HP.

(i) Draw the projections of the solid after it has been cut.
(ii) Locate a point g on the horizontal trace of the plane so that bg makes an angle of 35° with the horizontal plane.

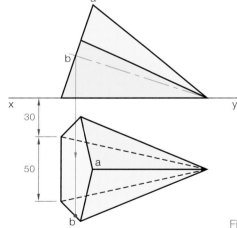

Fig. 9.102

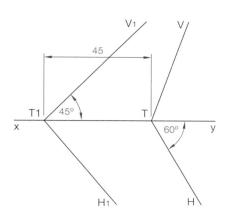

Fig. 9.103

Q12. The traces of two oblique planes are shown in Fig. 9.103. VTH makes an angle of 70° with the horizontal plane. $V_1T_1H_1$ makes an angle of 60° with the vertical plane. A square-based pyramid of base 50 mm and altitude of 105 mm is placed on VTH. One edge of the pyramid's base lies on the HT and one corner touches the vertical plane.

(i) Draw the given traces and the plan and elevation of the pyramid.

(ii) The pyramid is cut by $V_1T_1H_1$. Draw the projections of the pyramid when it is cut by this plane.

Q13. The traces of two oblique planes are shown in Fig. 9.104. VTH makes an angle of 50° with the horizontal plane. $V_1T_1H_1$ makes an angle of 75° with the vertical plane. A pentagonal-based pyramid of base 40 mm and altitude 95 mm is placed on VTH. One edge of the pyramid base lies on the VT and one corner touches the horizontal plane.

(i) Draw the given traces and the plan and elevation of the pyramid.

(ii) The pyramid is cut by $V_1T_1H_1$. Draw the projections of the pyramid when it is cut by this plane.

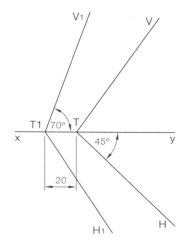

Fig. 9.104

LAMINAR SURFACES

Q14. Given the coordinates of two planes ABC and ABD.

A = 220 15 10   B = 270 35 90
C = 260 65 15   D = 230 60 75

(i) Determine the dihedral angle between the planes.

(ii) Determine the projections of a perpendicular from D to the plane ABC.

Q15. Given the horizontal and vertical projections of two planes ABC and ABD.

A = 130 90 10   B = 215 15 95
C = 165 100 100   D = 245 70 25

(i) Determine the dihedral angle between the planes.

(ii) Show the projections of a line drawn from C to the line AD and which shall be perpendicular to AD.

HIGHER LEVEL

Q16. Given the horizontal and vertical projections of two planes ABC and ADE.

A = 125 85 30   B = 170 10 100   C = 80 75 65
D = 180 70 70   E = 75   20 105

(i) Determine the line of intersection between the planes.

(ii) Determine the dihedral angle between the planes.

(iii) Draw the projections of a line on the plane ABC, that passes through A and makes an angle of 70° with the edge BC.

Q17. Given the horizontal and vertical projections of two planes ABC and ADE.

A = 225 25 90   B = 220 95 50   C = 175 35 20
D = 240 60 10   E = 140 60 15

(i) Determine the line of intersection between the planes.

(ii) Determine the dihedral angle between the planes.

(iii) Determine the inclination of the line AD to the plane ABC.

Q18. Given the horizontal and vertical projections of two planes ABC and ADE.

A = 195 20 110   B = 175 105 55
C = 130 65 20   D = 205 80 25   E = 120 55 50

(i) Determine the line of intersection between the planes.

(ii) Determine the dihedral angle between the planes.

(iii) Determine the projections of a line drawn from E, which is inclined at 30° to the HP, is 45 mm long and touches the plane ABC.

Q19. Given the coordinates of two planes ABC and DEF.

A = 130 60 5   B = 210 10 90   C = 200 80 25
D = 240 20 30   E = 155 85 5   F = 130 45 60

(i) Determine the line of intersection between the planes.

(ii) Determine the dihedral angle between the planes.

(iii) Find the horizontal and vertical trace of DEF and find its true inclination to the vertical plane·

Q20. Given the coordinates of two planes ABC and DEF.

A = 185 25 15   B = 230 105 60   C = 120 45 75
D = 240 90 10   E = 195 35 95   F = 130 65 30

(i) Find the projections of the line of intersection between the planes.

(ii) Determine the dihedral angle between the planes.

(iii) Draw a line from E which is 35 mm long, is parallel to ABC and the vertical plane.

SKEW LINES

Q21. Given the coordinates of two skew lines AB and CD.

A = 125 85 30   B = 170 10 100
C = 75 20 105   D = 180 70 70

Show the projections of the shortest distance between them using the point view method.

Q22. Given the coordinates of two skew lines AB and CD.

A = 195 20 110   B = 130 65 20
C = 205 80 25   D = 120 55 50

Show the projections of the shortest distance between them using the plane method.

Q23. Given the coordinates of two skew lines AB and CD.

A = 160 90 20 B = 225 5 10
C = 130 25 70 D = 235 30 25

Show the projections of the shortest horizontal line joining them.

Q24. Given the coordinates of two skew lines AB and CD.

A = 225 25 90   B = 240 60 10
C = 220 95 50   D =175 35 20

Show the projections of the shortest horizontal line between them.

Q25. Given the horizontal and vertical projections of two skew lines AB and CD.

A = 130 90 10 B = 245 70 25
C = 215 15 95 D = 165 100 100

Show the projections of the shortest line between them inclined at 15° to the HP.

Q26. Given the horizontal and vertical projections of two skew lines AB and CD.

A = 140 100 10 B = 130 15 70
C = 160 45 85 D = 205 10 45

Show the projections of the shortest line at 20° to the HP between them.

AREA 5

INTERSECTION AND
DEVELOPMENT OF SURFACES

10 Intersection of Solids

SYLLABUS OUTLINE

Areas to be studied:

- Intersection of surfaces of prisms, pyramids[1] and spheres, their frustra and composite solids and development of same.
  - *Intersection of right and oblique solids and their surface development.*

Learning outcomes

Students should be able to:

Higher and Ordinary levels

- Find the intersection of given lines and planes with given planes and curved surfaces.
- Establish the surface intersections of prisms, pyramids, spheres, their frustra and composite solids, where the intersecting solids have their axes parallel to at least one of the principal planes of reference[2].

Higher level only

- *Complete the intersection details of regular and oblique solids wherein their axes are parallel to one of the principal planes of reference.*

  1 Pyramid and prism are taken to include the cone and cylinder respectively.
  2 Principal planes of reference refers to the horizontal and vertical planes.

Interpenetrations

Everyday life throws up numerous examples of solids joining into other solids. When these solids join we get a **line of interpenetration**. The line of interpenetration will be either straight or curved depending on the types of solids joining together.

Solids made up of flat or plane surfaces penetrated by a similar solid, will produce straight lines as join lines. Solids with curved surfaces, penetrated by other solids will produce curved lines of penetration. In this chapter we investigate various methods of finding the lines of intersection between solids.

Method One: Limits Method

For some of the less complex interpenetrations, involving solids with plane surfaces, this is the best method. The solids involved will produce an interpenetration line made up of straight lines. If we can find the start, bend points and finish of each penetration line, we can find the full line of interpenetration.

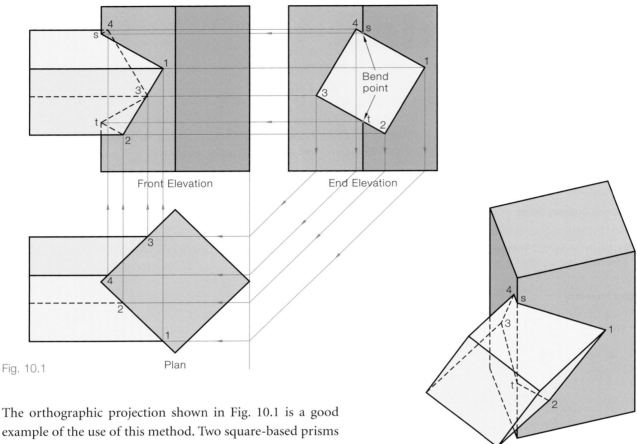

Fig. 10.1

Front Elevation

End Elevation

Plan

Bend point

Fig. 10.2

The orthographic projection shown in Fig. 10.1 is a good example of the use of this method. Two square-based prisms are joined and the line of intersection between them is to be found. Information is found from the end elevation and the plan to complete the front elevation. The penetration points of edges 1, 2, 3 and 4 can be clearly seen in plan and are projected to elevation. Where a penetrating surface straddles two surfaces, the line of intersection will have a bend in it. An example of this is the surface containing 2 and 3. The bend point is found in the end view and is point t. The penetration line goes from '2' to 't' to '3'. The pictorial, Fig. 10.2, may help in the visualisation of this.

Given the plan and end elevation of two intersecting solids, a hexagonal prism and a triangular prism. Draw the given views and complete the front elevation of the solids, Fig. 10.3.

(1) Draw the given views. Both the plan and end view are complete and provide the necessary information for the front elevation.

(2) Identify the bend points r, s, t and u in the end elevation. Project these across to the front elevation.

(3) The end points for edges 1 and 2 are seen in plan and projected up to the front elevation.

(4) Edge 3 does not make contact with the triangular prism.

(5) It is important to use indexing in this type of question, Fig. 10.4.

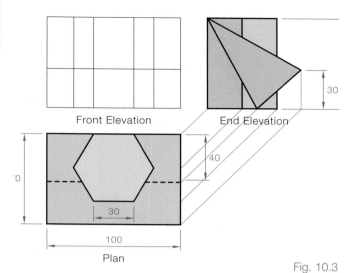

Fig. 10.3

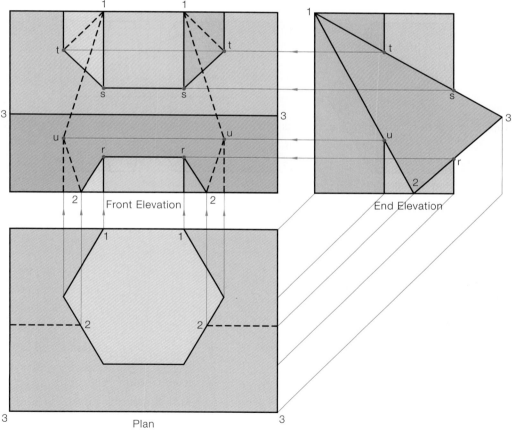

Fig. 10.4

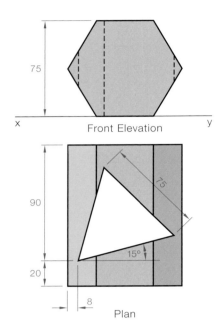

75

x   Front Elevation   y

90

75

15°

20

8

Fig. 10.5

Plan

Given the plan and elevation of a hexagonal prism with an equilateral triangular hole cut through it. Draw the given views and project an end view of the solid, Fig. 10.5.

(1) Draw the plan and elevation as given. Both of these views are complete.

(2) By projecting points from both of these views onto the end view we can build it up.

(3) Note the bend points p, q, r and s where one of the cutting planes crosses two or more planes.

(4) When all the points are found they are joined up in order. The order in which they are joined is best seen in the plan. 1 ➤ p ➤ q ➤ 2 ➤ r ➤ 3 ➤ s ➤ 1, Fig. 10.6.

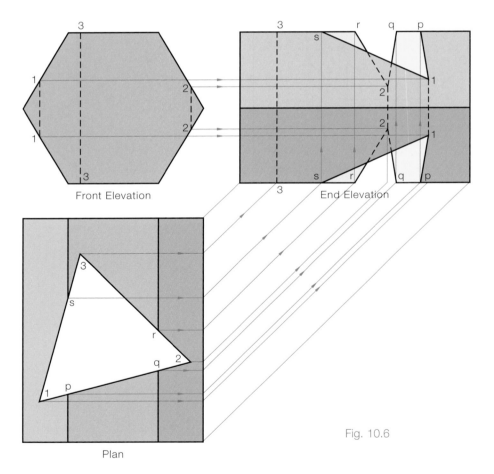

Front Elevation   End Elevation

Plan

Fig. 10.6

Given the plan and end view of two intersecting prisms. Draw the given views and project the front elevation, Fig. 10.7.

(1) Draw the given views.

(2) The edge, 1 of the square prism intersects the triangular prism in two places. Similarly for edge 2 and edge 3 of the square prism. It can be seen from the end view that edge 4 does not intersect the triangular prism. All six of these points are found in plan and projected to elevation.

(3) The bend points p, q, r and s are seen in end view and projected across to the front elevation.

(4) The sequence of joining the points is found from the end elevation, s, 1, p, 2, q, 3, r, 3, 2, 1, s, Fig. 10.8.

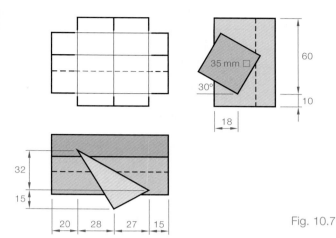

Fig. 10.7

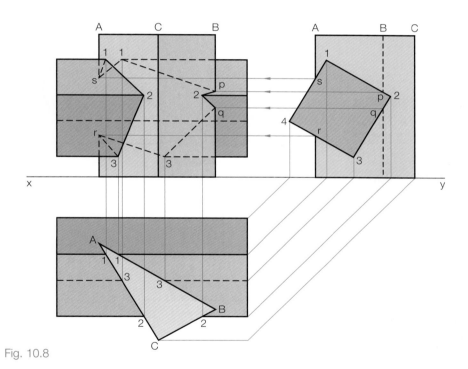

Fig. 10.8

Method Two: Radial Elements Method

This method can be very useful when cones or pyramids are being penetrated by other solids. The limits method used in the previous examples will not work for these types of solids.

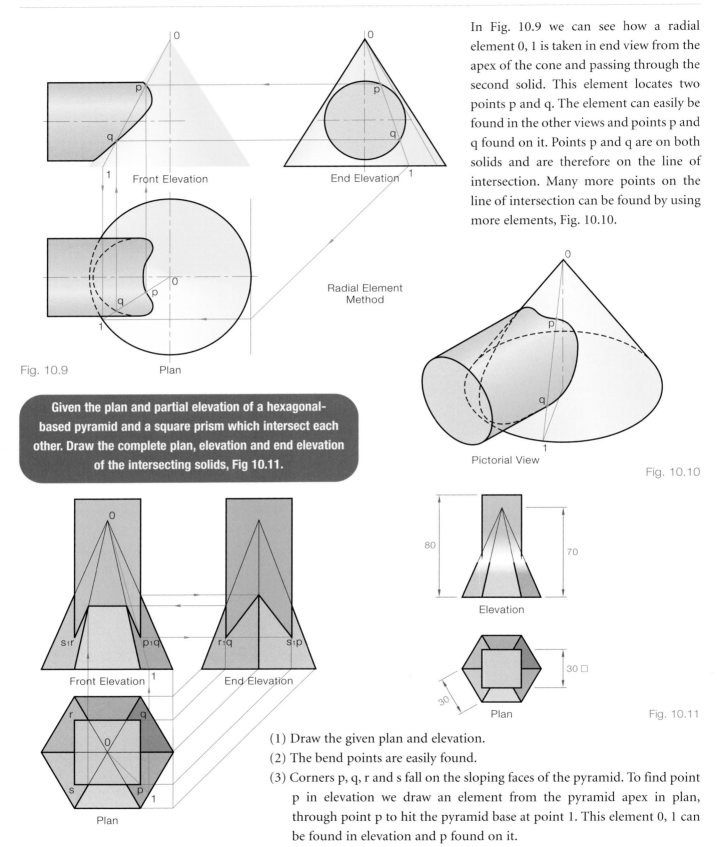

Fig. 10.9

Front Elevation

End Elevation

Radial Element Method

Plan

In Fig. 10.9 we can see how a radial element 0, 1 is taken in end view from the apex of the cone and passing through the second solid. This element locates two points p and q. The element can easily be found in the other views and points p and q found on it. Points p and q are on both solids and are therefore on the line of intersection. Many more points on the line of intersection can be found by using more elements, Fig. 10.10.

Pictorial View

Fig. 10.10

Given the plan and partial elevation of a hexagonal-based pyramid and a square prism which intersect each other. Draw the complete plan, elevation and end elevation of the intersecting solids, Fig 10.11.

Front Elevation

End Elevation

Elevation

Plan

Plan

Fig. 10.11

Fig. 10.12

(1) Draw the given plan and elevation.

(2) The bend points are easily found.

(3) Corners p, q, r and s fall on the sloping faces of the pyramid. To find point p in elevation we draw an element from the pyramid apex in plan, through point p to hit the pyramid base at point 1. This element 0, 1 can be found in elevation and p found on it.

(4) The front elevation and end elevation can now be completed. There is no necessity for any more elements as the answer is symmetrical, Fig. 10.12.

Fig. 10. 13 shows the plan of a hexagonal-based pyramid of height 80 mm. The pyramid has a square hole cut through it. Draw the given plan and project a front elevation and end elevation.

(1) The construction is as before.

(2) Draw the front elevation and end elevation simultaneously as some of the bend points are easier to find in one than the other.

(3) An element is drawn through point b in plan. This element is found in the front elevation and point b is found.

(4) Another element is drawn through point d in plan. This element is found in the end elevation and point d is found, Fig. 10.14.

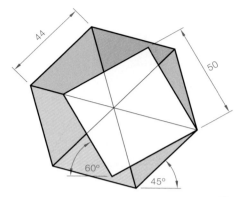

Fig. 10.13

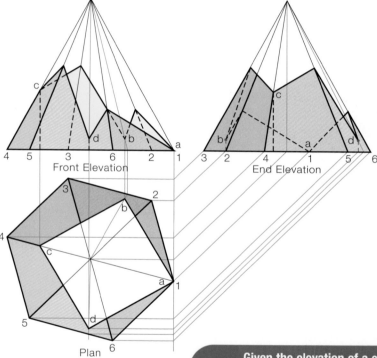

Fig. 10.14

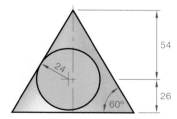

Fig. 10.15

Given the elevation of a cone and a cylinder intersecting each other. Draw the given view and project a plan and end view. The cylinder projects 10 mm beyond the base of the cone, Fig. 10.15.

When drawing in the elements on the cone in front elevation, it is advisable to space them equidistant each side of the centre line. This ensures there are less elements to project across to end view. Do not draw in too many generators as it can complicate the drawing. The method is clear from the drawing Fig. 10.16.

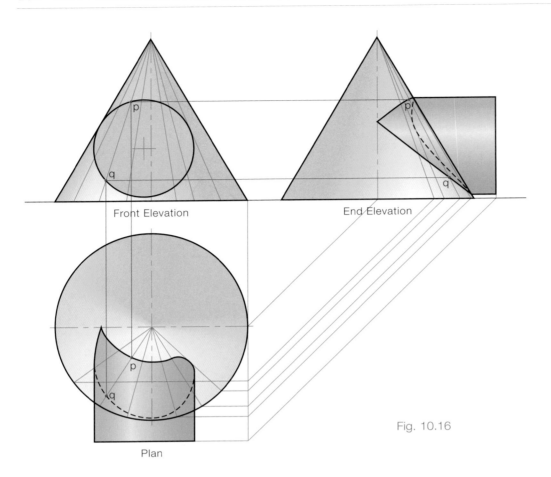

Front Elevation

End Elevation

Plan

Fig. 10.16

Method Three: Horizontal Sections

The use of horizontal planes is a very useful method, particularly when dealing with spheres, cones and cylinders. The horizontal section of each of these solids produce circles, Figures 10.17 and 10.18.

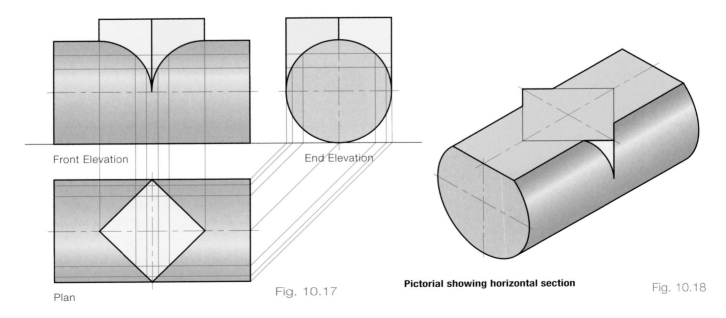

Front Elevation

End Elevation

Plan

Fig. 10.17

Pictorial showing horizontal section

Fig. 10.18

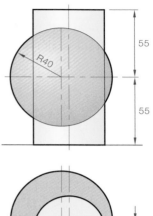

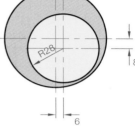

Fig. 10.19

To draw the plan and elevation of a cylinder piercing a sphere, showing clearly the line of intersection, Fig. 10.19.

(1) A horizontal section through these two solids will produce two intersecting circles. Draw the plan which is complete and draw the partial elevation.

(2) Take any horizontal section in elevation, e.g. at 1.

(3) The section of the sphere is a circle in plan which intersects the plan of the cylinder at points p and q.

(4) Project p and q onto the section line in elevation. Repeat for other sections.

(5) It is worth noting that if the section lines are taken too high or too low the circles produced will not intersect.

(6) The elevation is symmetrical about the horizontal axis, Fig. 10.20.

Elevation

Fig. 10.20   Plan

Given the plan and elevation of a sphere and a cone which intersect each other. Draw the given views and find the line of interpenetration, Fig. 10.21.

(1) Draw the plan and elevation as given.

(2) It is advisable to space the horizontal sections at equal intervals each side of the sphere centre line.

(3) The intersections of the cone sections in plan with their corresponding sphere sections gives the points for the curve on the plan.

(4) Project these points of intersection to their corresponding horizontal sections to obtain the curve points on the front elevation, Fig. 10.22.

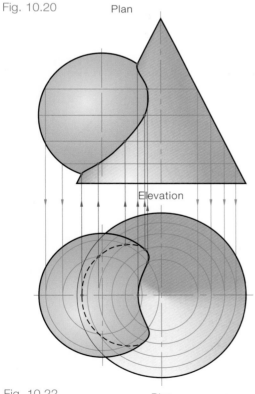

Fig. 10.22   Plan

Elevation

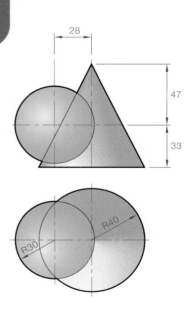

Fig. 10.21

Method 4: Vertical Sections

The method used here is exactly the same as that for horizontal sections. A series of vertical sections are taken at intervals through both solids and the line of intersection is built up, Figures 10.23 and 10.24.

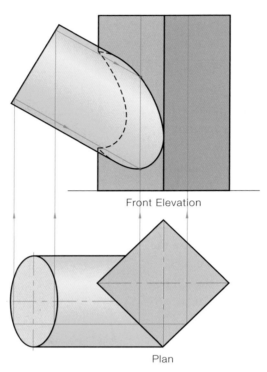

Front Elevation

Plan

Fig. 10.23

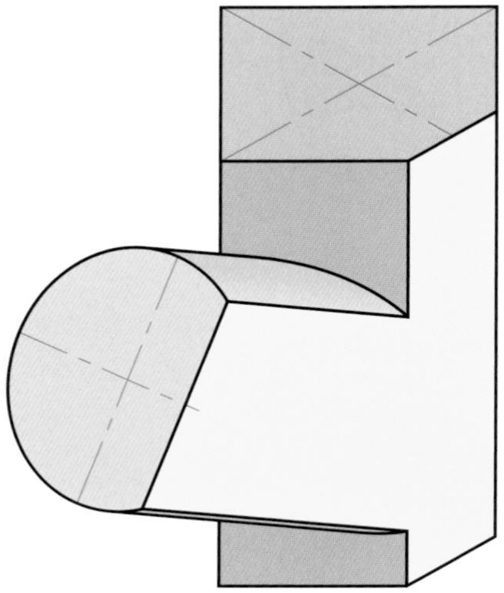

Isometric showing
vertical section

Fig. 10.24

> Given the plan and incomplete elevation of a cylinder and a square prism intersecting. Draw the given views and find the line of interpenetration, Fig. 10.25.

(1) Set up the plan and elevation.
(2) Vertical sections will produce intersecting straight lines as shown in Fig. 10.26.

Ensure that one of the vertical sections taken is through the centre of the sphere. The points found using this section, points r and s, are the transition points for the line of intersection from front to back.

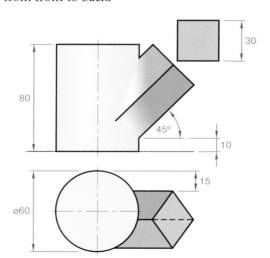

Fig. 10.25

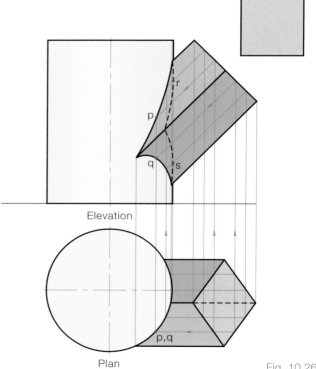

Elevation

Plan

Fig. 10.26

Given the plan and incomplete elevation of a sphere intersecting a triangular prism. Draw the given plan and complete the elevation, Fig. 10.27.

(1) This problem could be solved by using horizontal or vertical cutting planes.
(2) It is advisable to take the cutting planes equidistant each side of the sphere centre line as this will reduce the number of sectional circles needed in elevation.
(3) One of these sectional circles forms part of the interpenetration line to the back of the two solids, Fig. 10.28.

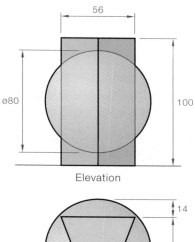

Elevation

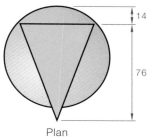

Plan

Fig. 10.27

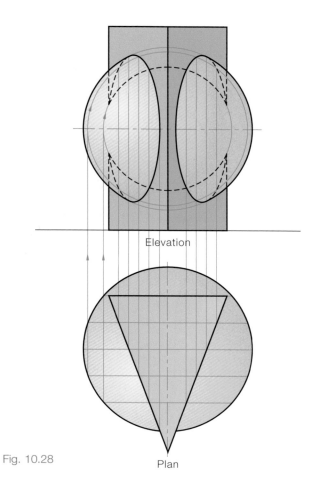

Elevation

Plan

Fig. 10.28

Development and Interpenetration

Given the plan and incomplete elevation of two intersecting cylinders. Find the line of interpenetration and draw a surface development of the curved surfaces, Fig. 10.29.

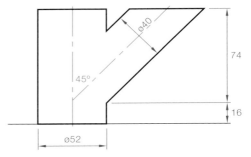

Fig. 10.29

Plan

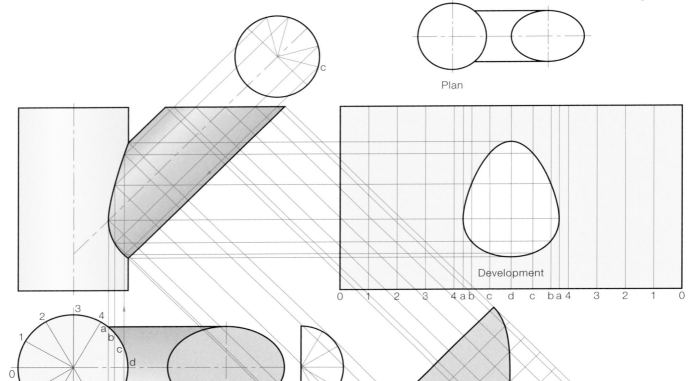

Development

(1) Vertical sections are used to find the line of interpenetration.

(2) A section of the inclined cylinder is drawn on the extended axis in plan and elevation. This section is divided into parts as shown.

(3) The vertical sections are drawn through these division lines giving the line of interpenetration as shown.

(4) The developments are projected from the elevation because the elevation shows true lengths of all elements on the cylinders, Fig. 10.30.

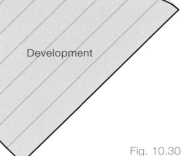

Development

Fig. 10.30

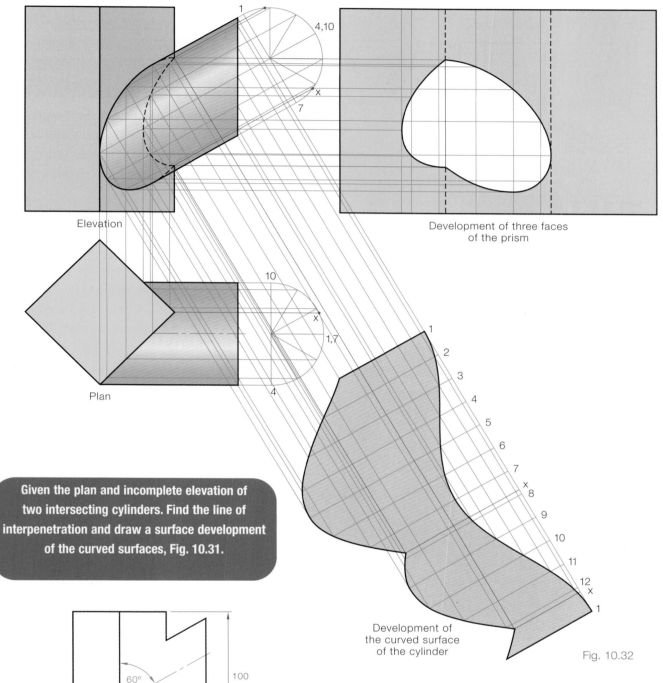

Elevation

Development of three faces
of the prism

Plan

Given the plan and incomplete elevation of two intersecting cylinders. Find the line of interpenetration and draw a surface development of the curved surfaces, Fig. 10.31.

Development of
the curved surface
of the cylinder

Fig. 10.32

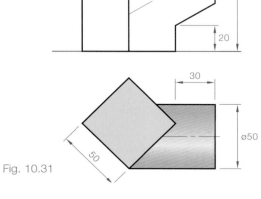

Fig. 10.31

(1) Draw a partial section of the cylinder on the extended axis in plan and elevation. A semicircle is sufficient. Divide each into six equal divisions as shown.

(2) The interpenetration is found by projection of elements as shown.

(3) Point X must be located in plan, where the cylinder hits the corner of the prism. Once found on the section in plan it is transferred with the compass to the section in elevation. Thus we can find the bend points in elevation.

(4) Point X is also needed in the development of the cylinder.

(5) Complete as shown, Fig. 10.32.

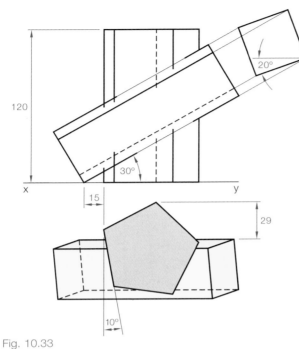

Given the plan and incomplete elevation of a pentagonal prism of side 45 mm being intersected by an inclined square-based prism of 40 mm side. Complete the elevation showing the full line of intersection, Fig. 10.33.

(1) Draw the pentagon in plan and project the elevation.

(2) Draw the line 3–3 in the specified place. Construct the sectional square at 20° as shown. Index the corners.

(3) Project the corners of the square back to elevation to give the prism edges.

(4) In plan we are given the location of the back edge of the inclined prism. This edge must be edge 4 as this is shown as a dotted line in elevation.

(5) By projecting the square's corners in the section, perpendicular to the prisms inclination, we find d_1, d_2 and d_3. These distances are marked off from edge 4 in plan giving the remaining three edges in plan, Fig. 10.34.

Fig. 10.33

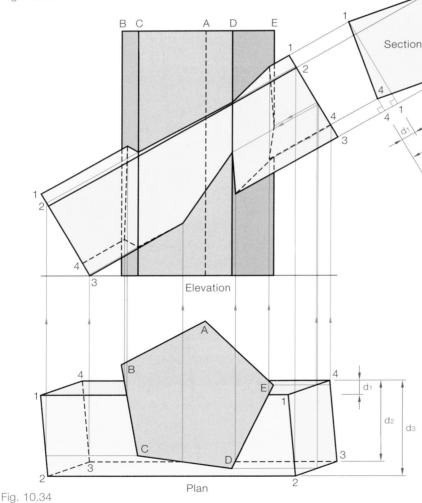

Fig. 10.34

(6) The plan can be completed.

(7) The points where edge 4,1 and 3 run into the pentagonal prism can be projected up to elevation. Edge 2 does not hit the pentagonal prism.

(8) The bend points on edge E, for instance, are found by projecting E in plan parallel to the square prism's axis, onto the prism's end. The points are projected to the prism's elevation and projected back down to edge E parallel to the prism's axis in elevation.

(9) Similar construction for edge C and edge D.

Use of Auxiliary Plans

H I G H E R   L E V E L

Fig. 10.35 shows the projections of a square-based prism of 50 mm side. This solid is being intersected by an equilateral triangular-based prism of 50 mm side. Draw the projections of the solids showing all lines of interpenetration

(1) Draw the square prism in plan and elevation.

(2) Details for the lowest line of the inclined triangular prism are given. Draw this line in elevation. Extend this line to the right and construct the equilateral section as given.

(3) Index the corners and project back to elevation.

(4) Project the corners of the section triangle perpendicularly to the prism axis thus finding d_1 and d_2.

(5) Details of one of the triangular prism edges is given in plan. This edge must be edge 1. Step distances d_1 and d_2 in plan to find the other two edges.

(6) An auxiliary plan is drawn, viewing down along the triangular prism's axis. This auxiliary shows which faces are intersected and finds bend points p, q, r and s.

(7) From the auxiliary, corner 2 penetrates surface ABCD and AABB.

AABB is seen as an edge view in plan and the penetration point is seen in plan and projected to elevation.

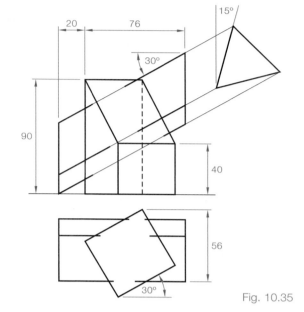

Fig. 10.35

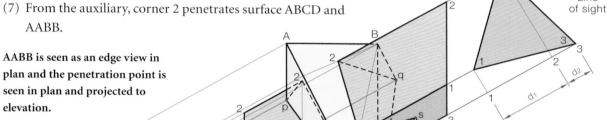

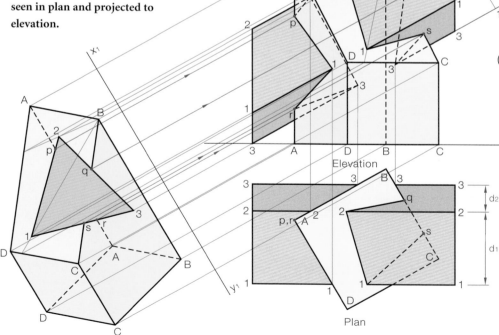

Auxiliary Plan

Elevation

Plan

Fig. 10.36

(8) To find point 2 on surface ABCD we draw a line from one of the corners through 2, e.g. from B through 2 to hit edge AD. Find this line in elevation. Point 2 is on this new line in elevation and on line 2,2 so therefore is pinpointed at these lines' intersection point. Similar construction for point 1 on surface ABCD, Fig. 10.36.

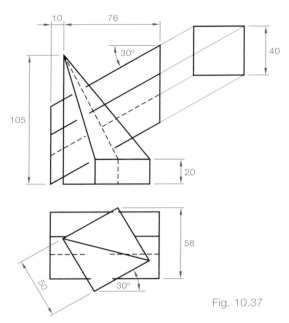

Fig. 10.37

(10) Edge 2 hits the vertical surface 0,0,AA.
This surface is an edge view in plan and therefore shows the penetration point clearly.

(11) Edge 2 also makes contact with edge OBC. Draw a line from 0 through 2 to hit the edge BC. Find this line in elevation. Edge 2 makes contact with the surface where this line crosses line 2,2.

(12) Similar construction for edge 4.

(13) Join up the points. The order in which they are joined is found from the auxiliary, Fig. 10.38.

Fig. 10.37 shows the incomplete projections of an oblique pyramid with a 50 mm square base. This solid is penetrated by a square-based prism of 40 mm side. Draw the projections of the solid

(1) Draw the oblique pyramid in plan and elevation.

(2) Draw the lowest line of the penetrating square prism as given. Extend this line and draw the square section as shown.

(3) Index the corners and project them back to the elevation.

(4) Find distances d_1, d_2 and d_3 from the sectional view by projecting the corners of the section perpendicular to the prism axis.

(5) One of the prism edges is given in plan. This must be edge 3, because edge 1 is appearing as a dotted line in elevation and is therefore at the back.

(6) Using distances d_1, d_2 and d_3, locate the other edges of the prism in plan.

(7) Draw the auxiliary plan.

(8) The auxiliary shows all bend points. Index these and project them back to elevation and plan.

(9) Edges 1 and 3 do not make contact with the pyramid.

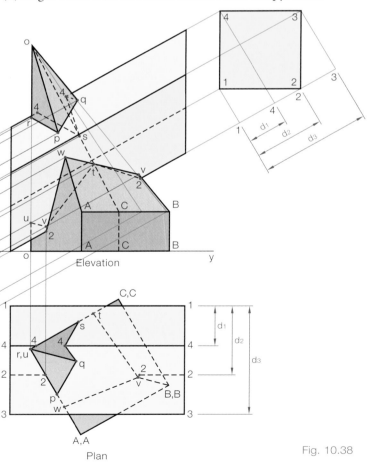

Fig. 10.38

To show a complete surface development of all the surfaces of the intersecting solids shown in Fig. 10.38, see Fig. 10.39.

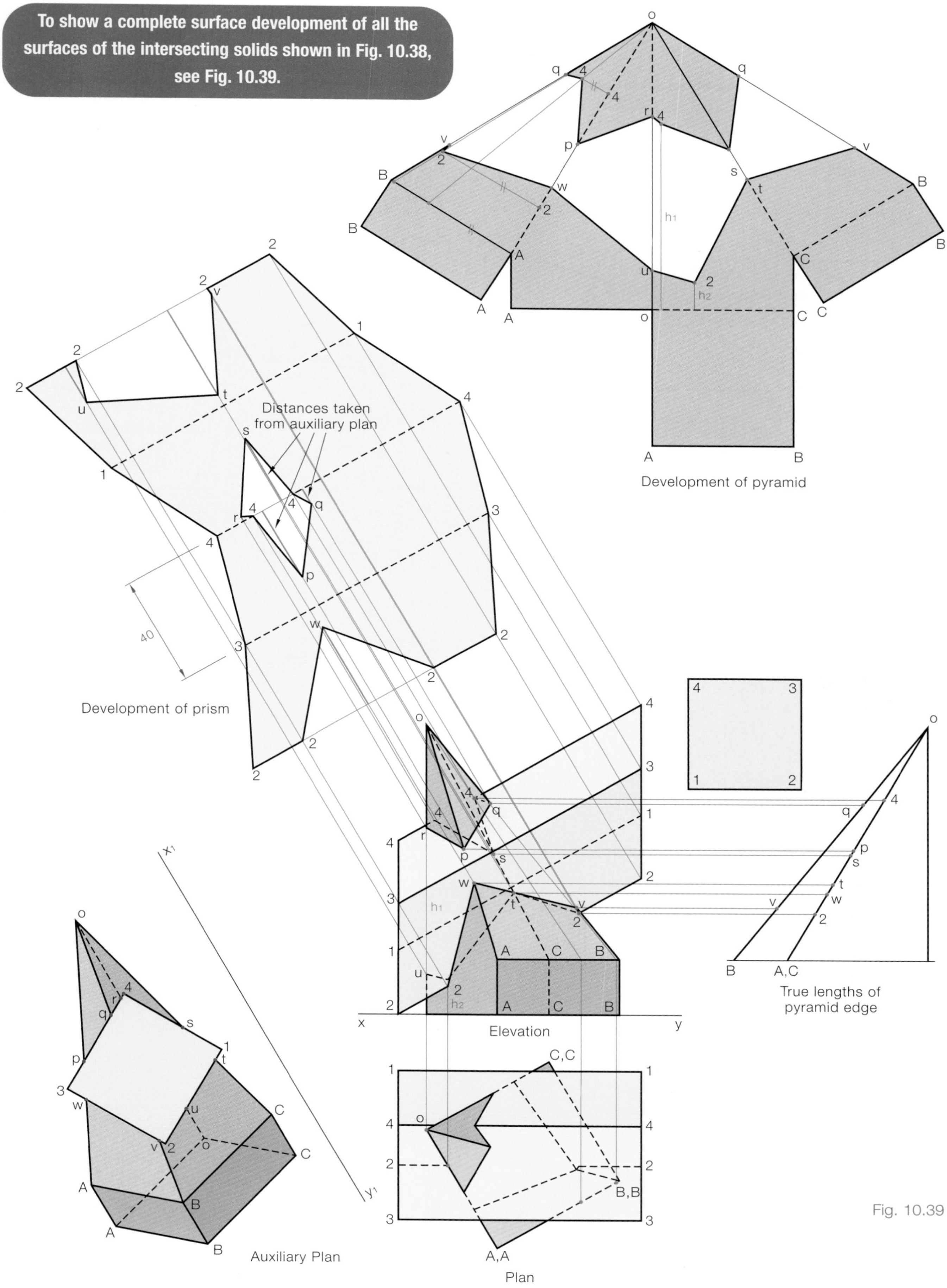

Development of pyramid

Distances taken from auxiliary plan

Development of prism

40

True lengths of pyramid edge

Elevation

Auxiliary Plan

Plan

HIGHER LEVEL

Fig. 10.39

Activities

Using the limits method find the line of intersection between the following solids. In each case draw a front elevation, end elevation and plan of the solids.

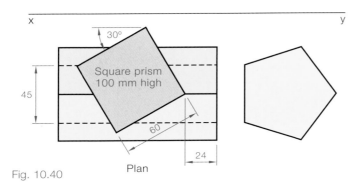

Fig. 10.40

Q1. Fig. 10.40

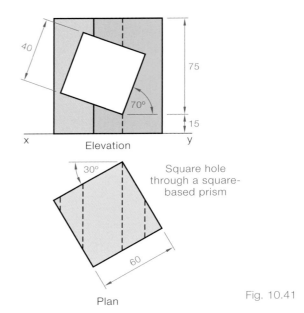

Fig. 10.41

Q2. Fig. 10.41

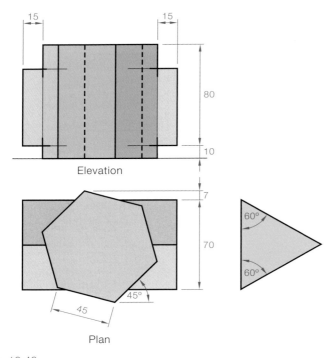

Fig. 10.42

Q3. Fig. 10.42

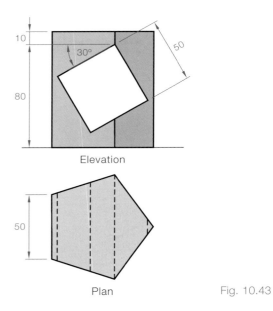

Plan   Fig. 10.43

Q4. Fig. 10.43

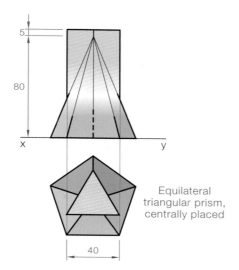

Fig. 10.44

Equilateral
triangular prism,
centrally placed

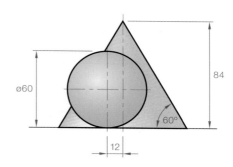

Fig. 10.45

Q5. Fig. 10.44

Q6. Fig. 10.45

Solve the following questions using horizontal sections. In each case draw a front elevation, end elevation and plan showing the full line of intersection.

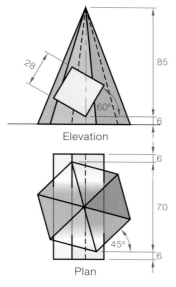

Elevation

Plan

Fig. 10.46

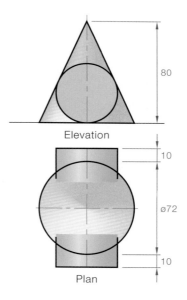

Elevation

Plan

Fig. 10.47

Q7. Fig. 10.46

Q8. Fig. 10.47

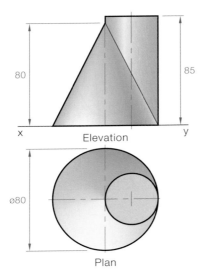

Fig. 10.48

Q9. Fig. 10.48

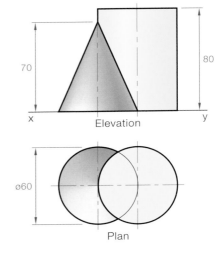

Fig. 10.49

Q10. Fig. 10.49

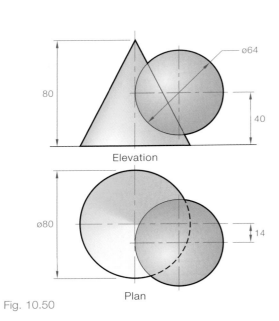

Fig. 10.50

Q11. Fig. 10.50

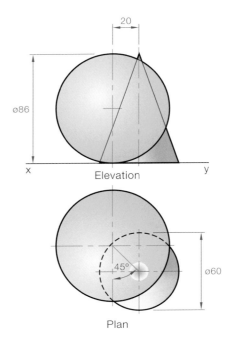

Fig. 10.51

Q12. Fig. 10.51

Solve the following questions using vertical sections. In each case draw a front elevation, end elevation and plan showing all lines of intersection.

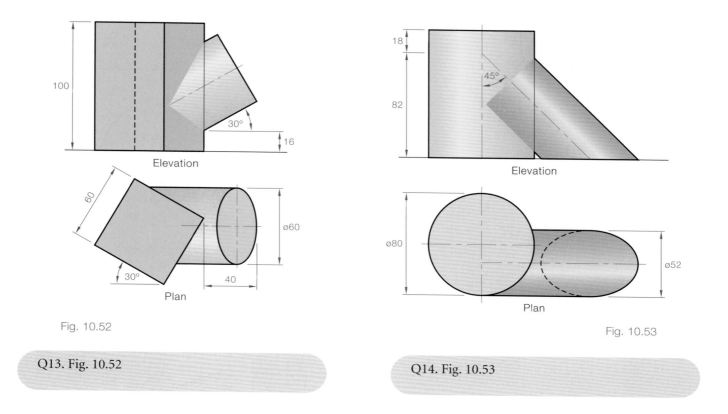

Fig. 10.52

Fig. 10.53

Q13. Fig. 10.52

Q14. Fig. 10.53

For each of the following questions determine the line of intersection between the solids A and B. Develop the surfaces of the solid A.

Q15. Fig. 10.54

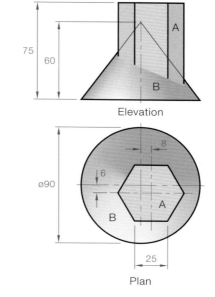

Fig. 10.54

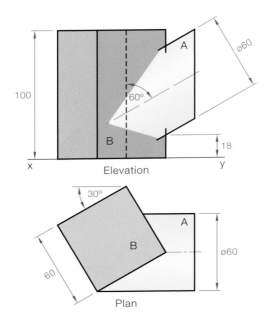

Fig. 10.56

Q16. Fig. 10.55

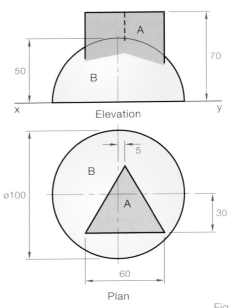

Fig. 10.55

Q17. Fig. 10.56

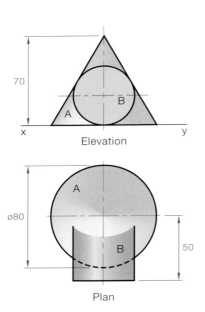

Fig. 10.57

Q18. Fig. 10.57

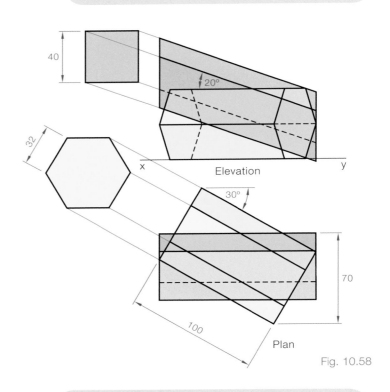

Fig. 10.58

Q19. Shown in Fig. 10.58 are the incomplete plan and elevation of a hexagonal-based prism being intersected by an inclined square-based prism. Draw the projections of the solids and find all lines of intersection.

HIGHER LEVEL

Q20. Fig. 10.59 shows the incomplete plan and elevation of a truncated equilateral triangular prism of 100 mm side resting on the horizontal plane. This solid is penetrated by a 60 mm side equilateral triangular prism which is inclined at 30° to the HP. Draw the projections of the solids showing all interpenetration lines.

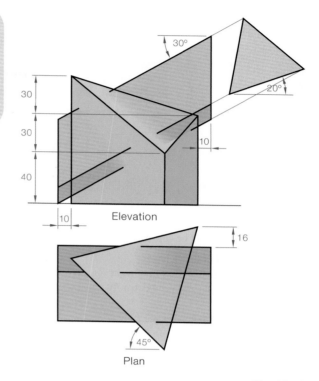

Fig. 10.59

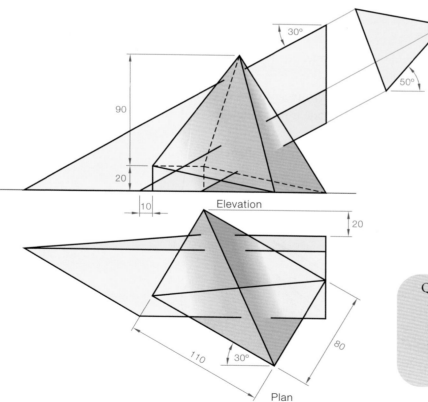

Fig. 10.60

Q21. Fig. 10.60 shows a shaped solid which is penetrated by an equilateral triangular prism of side 70 mm. Draw the given views and complete them to show all lines of interpenetration.

11 Developments and Envelopments

SYLLABUS OUTLINE

Areas to be studied:
• Surface development and envelopment of right solids. • *Surface development and envelopment of oblique solids.*

Learning outcomes
Students should be able to:

Higher and Ordinary levels
• Develop and envelop of right regular solids, their composites and frustra.
• Determine and project true distance lines between specified points on the surfaces of solids.

Higher level only
• *Develop and envelop the surfaces of oblique prisms and pyramids.*

Developments

The development of a surface is that surface laid out on a plane. The faces or surfaces of an object are unfolded onto a single plane. Fold lines are indicated by dashed lines.

A large number of industries rely on developments, for example, cardboard cartons are used for packaging and marketing manufactured goods. These cartons are usually made from a single sheet of cardboard. Sheet metalworkers continuously use developments as does the clothes industry.

In a development all lines are true lengths and all surfaces are true shapes.

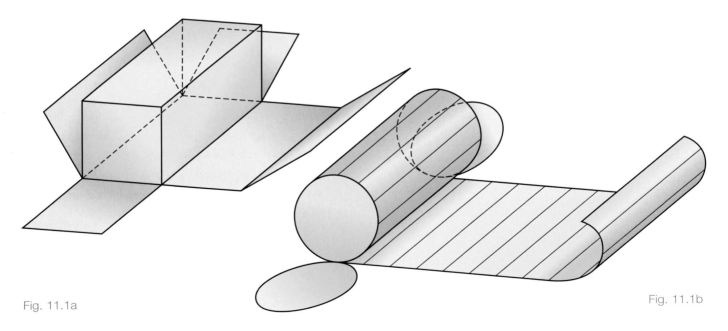

Fig. 11.1a
Fig. 11.1b

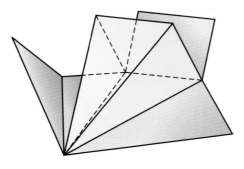

Fig. 11.1c

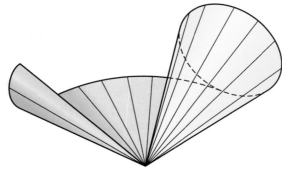

Fig. 11.1d

Given the plan and elevation of a rectangular prism. To draw the complete surface development.
Fig. 11.2.

(1) Project lines from the elevation to obtain the heights of the sides.

(2) Step-off the lengths of the sides with a compass taking distances from the plan, 2–3, 3–4, 4–1, 1–2.

3) Point 2 appears twice in this example because it forms the seam. The size of both top and bottom matches those of the plan. Dotted lines represent fold lines.

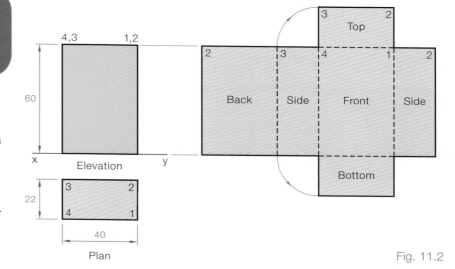

Fig. 11.2

To draw the development of a truncated prism given its plan and elevation.
Fig. 11.3

(1) Project lines from the elevation to obtain the heights for the sides.

(2) The width of each face is taken from plan.

(3) The length of the top surface must match that of the sloped surface on the front or back.

(4) Project lines perpendicularly to one of these sloped lines and complete the top as shown in Fig. 11.3.

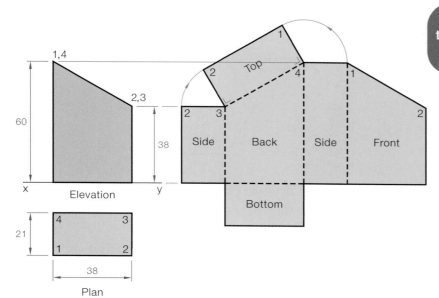

Fig. 11.3

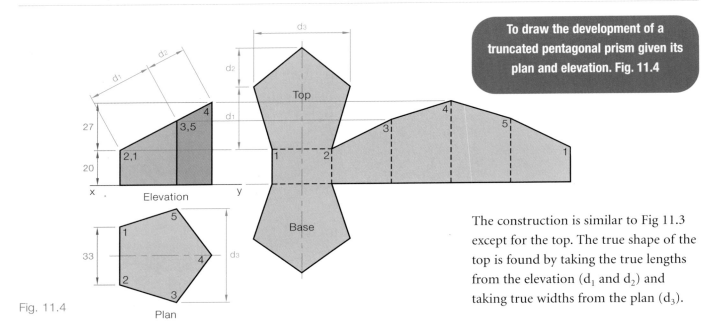

To draw the development of a truncated pentagonal prism given its plan and elevation. Fig. 11.4

Fig. 11.4

The construction is similar to Fig 11.3 except for the top. The true shape of the top is found by taking the true lengths from the elevation (d_1 and d_2) and taking true widths from the plan (d_3).

Given the plan and elevation of a hexagonal prism which has been cut at the top as shown. Draw the complete surface development of the prism. Fig. 11.5

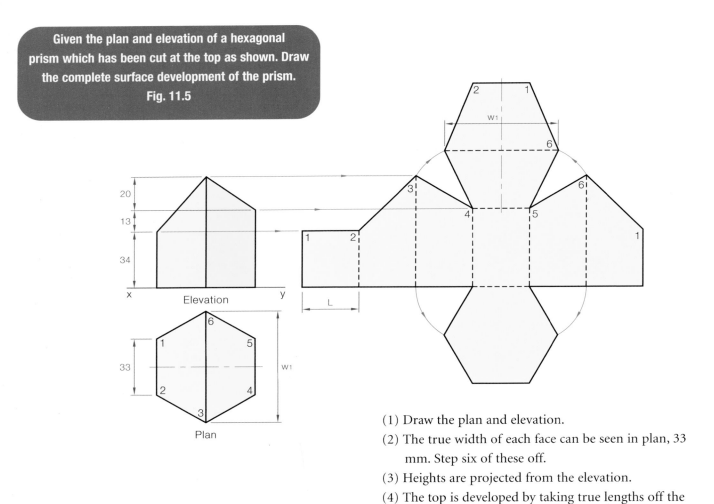

Fig. 11.5

(1) Draw the plan and elevation.

(2) The true width of each face can be seen in plan, 33 mm. Step six of these off.

(3) Heights are projected from the elevation.

(4) The top is developed by taking true lengths off the elevation and true widths off the plan. Seams that join together must be of equal length.

(1) Divide the circumference of the circle in plan into twelve equal parts in the usual way.

(2) Project the top and bottom of the elevation across to obtain the height of the development.

(3) Step-off the twelve steps from the plan (the circumference).

(4) It does not matter where the top and bottom circles are added on the top and bottom lines.

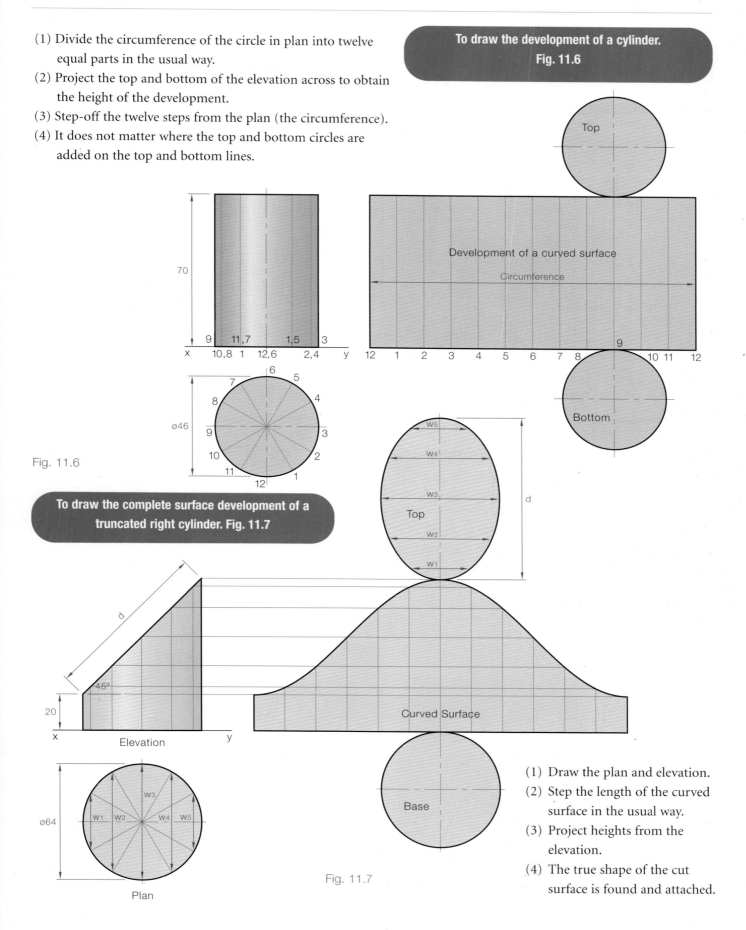

To draw the development of a cylinder.
Fig. 11.6

Fig. 11.6

To draw the complete surface development of a truncated right cylinder. Fig. 11.7

Fig. 11.7

(1) Draw the plan and elevation.

(2) Step the length of the curved surface in the usual way.

(3) Project heights from the elevation.

(4) The true shape of the cut surface is found and attached.

To develop the complete surface development of the cylinder which has been cut as shown in the plan and elevation. Fig. 11.8

The construction is the same as in the previous example. The top surface is curved and is found by taking lengths off the curve in elevation.

The smaller the steps taken the more accurate the result. The widths are taken from the plan and are true lengths.

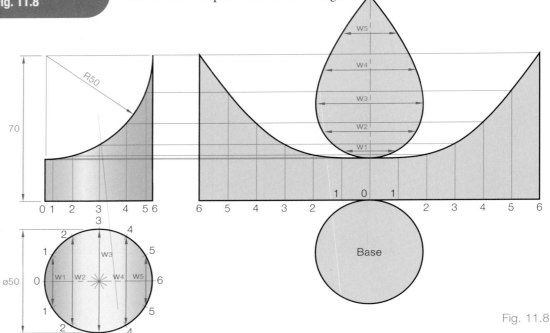

Fig. 11.8

This method, sometimes called the radial method, is applied to pyramids and cones. The true length of an edge is found. This length is used as the radius of an arc which is the basis of the construction.

(1) Find the true length of edge OC by rotating it parallel to the xy in plan and projecting it to elevation.

(2) Choose a point O for the development and scribe an arc having the true length of OC as radius.

(3) Step the length of the base around the arc four times.

(4) Complete the development by attaching the base.

To draw the complete surface development of a square-based pyramid given its plan and elevation. Fig. 11.9

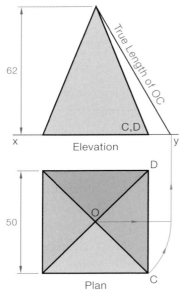

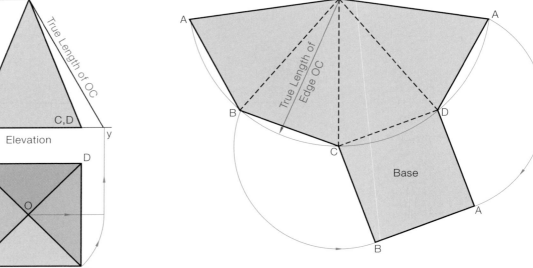

(1) The true length of an edge is first
found as shown in plan and elevation.

(2) This true length is used to draw the arc
for the development.

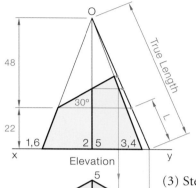

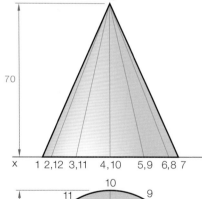

(3) Step the six hexagon sides
around this arc and thus
complete the development
of the pyramid as if it has
not been cut.

**To draw the surface development of a truncated
hexagonal pyramid given its plan and elevation.
Fig. 11.10**

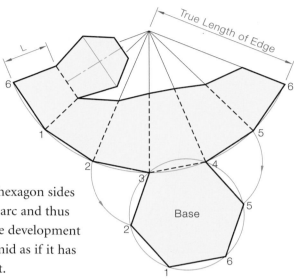

Fig. 11.10

(4) The true length of each cut edge is now found
and stepped-off on the development.

(5) The cut surface itself is found in the usual way.

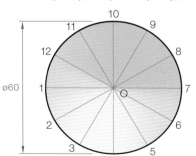

Fig. 11.11

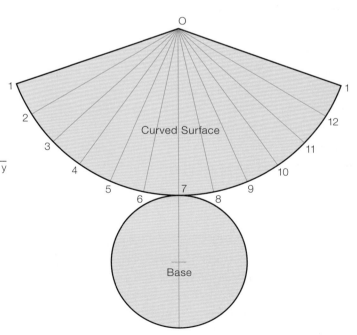

**To develop the complete surface
development of a cone given its plan
and elevation.
Fig. 11.11**

(1) A cone is developed in exactly the same way as a pyramid.

(2) The plan is divided into twelve equal pieces giving twelve generators.

(3) These generators are found in elevation.

(4) Generator O1 or O7 shows the true length of the generators and it is this
true length that is used to draw the arc for the development.

(5) Complete the development in the usual way.

(1) Like the development of the truncated pyramid Fig. 11.10 we develop the surface of the cone before it is cut.

(2) The true length of each cut generator must be found by projecting the cut end of each generator over to the side of the cone which will show it as a true length.

(3) Each length is then marked onto the development and rotated about O onto the appropriate generator.

To draw the complete surface development of a truncated right cone given its plan and elevation. Fig. 11.12

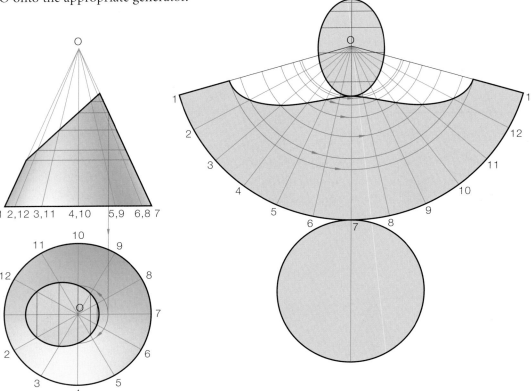

Fig. 11.12

Worked Examples

The elevation and plan of a right pentagonal prism of sides 30 mm with a Ø25 mm passing centrally through it. Draw the given views and develop the surface of the prism. Fig. 11.13

(1) Develop the prism as before.

(2) Divide the circle into 12 equal parts. Project these down to plan where the edge 3,4 is seen as a true length.

(3) w_1, w_2 and w_3 can then be transferred onto the development.

(4) Project across from the elevation to intersect perpendiculars from w_1, w_2 and w_3 and join to give a fair curve.

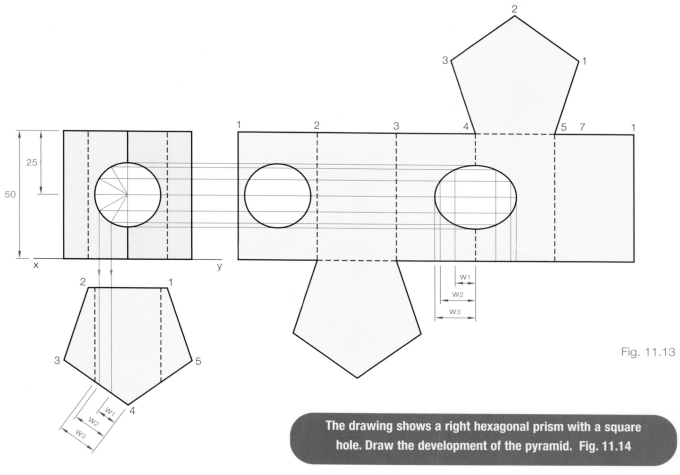

Fig. 11.13

The drawing shows a right hexagonal prism with a square hole. Draw the development of the pyramid. Fig. 11.14

(1) The square hole in plan is found by taking horizontal sections. Each horizontal section gives a hexagon in plan on which a vertex is located. The points a and b can be projected directly onto edge 1,o and 3,o. Similarly c and d are projected to edge 6,o and 4,o.

(2) Develop the surface of the pyramid. All points are brought across to edge 5,o on the elevation to find true distances.

(3) These true distances are swung around on the development and the points are located as shown. The development of the base is not shown.

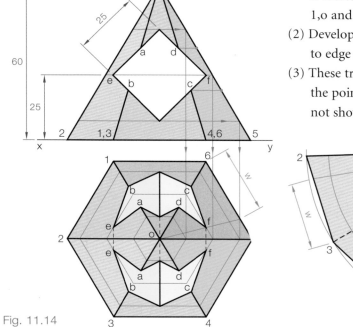

Fig. 11.14

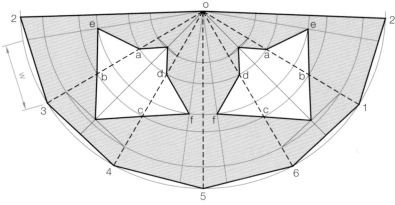

(1) Draw the plan and elevation of the cut pyramid.
(2) Develop the surface of the complete pyramid.

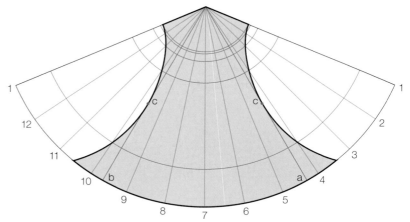

The plan and elevation of a hexagonal-based pyramid which is cut top and bottom at an angle of 30°. Draw the complete surface development. Fig. 11.15

Fig. 11.15

(3) The true length of all the cut edges are found in elevation by projecting horizontally across to edge O,4. This edge is seen as a true length in elevation.

(4) Both the top and base are found by taking lengths from the elevation and widths from the plan.

The elevation of a right circular cone from which a portion has been cut away by a cylindrical surface is shown in Fig. 11.16. Draw the surface development of the curved surface of the cone.

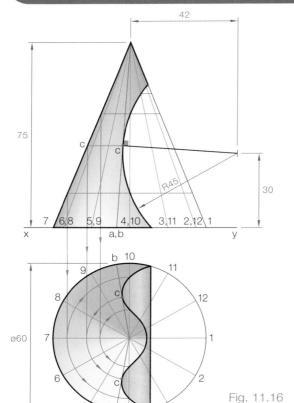

Fig. 11.16

(1) Divide the plan into 12 equal parts giving generators.
(2) Develop the full curved surface of the cone.
(3) Where generators are cut in, elevation will find points in the plan.
(4) The true length of each cut generator must be found before locating points on the development.
(5) An extra generator is found as a tangent to the arc in elevation to find an extra point c both in plan and on the development.

Activities

Figures 11.17 to 11.19 show pictorial views of solids. In each case draw a plan and elevation and a complete surface development.

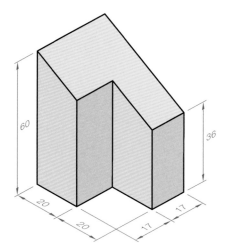

Fig. 11.17

Q1. Fig. 11.17

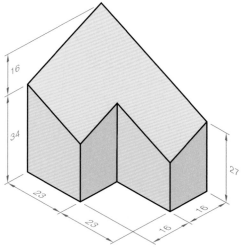

Fig. 11.18

Q2. Fig. 11.18

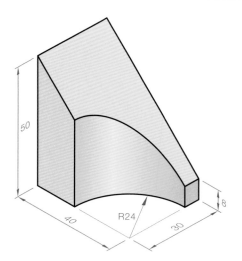

Fig. 11.19

Q3. Fig. 11.19

Figures 11.20 to 11.27 show the plans and elevations of prisms and cylinders. In each case draw the given views and draw the surface development of the solids.

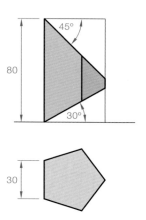

Fig. 11.20

Q4. Fig. 11.20

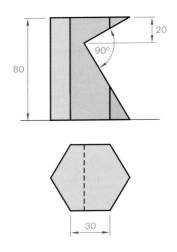

Fig. 11.21

Q5. Fig. 11.21

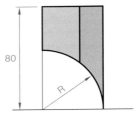

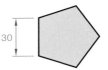

Fig. 11.22

Q6. Fig. 11.22

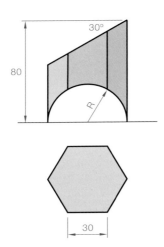

Fig. 11.23

Q7. Fig. 11.23

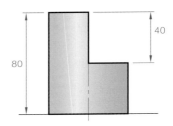

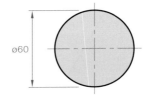

Fig. 11.24

Q8. Fig. 11.24

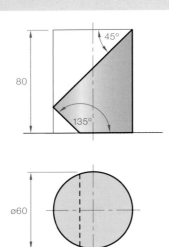

Fig. 11.25

Q9. Fig. 11.25

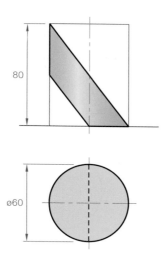

Fig. 11.26

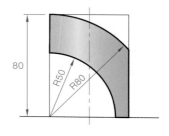

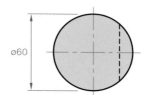

Fig. 11.27

Q10. Fig. 11.26

Q11. Fig. 11.27

Q12. TO Q19.

Figures 11.28 to 11.35 show incomplete plans and elevations of pyramids and cones. In each case complete the given views and draw the surface development of the solid.

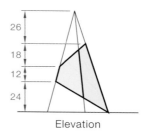

Elevation

Incomplete Plan   Fig. 11.29

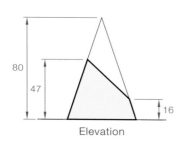

Elevation

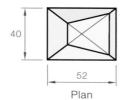

Fig. 11.28   Plan

Q13. Fig. 11.29

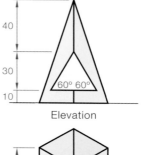

Elevation

Q12. Fig. 11.28

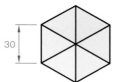

Q14. Fig. 11.30

Fig. 11.30   Incomplete Plan

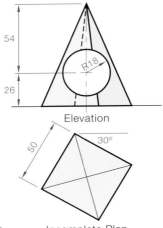

Fig. 11.31   Incomplete Plan

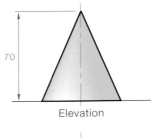

Elevation

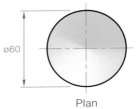

Plan   Fig. 11.32

Q15. Fig. 11.31

Q16. Fig. 11.32

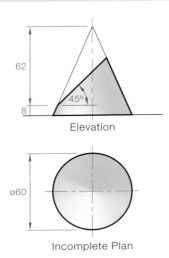

Fig. 11.33

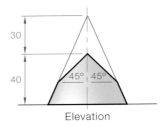

Elevation

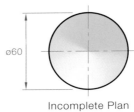

Incomplete Plan

Fig. 11.34

Q17. Fig. 11.33

Q18. Fig. 11.34

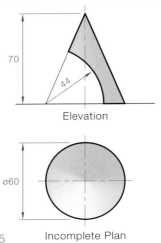

Fig. 11.35   Incomplete Plan

Q19. Fig. 11.35

Envelopments

As explained earlier, the word 'development' describes the process of opening out the surfaces of an object. 'Envelopment' can be seen as the opposite, the closing over of a development to create the object.

Given the incomplete development of a solid. Draw the front elevation, end elevation and plan of the solid and complete the development.
Fig. 11.36a

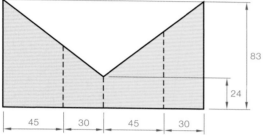

(1) The base must be rectangular as alternate sides are equal in length. The solid must also be a prism as the development is made up of parallel height lines.
(2) Decide which face of the development will form the front of the object. Draw the front elevation in line with the development.
(3) Project the plan which will equal the base in size.
(4) Draw the end elevation and complete the development, Fig. 11.36b.

Fig. 11.36a

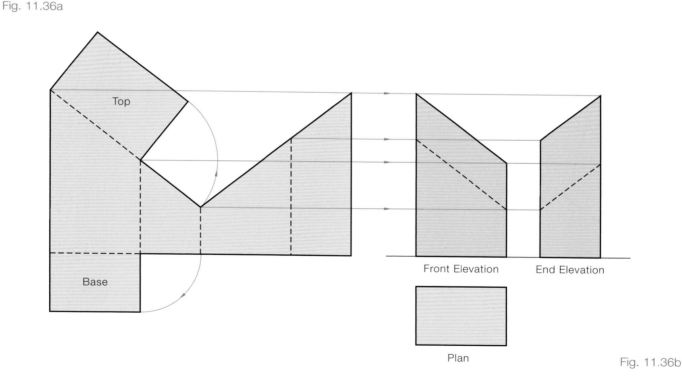

Fig. 11.36b

Given the partial development of a solid. Draw the front elevation, end elevation and plan of the solid. Complete the development.

Fig. 11.37a

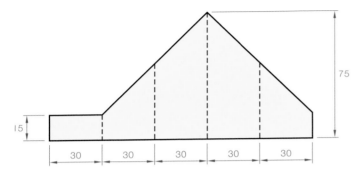

Fig. 11.37a

The solid must be a pentagonal prism because it has five equal sides and parallel height lines. The prism must also be truncated because of the variation in heights.

(1) Draw the development.

(2) Draw the base of the development and the plan.

(3) Project the elevation from the plan and from the development.

(4) Project the end view.

(5) Find the true shape of the cut surfaces by taking widths from the plan and lengths from the elevation, Fig. 11.37b.

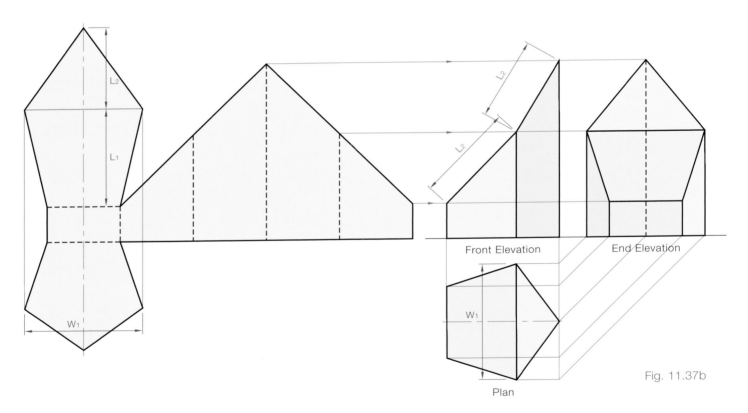

Front Elevation   End Elevation

Plan

Fig. 11.37b

The development of a cylinder which is open at both ends is shown. Draw a front elevation and plan of the object. Fig. 11.38a

(1) The length of the development must equal the circumference of the cylinder

$$2\pi R = 180 \text{ mm} \Rightarrow R = 28.6 \text{ mm}$$

(2) Draw the plan of the cylinder as a circle of radius 28.6 mm.
(3) Divide this circle into twelve.
(4) Divide the development into twelve equal parts.
(5) Complete by projection, Fig. 11.38b.

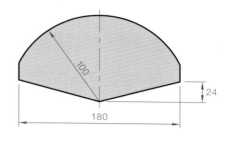

Fig. 11.38a

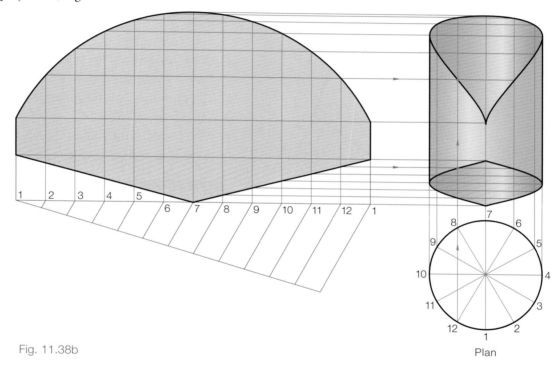

Fig. 11.38b

Plan

Partial Envelopments

A partial development is when a label or sticker is wrapped around a solid. The label can be much more complicated in appearance when developed out than it would suggest when wrapped around the jar or bottle.

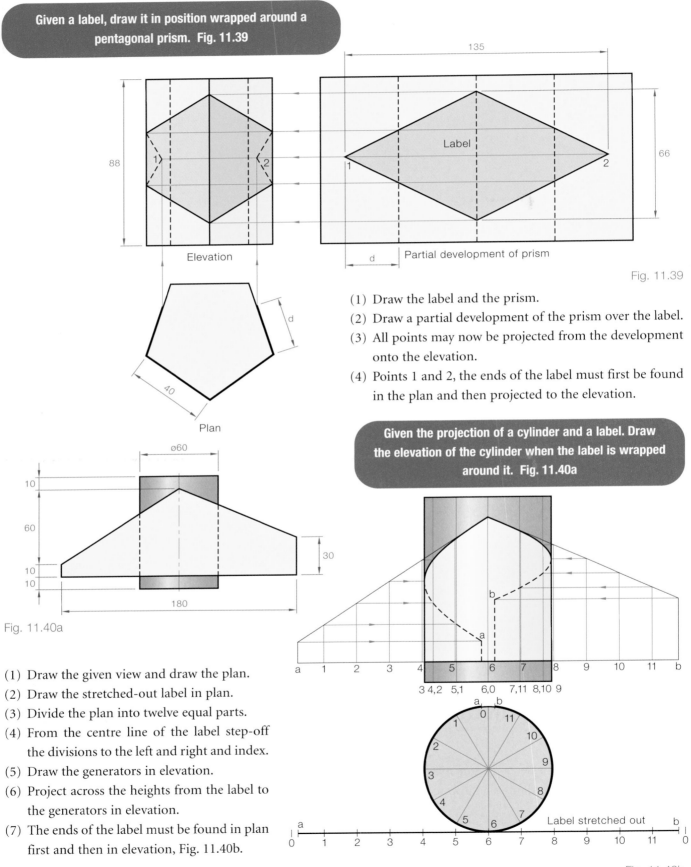

Given a label, draw it in position wrapped around a pentagonal prism. Fig. 11.39

135

Label

66

1   2

1   2

88

Elevation

d   Partial development of prism

Fig. 11.39

d

40

Plan

(1) Draw the label and the prism.

(2) Draw a partial development of the prism over the label.

(3) All points may now be projected from the development onto the elevation.

(4) Points 1 and 2, the ends of the label must first be found in the plan and then projected to the elevation.

ø60

10

60

10
10

30

180

Fig. 11.40a

Given the projection of a cylinder and a label. Draw the elevation of the cylinder when the label is wrapped around it. Fig. 11.40a

b

a

a   1   2   3   4   5   6   7   8   9   10   11   b

3 4,2 5,1   6,0   7,11 8,10 9

a   b

0

1   11

2   10

3   9

4   8

5   7

6

(1) Draw the given view and draw the plan.

(2) Draw the stretched-out label in plan.

(3) Divide the plan into twelve equal parts.

(4) From the centre line of the label step-off the divisions to the left and right and index.

(5) Draw the generators in elevation.

(6) Project across the heights from the label to the generators in elevation.

(7) The ends of the label must be found in plan first and then in elevation, Fig. 11.40b.

a   Label stretched out   b

0   1   2   3   4   5   6   7   8   9   10   11   0

Fig. 11.40b

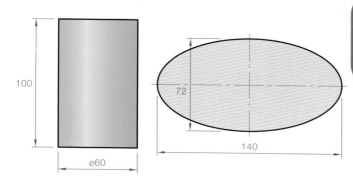

Fig. 11.41a

Given the elevation of a cylinder and the development of an elliptical label. Draw the elevation of the cylinder when the label is wrapped around it.

Fig. 11.41a

(1) The construction is the same as in the previous example. Drawing the developed label to the side produces a less complex drawing and is a neater presentation.

(2) The ends of the label, points a and b, will fall between 5 and 6 on the cylinder. They are found in plan first and then projected to elevation,

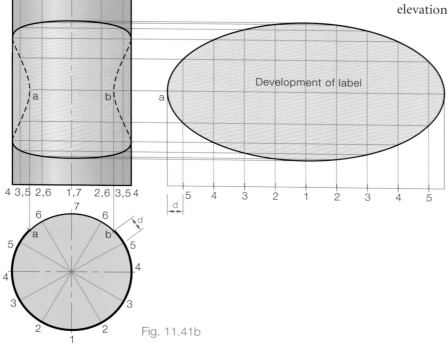

Development of label

Fig. 11.41b

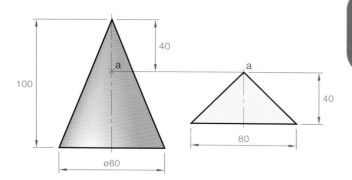

Fig. 11.42a

Given the projection of a cone and the development of a triangular label. Draw the elevation and plan of the cone when the label is wrapped around it.

Fig. 11.42a

(1) Develop the surface of the cone and place the label in position.

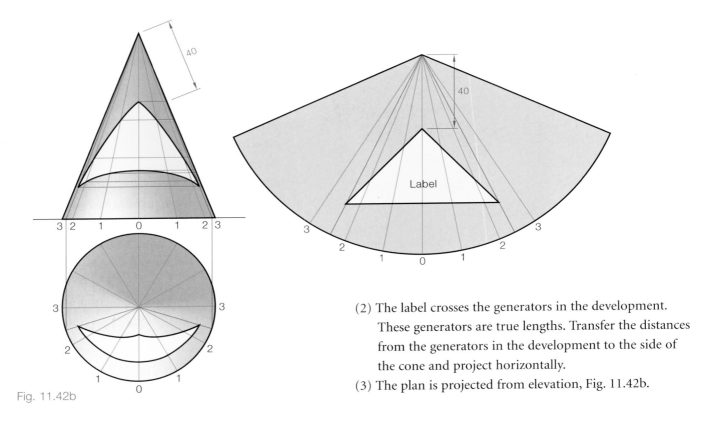

Fig. 11.42b

(2) The label crosses the generators in the development. These generators are true lengths. Transfer the distances from the generators in the development to the side of the cone and project horizontally.

(3) The plan is projected from elevation, Fig. 11.42b.

Shortest Distance

The shortest distance between two points on the same plane is a straight line. When the two points are on different surfaces of the same solid and we wish to find the shortest distance between them along the surface of the solid, we develop the surface of the solid and join the points with a straight line. This straight line can then be found on the projections of the solid.

Given the plan and elevation of a cylinder and two points p and q on its surface. Draw the projection of the shortest distance between these two points along the surface of the cylinder.

Fig. 11.43a

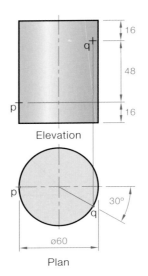

Elevation

Plan

Fig. 11.43a

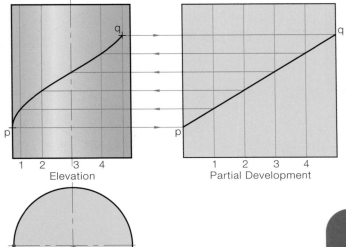

Elevation

Partial Development

Fig. 11.43b

(1) Develop the surface of the cylinder between p and q.
(2) Project p and q onto the development and join with a straight line.
(3) Project this line back to elevation. The line joining p and q in elevation forms part of a helical curve, Fig. 11.43b.

The front elevation and plan of a solid are shown in Fig. 11.44a. Also shown are two points p and q on the surface of the solid. Draw the path of the shortest distance between these two points along the surface of the solid.

(1) Draw the given plan and elevation and locate points p and q on its surface.
(2) Develop the surface of the solid and locate p and q on the development.
(3) Join p and q with a straight line on the development.
(4) Distances Oa, Ob, Oc and Od are true lengths on the development and are stepped down on generator Op in elevation because it too is a true length.
(5) The elevation and plan are finished by projection, Fig. 11.44b.

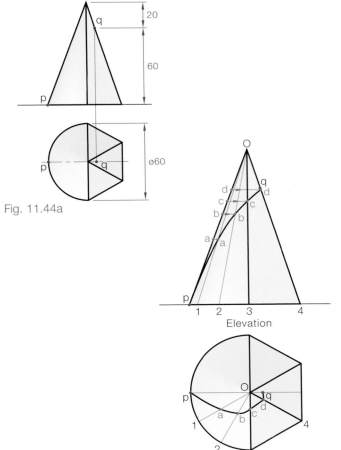

Fig. 11.44a

Elevation

Plan

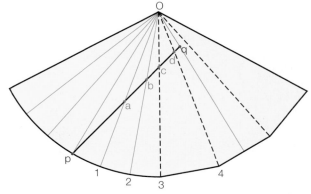

Fig. 11.44b

Given the isometric projection of a solid having two points, p and q, on its surface. Draw the front elevation, end elevation and plan of the solid showing the shortest path between points p and q.
Fig. 11.45a

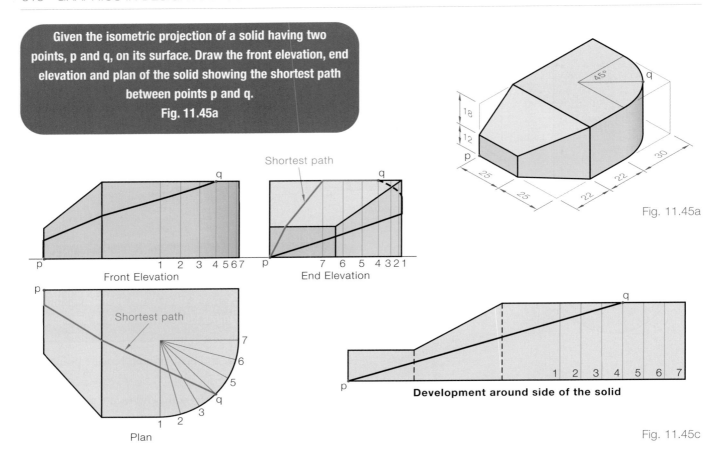

Fig. 11.45a

Shortest path

Front Elevation

End Elevation

Shortest path

Plan

Fig. 11.45b

Development around side of the solid

Fig. 11.45c

In this example it is unclear which route would be the shorter, across the top or around the side. A development is drawn to show both paths and it is clear from these that the route across the top is the shortest one, Fig. 11.45d.

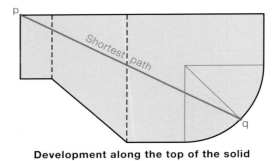

Shortest path

Development along the top of the solid

Fig. 11.45d

Activities

Q1. TO Q3.

Figures 11.46 to 11.48 show the incomplete developments of prisms. Draw the front elevation, end elevation and plan of each solid and complete the development

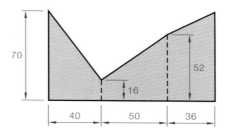

Fig. 11.47

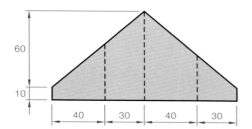

Fig. 11.46

Q1. Fig. 11.46

Q2. Fig. 11.47

Q4. TO Q6.

Figures 11.49 to 11.51 show the development of cylinders which are open at both ends. Draw a plan and elevation of the cylinder.

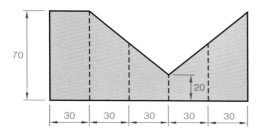

Fig. 11.48

Q3. Fig. 11.48

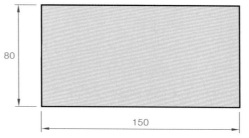

Fig. 11.49

Q4. Fig. 11.49

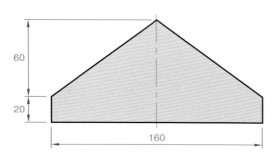

Fig. 11.50

Q5. Fig. 11.50

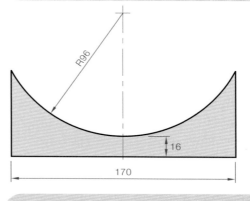

Fig. 11.51

Q6. Fig. 11.51

PARTIAL ENVELOPMENTS

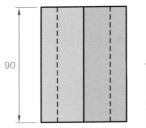

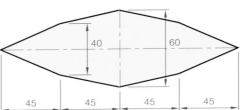

Fig. 11.52

Q7. Given the plan and elevation of a pentagonal prism and the development of a label. Draw the plan and elevation of the prism when the label is wrapped around it, Fig. 11.52.

Q8. Given the plan and elevation of a cylinder and the development of a label. Draw the elevation of the cylinder when the label is wrapped around it, Fig. 11.53.

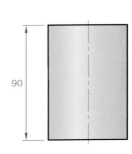

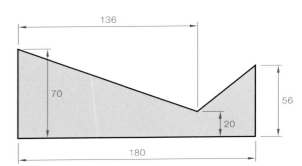

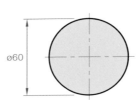

Fig. 11.53

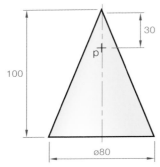

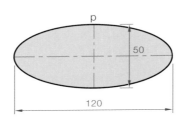

Fig. 11.54

Q9. Given a cone and the development of a label. Draw the plan and elevation of the cone when the label is wrapped around it, Fig. 11.54.

Q10. The elevation of a cone and the development of a label are shown in Fig. 11.55. Draw the elevation and plan of the cone when the label is in position.

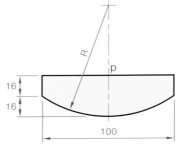

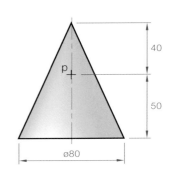

Fig. 11.55

Q11. AND Q12.

In each case, given the pictorial view of a solid having two points on its surface, p and q. Draw a front elevation, end elevation and plan of the solid showing the shortest route, on the surface of the solid, between p and q.

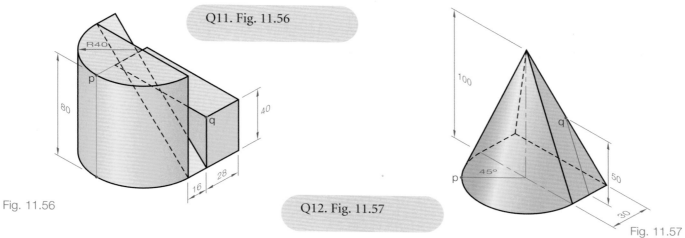

Q11. Fig. 11.56

Fig. 11.56

Q12. Fig. 11.57

Fig. 11.57

Development of Oblique Solids

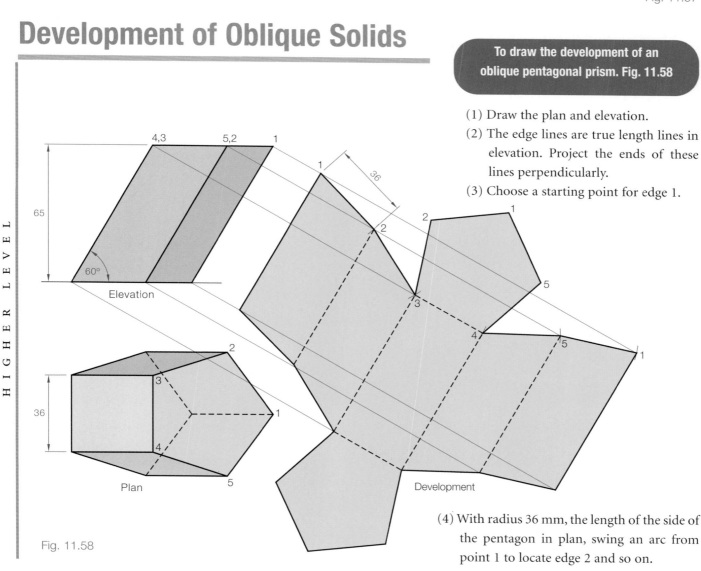

Fig. 11.58

To draw the development of an oblique pentagonal prism. Fig. 11.58

(1) Draw the plan and elevation.
(2) The edge lines are true length lines in elevation. Project the ends of these lines perpendicularly.
(3) Choose a starting point for edge 1.

(4) With radius 36 mm, the length of the side of the pentagon in plan, swing an arc from point 1 to locate edge 2 and so on.

HIGHER LEVEL

To draw the development of the surfaces of a truncated oblique hexagonal prism. Fig. 11.59

The development method is the same as above. The surface on the HP gives true lengths which are used as before to find the edges 1,1 and 2,2 etc.

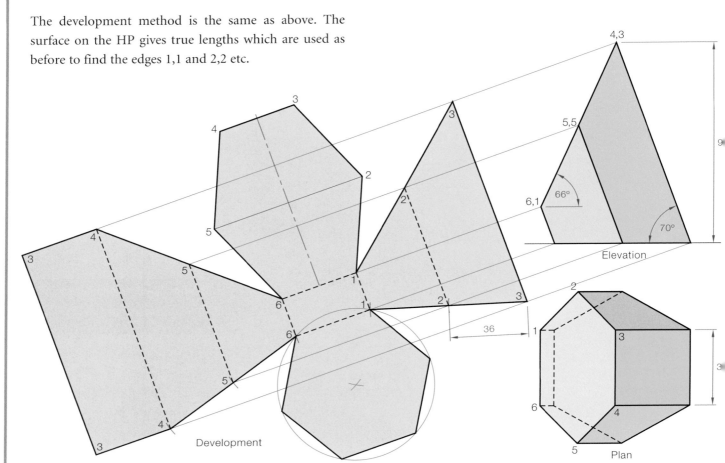

Development

Elevation

Plan

Fig. 11.59

To draw the surface development of an oblique cylinder. Fig. 11.60

(1) Draw the plan and elevation.

(2) Divide the base circle into 12 equal parts.

(3) Project these points to elevation and draw in the generators.

(4) Project out the ends of each generator at right angles.

(5) Choose a starting point 1.

(6) Take distance d from plan and swing an arc from point 1 to locate point 2.

(7) Continue in this manner to locate the other points.

(8) Construct lines parallel to the cylinder edge from each point and find the top edge of the development.

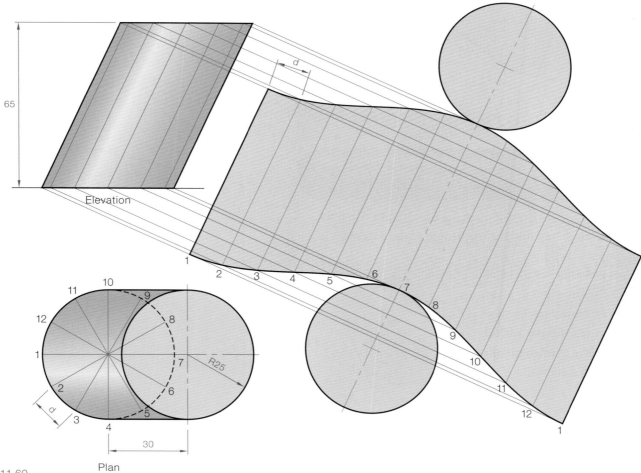

Fig. 11.60

HIGHER LEVEL

To draw the complete surface development of an oblique truncated cylinder. Fig. 11.61

The construction is as Fig. 11.60.

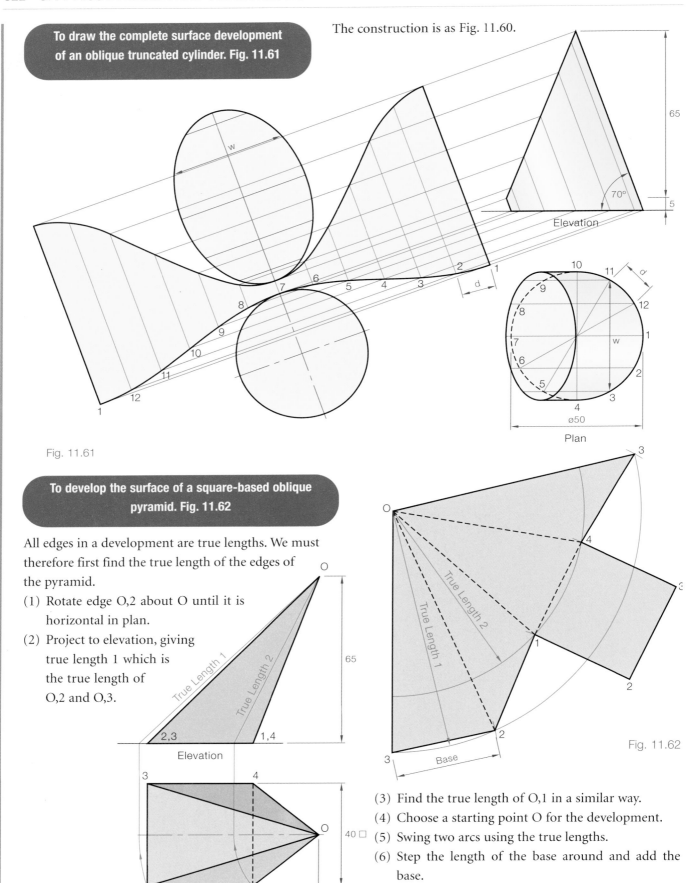

Fig. 11.61

To develop the surface of a square-based oblique pyramid. Fig. 11.62

All edges in a development are true lengths. We must therefore first find the true length of the edges of the pyramid.

(1) Rotate edge O,2 about O until it is horizontal in plan.
(2) Project to elevation, giving true length 1 which is the true length of O,2 and O,3.

(3) Find the true length of O,1 in a similar way.
(4) Choose a starting point O for the development.
(5) Swing two arcs using the true lengths.
(6) Step the length of the base around and add the base.

Fig. 11.62

(1) Find the true length of all the edges. True length 1 shows the true length of edges O,3 and O,4. True length 2 shows the true length of O,2 and O,5. Edge O,1 already appears as a true length in elevation.

(2) Project the cut points in elevation over to these true lengths.

(3) Construct the development as before, using the true lengths found.

To develop the surface of a pentagonal-based oblique pyramid. Fig. 11.63

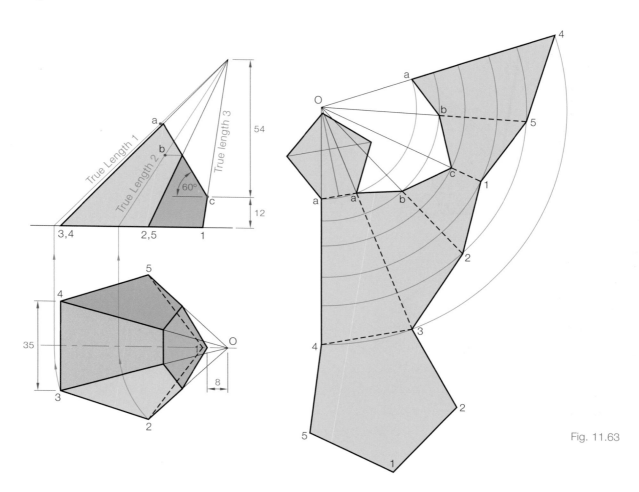

Fig. 11.63

(1) Divide the base circle and draw in the radians.

(2) Find the true length of each radian. Radian O,1 and O,7 are already shown as true lengths.

(3) Start the development with radian O,1.

(4) With the true length of O,2 as radius and O as centre, scribe an arc. With chord length 1,2 as radius and point 1 as centre, scribe an arc to cut the previous arc giving point 2 on the development.

(5) Continue in this way to complete the development.

To develop the surface of an oblique cone.
Fig. 11.64

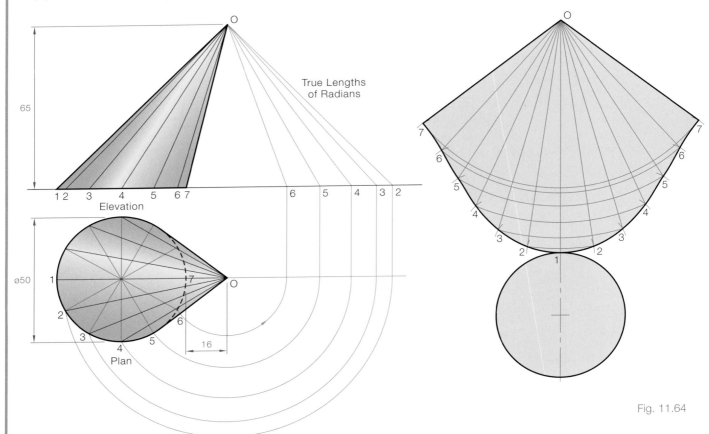

Fig. 11.64

To develop a truncated oblique cone. Fig. 11.65

(1) Develop the full cone as above.
(2) Transfer the cut length of each radian in elevation across to its true length.
(3) Transfer these true lengths to the development.
(4) Add the true shape of the cut surface.

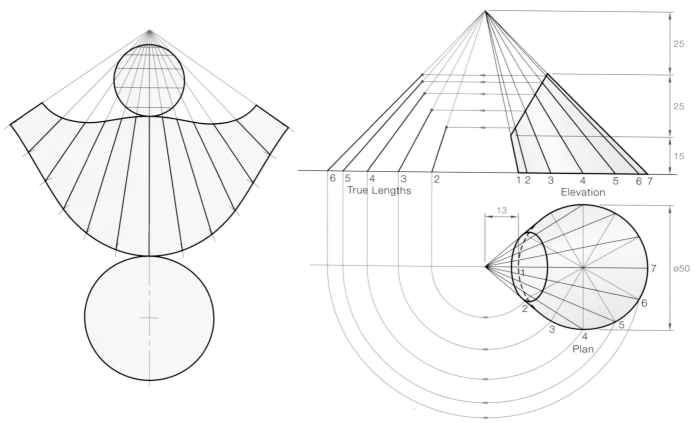

Fig. 11.65

Given the plan and elevation of an oblique pentagonal prism and the development of a label that is to be wrapped around it. Draw the plan and elevation of the prism when the label is in position. Axis ab on the label is to be placed centrally on edge 1,1 of the prism.

Fig. 11.66

(1) Develop the surface of the prism as described earlier.

(2) Place the label in position on the development.

(3) All corners and fold points are easily projected back, except corners c and d.

(4) On the development, point d is projected parallel to the edges onto 2,3 which is a true length. Point q is found on 2,3 in plan which is also a true length.

(5) Draw line qq in plan and elevation. It will run parallel to the edges. Corner d is now projected onto line qq.

(6) Similar construction for point c.

HIGHER LEVEL

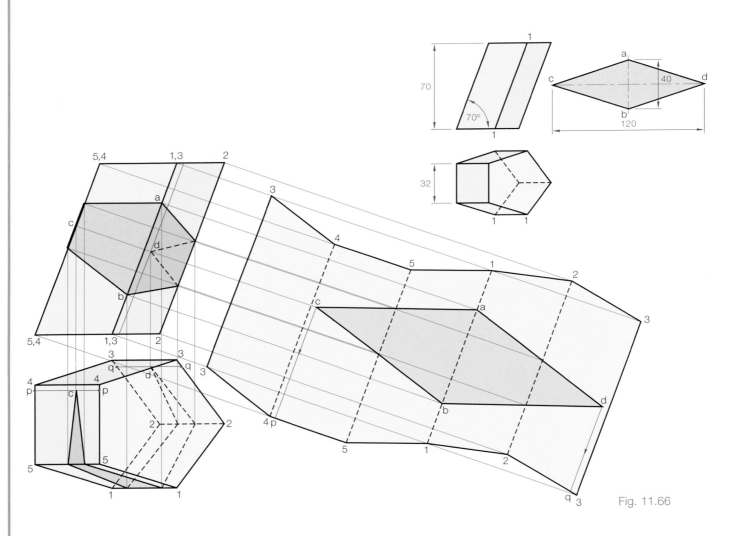

Fig. 11.66

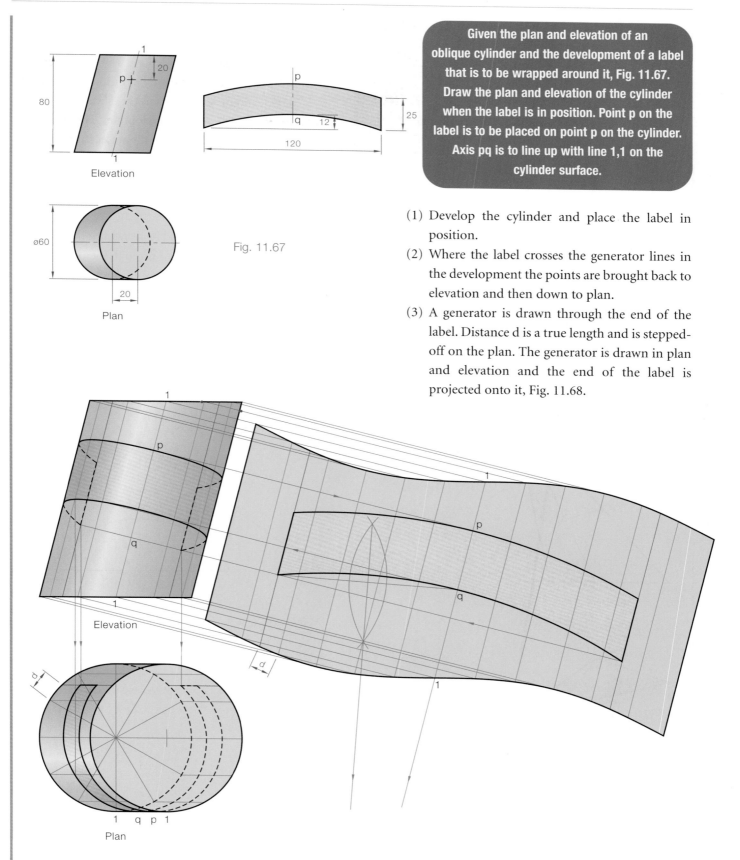

Elevation

Fig. 11.67

Plan

ø60

Given the plan and elevation of an oblique cylinder and the development of a label that is to be wrapped around it, Fig. 11.67. Draw the plan and elevation of the cylinder when the label is in position. Point p on the label is to be placed on point p on the cylinder. Axis pq is to line up with line 1,1 on the cylinder surface.

(1) Develop the cylinder and place the label in position.
(2) Where the label crosses the generator lines in the development the points are brought back to elevation and then down to plan.
(3) A generator is drawn through the end of the label. Distance d is a true length and is stepped-off on the plan. The generator is drawn in plan and elevation and the end of the label is projected onto it, Fig. 11.68.

Elevation

Plan

Fig. 11.68

HIGHER LEVEL

Given the plan and elevation of a pentagonal-based oblique pyramid and the development of a label. Draw the plan and elevation of the pyramid when the label is wrapped around it. Point p on the label is to be placed on point p on the pyramid, and the axis pq is to be placed on the edge 0,1. Fig. 11.69

(1) Develop the surface of the pyramid as explained earlier. Place the label in position on the development.

(2) Transfer distances Op and Oq onto the true length of O,1 and project across to the elevation.

(3) Points on O,5 on the development are transferred to the true length of O,5 and projected over to the elevation.

(4) Points on O,2 in the development can be transferred directly to O,2 in the elevation as this is a true length.

(5) Points r and s are found by drawing a line from the apex in the development through them, to lines 4,5 and 2,3 respectively. These lines can be found in plan. Find their true lengths. Transfer Or and Os from the development to the true lengths, then project to elevation and plan, Fig. 11.70.

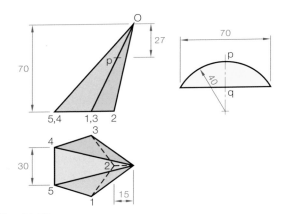

Fig. 11.69

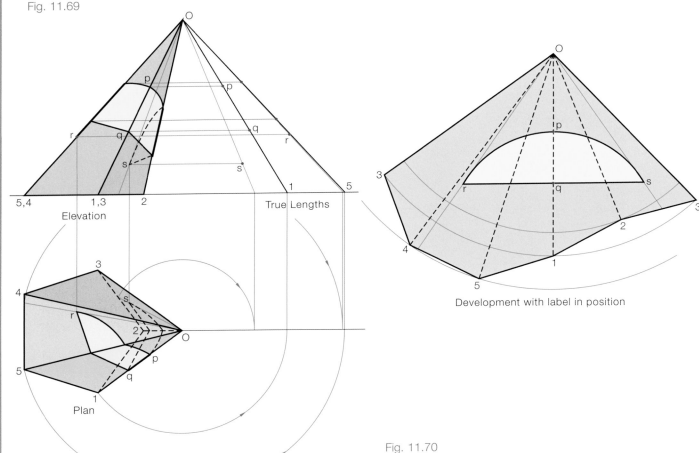

Fig. 11.70

Development with label in position

HIGHER LEVEL

Given the plan and elevation of an oblique cone and the development of a label. Draw the plan and elevation of the cone when the label is wrapped around it. Point p on the label is to be placed on point p on the cone and axis pq is to be placed on the generator 0,4.
Fig. 11.71

(1) The true lengths of the radians are needed for the development.
(2) Place the label in position.
(3) Distances are transferred from the development to these true lengths and projected across to the elevation.
(4) Special treatment is given to the label corners a, b, c and d.

(5) A radian is drawn through corner b, for instance, on the development. This radian is found in plan and then in elevation, Fig. 11.72a.
(6) Find the true length of the radian in elevation and transfer distance Ob from the development onto this true length.
(7) Point b is projected across to elevation and plan, Fig. 11.72b.

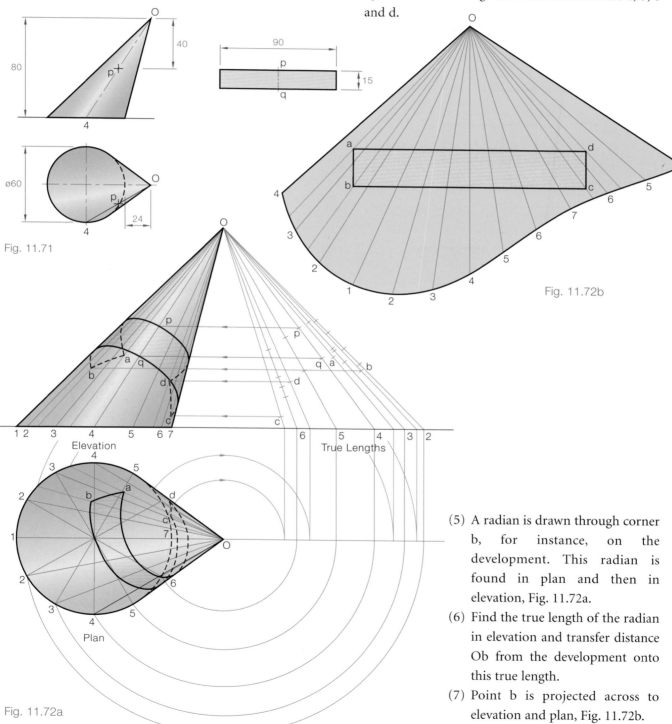

Fig. 11.71

Fig. 11.72a

Fig. 11.72b

Activities

Develop the surfaces of the oblique prisms shown in Figures 11.73, 11.74 and 11.75.

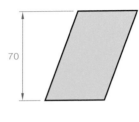
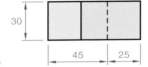

Fig. 11.73

Q1. Fig. 11.73

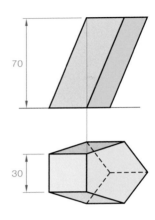

Fig. 11.74

Q2. Fig. 11.74

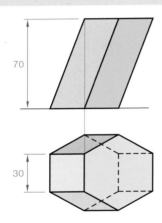

Fig. 11.75

Q3. Fig. 11.75

Develop the surfaces of the oblique pyramids shown, Figures 11.76, 11.77 and 11.78.

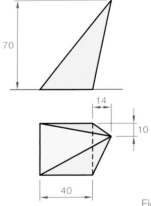

Fig. 11.76

Q4. Fig. 11.76

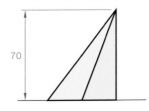

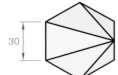

Fig. 11.77

Q5. Fig. 11.77

HIGHER LEVEL

H I G H E R   L E V E L

Q6. Fig. 11.78

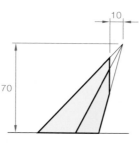

Fig. 11.78

Q7. TO Q9.

Develop the surface of the oblique cylinders and oblique cones shown in Figures 11.79, 11.80 and 11.81.

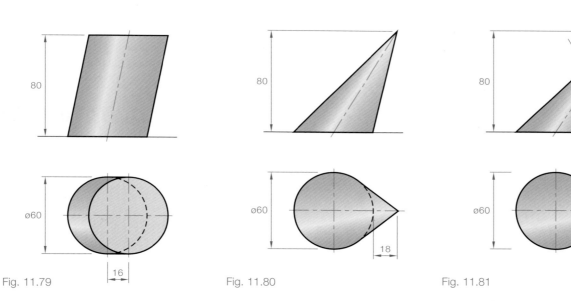

Fig. 11.79   Fig. 11.80   Fig. 11.81

Q10. Given the plan and elevation of an oblique cylinder and the development of a label. Draw the plan and elevation of the oblique cylinder when the label is wrapped around it. Point p on the label is to be placed on point p on the cylinder. Axis pq on the label is to line up with radian 1,1 on the cylinder. Fig. 11.82

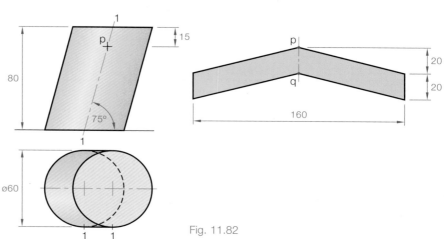

Fig. 11.82

HIGHER LEVEL

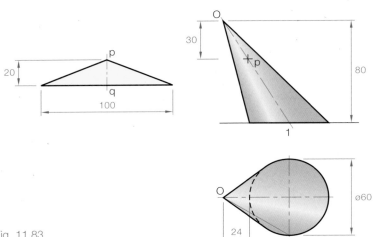

Fig. 11.83

Q11. Wrap the label shown in Fig. 11.83 around the oblique cone, placing point p on the label on point p on the cone and placing axis pq on the radian line O,1. Draw the plan and elevation of the oblique cone when the label is in position.

Q12. Draw the elevation and plan of the oblique prism when the label is wrapped around it. The minor axis is to line up with edge 1,1.

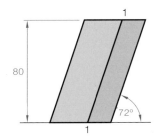

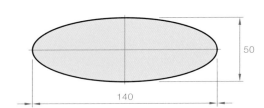

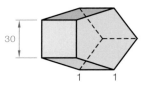

Fig. 11.84